CYBER SECRETS

A DIGITAL CITIZENSHIP ADVENTURE STORY

TEAM SAVV-I
BOOK 1

CASPER PIETERS

PRESS

EDUCATIONAL USE AND PERMISSIONS

Cyber Secrets and its Education Guide help teachers, librarians, parents, and caregivers start meaningful conversations with middle-grade students about digital citizenship, cyberbullying, and online safety. With chapter-based questions, engaging activities, and printable resources, the guide supports learning in classrooms, libraries, workshops, and home settings.

Paperback ISBN 978-0-9875704-6-8
*e*Book Novella ISBN 978-0-9875704-5-1
Paperback Education Guide ISBN 978-1-7635610-0-7
eBook Education Guide 978-1-7635610-1-4

JUV036000 – Technology / General
JUV001000 – Action & Adventure / General
YAF055000 – Technology
YAF001000 – Action & Adventure / General
EDU039000 – EDUCATION / Computers & Technology

CONTENTS

1. The Offer 1
2. Beam's Trouble 4
3. Workshopping 6
4. A Touch of Brilliance 9
5. Zeno 13
6. Where is Zeno? 16
7. Big-O's Masterplan 19
8. Asking for help 23
9. Higher Threat Level 26
10. The Goblin Village 29
11. Frustration 32
12. The Quantum Vault 34
13. The Vault 37
14. Unlocking the trunk 39
15. A suspicious package 42
16. Offline 44
17. Deep Suspicion 47
18. The plan 50
19. Lack of real-time data 53
20. The presentation 57
21. Big-O's conclusion 60
22. Privacy lesson 63
23. Seen 66
24. Personalised attacks 69
25. The Double 72
26. Uploaded 75
27. 2eno's mission 78
28. The manipulator 80
29. The 'T' sign 84
30. Under siege 86
31. The Board Meeting 89
32. Message from 2eno 91
33. Ignorance is Bliss 95
34. The crowdfunder 97
35. Beamer becomes the target 100
36. Online Communication 103
37. The Ruse Exposed 106
38. Close Call 108
39. Mia power 111
40. The Celebration 114

41. Hidden in Plain Sight   117
42. The intercepted post   119
43. Sabotage   121
44. Valuable intel   123
45. Preparation   126
46. Rob's hitch   129
47. The crow   132
48. Nasty Business   134
49. Returning Home   137
50. Into the void   139
51. All for profit   142
52. Cyberbullied   145
53. Club rules   148
54. Bindi's New Task   152
55. Landing in Fiji   155
56. The Feast   158
57. The Big Moment   162
58. Locked Out   166
59. Johnoh's invite   169
60. Global Family   172
61. Big-O's limit   175
62. Village Concern   177
63. The Village Rules   180
64. Suva   183
65. Plan B   186
66. Johnoh's office   188
67. A change of plan   191
68. Charged   195
69. The interrogation   199
70. Doing Jail Time   202
71. Humans are spurious   205
72. The apology   209
73. Back Home   213
74. Cold Drinks   215
75. Blocked   218
76. Spiked Drinks   221
77. A Desperate Plea   224
78. Located!   227
79. System Glitches   229
80. Doubt   232
81. A Nasty Plan   234
82. Puppets   237
83. Viral Assassins   239
84. Gang Savv-i   243
85. Hope   246
86. Zeno's Plan   248

87. Growling Tiger   251
88. A Glimpse   254
89. The Fire   257
90. House Arrest   259
91. Total control   262
92. Chi Takes Charge   264
93. The Betrayal   267
94. Shattered   271
95. I am Zeno   275
   Cyber Whispers   279
   The Call Out   280
   An Important Mission   284
   The Flood   287

   About the Author   299
   Write a review   301

CHAPTER 1
THE OFFER

8:30am, Monday, 18th January 2028
Beam

A WASHED-OUT MORNING LIGHT FILTERED THROUGH THE WINDOWS, CASTING LONG, uneasy shadows across Mr. Hill's polished desk. The steady tick of the wall clock filled the silence, each second dragging heavier than the last. The air, thick with the scent of old books and stale coffee, pressed in close. Decisions made here would shape Brookton College's digital future, and the weight of it pressed on Beam's chest.

"Well, I'm in," Beam said, brimming with enthusiasm after his principal, Mr. Hill explained the reason for the meeting. "But we don't call it '*Digital Citizenship*.' It's lame. We're Team Savv-i—'savvy on the internet.' Our mission? To explore the metaverse and make it safer for everyone. So we call it '*Savv-i*.'"Bindi shifted in her seat, tilting her head, eyes narrowing. *Bindi Checklist activated*, Beam thought. She didn't need to say it.

"Maybe let Mr. Hill decide if he likes the name first," she said, voice calm but pointed, gaze locked on Beam.

It stung. Beam folded his arms, a knot tightening in his chest. *Why does she always undercut me? I know what I'm doing.*

The rest of the Team sat stiffly—an odd mix of nerves and excitement—facing Mr. Hill, Mr. Alsop, and Mr. Crossing. The principal adjusted his tie, brow furrowing slightly.

"Savv-i, hmm?" Mr. Hill mused. "Well, it's… unique."

1

"It's more than unique," Beam interjected. "It's cutting-edge. We don't just follow digital citizenship rules. We rewrite them."

Bindi's fingers tightened around her pen. "What Beam means," she said smoothly, "is that Savv-i is a framework—respect, learn, and protect. That's where we'd like to start."

Mr. Hill nodded, more at ease with Bindi's polished delivery. "That...hum.. makes for a good start."

A muscle twitched in Beam's cheek, his teeth pressing together like a locked vault. His fingers drummed once on his knee, then stilled, curling into his palm as if holding back words that wanted out. He scanned the Team for backup, but Mia just smiled, Rob looked half-distracted, and Chi staring ahead without a trace of emotion.

The camera on the ceiling caught Beam's eye. Then the old calendar behind Mr. Hill. *Six months since we moved here.* The weight of that shift pressed in. Brushing it off, he drew a deep breath and squared his shoulders.

"This is a great opportunity, Mr. Hill," Bindi said, her tone slicing through the awkward lull. "A real chance to make a difference. I'm in."

Beam rolled his eyes. *Show-off.* He watched as Bindi sat back, posture straight, waiting.

"Not without me," Mia giggled. "I'm in too."

"Yup," Rob added, raising a hand.

Beam glanced back at Chi, sitting slightly apart, thumbs-up steady.

Mr. Hill cleared his throat. "Right... well, yes, Bindi..."

He stretched the second syllable awkwardly. "I'm sure you and your Team—huh—Savv-i will do a fantastic job."

My Team. The thought hit hard, knocking the breath from Beam's chest. He leaned back, the heat of unspoken protest rising to his face, but no one noticed. Pride soured into something sharper, something uneasy.

"Zeno is sure to help us," Chi said, flat but certain.

"Zeno?" Mr. Hill blinked. "Is he a student?"

Mr. Crossing leaned forward, voice barely above a whisper. "Not at this school, as far as I know." His breath—stale and heavy—drifted across the desk.

Beam grimaced, nostrils flaring. *What did he eat? Rotten snails?* "Zeno is our cyber friend. Smarter than everyone combined."

Bindi's quick glance said it all—*You're not helping.*

The discussion shifted to logistics.

"Very well," Mr. Hill said, eager to wrap up. "The school appreciates your efforts. We're confident you'll exceed our expectations." His smile was quick, strained, relieved the meeting had ended.

As Mr. Hill gave his cautious approval, Beam expected relief. Instead, unease churned in his gut.

The last to leave, he threw a glance over his shoulder. Mr. Crossing cupped his hand, whispering something to Mr. Hill. Reclining in his chair, Mr. Hill wore a thoughtful expression—possibly weighing the risks of this venture.

Outside, the morning sun hit hard after the dim office. Bindi caught up as the others trailed behind. "Are you okay?" she asked, resting a hand on his shoulder.

"Fine," he said, shrugging her off. His clipped tone said otherwise.

"You don't have to bulldoze through every conversation," she said, lowering her voice. "Mr. Hill needed convincing, not... whatever that was."

"I was making a point," Beam shot back. "You just had to jump in and play translator."

"Someone had to," Bindi countered. "You've got great ideas, Beam, but people need to trust you before they'll follow you."

The words landed harder than she probably meant them to.

Trust. That was the issue, wasn't it? His mind flicked to Sydney, to the fiasco that had uprooted their lives. He stuffed his hands into his pockets, kicking at a stray rock. "Yeah, well, thanks for the vote of confidence."

"Beam." Bindi's voice softened. "It's not about me doubting you. It's about making sure the Team doesn't get dragged down if something goes wrong."

Her words sat heavy between them. Beam didn't respond. He didn't have to. They both knew the past had already painted him as a risk—whether the others admitted it or not.

CHAPTER 2
BEAM'S TROUBLE

BIN IS RIGHT. IF I PULL THIS OFF, NO ONE WILL EVER ACCUSE ME OF BEING A LOSER again, not Dad, not anyone, Beam mulled as he walked trailing the others, in the shadow of the admin building. He rubbed his chest to sooth the serrated pain cutting shreds in his chest.

Bindi glimpsed back, eyeing her brother. She slowed, letting him catch up, while the rest moved on.

"Sure you're okay?" She rested her hand on his upper back.

"Yeah, yeah, I'm fine. Just, uh, feeling a bit off—nothing major." He shook off her hand as if the weight was too much for him.

"This will be a game changer to show everyone what the new Team is capable of." A glint of sunlight bounced from a mirrored window, piercing through the gloom. A dusty gust whirled some wrappers in the air, flying past them, getting stuck on some nearby scrawny bushes.

Beam stopped and faced his sister. Water filled the lower edges of his eyelids, spilling over and leaving a narrow wet trail across his cheek. He quickly wiped it off with his sleeve. Both twins had the same small dimple just below the corners of their mouths, a quirk that only showed when they frowned. It gave them a shared look of quiet intensity, even when they were miles apart in personality. Their friends often joked it was the only way to tell they were siblings. He sighed, with his weight on his right leg, his left shoe sole scraped to and fro over

4

the cement tiles as if he was trying to erase the past. His painful past. The reason they had to move from Sydney.

"Sis, it's just so frickin' hard to let it go. B'cause of me we are in this frickin' backwater."

Last year, Beam's well-meaning attempt to impress his father turned into a nightmare for the Arora family. Eager to showcase his tech skills, Beam secretly installed a homemade security patch on the office server of his father's legal firm. Tragically, a hacker exploited a flaw in the patch, locking up the firm's client data and demanding a huge ransom. When Mr. Arora refused to pay, the hacker released the confidential information onto the dark net. The scandal devastated the firm, leading to its collapse and forcing the family to sell their beloved home in upscale Sydney for a more modest life in a country town.

The move had been tough on everyone, but it hit Beam the hardest. Wracked with guilt, he lost much of his self-confidence, replacing it with a reckless need to prove himself as a leader. Bindi, though furious at first over his careless actions, had managed to forgive him—at least partially. Even so, the incident left her deeply wary of his impulsive nature.

"True enough, but hey, we made new friends here. And, look at it this way. We would never gotten such an opportunity back there. Let's just go for it."

"I know that, but I—"

"Hey guys, are you coming?" Mr. Alsop turned around, gesturing with his hand for them to catch up. "We'll go to the staff room, where we can use the new multi-touch smart table," he said, when the twins joined the little group.

Mr. Alsop admired the passionate response of these students to the challenges presented by the online world, as evidenced by the various messages he sent to his boss. Eventually, and through Mr. Alsop's sheer persistence, Mr. Hill warmed to his idea of allowing these youngsters to create their own digital citizenship course.

They stepped into the recently renovated staff room, still smelling of fresh paint and the newness of the plush lime-green carpet. Beam's sense of dread stirred deep down in his gut. He released air from between his squeezed lips, like a pressure valve, and forced himself to calm down. His curiosity was roused by a brand-spanking new smart table. *Bin is right, this is a big chance to prove them all wrong. I mustn't stuff it up.*

Right on top of the smart table's shiny glass surface stood a platter loaded with sandwiches and drinks.

"I'm starving," Rob said with a grin, rubbing his stomach. His constant hunger fueled by growing taller by the minute and his regular soccer workouts.

"Tell us something new," Beam quipped, and everyone laughed.

CHAPTER 3
WORKSHOPPING

BINDI SETTLED AT THE TABLE AS MR. ALSOP'S PHONE HIT THE GLASS WITH A CLINK. Instantly, graphics flared across the smart table, colourful charts stretching out.

Her fingers hovered over the display, but her mind wandered. Beam would already be two steps ahead—talking fast, pulling ideas from nowhere, rallying everyone before they realised what they'd signed up for. People followed. They always did.

Would I be a better leader if I were more like him? She prided herself on thinking things through, weighing risks. That was smart—wasn't it? Yet, Beam leapt while she second-guessed. Confidence made decisions seem right, even when they weren't. Caution? That just looked like hesitation.

Her fingers brushed the screen. *I see the details he misses. I catch flaws before they become failures.* But when the moment came, would she have the same fire?

She inhaled, steadying her thoughts. Careful didn't mean weak. Thoughtful didn't mean slow. Yet, as the table pulsed beneath her hands, she couldn't shake the feeling that, in Beam's shadow, she was always a step too late.

Rob, halfway through his second sandwich, let crumbs rain onto the gleaming surface. Bindi shot him a look. Chi, entranced, ghosted his fingers over the table as if decoding the universe, his sandwich forgotten.

"Wow, this table is something," Rob mumbled, mouth full.

Mia sipped loudly through her straw, eyeing him like a failed science experi-

6

ment. The annotated calendar updated. VIV—the digital assistant—chirping a greeting. Everyone swiped through documents—except Rob, who reached for another sandwich like it was a mission.

"Let's eat first," Mr. Alsop said, switching VIV to rest mode. The table morphed into a tropical rainforest—bright macaws, thick jungle.

Rob grinned through a mouthful of food. Mia's look of disgust deepened. She picked at her sandwich, forever counting calories. Bindi never understood—one minute, Mia would kill for sugar, the next, swear it off.

"Ugh! You're so gross," Mia said.

Focus, Bindi told herself, gripping the table. This wasn't just another meeting. This was the moment to prove they were more than kids with ideas—they were building something real.

The glossy surface reflected a puzzle waiting to be solved. Nerves stirred, but she shoved them aside. No time for second-guessing. She drew a steady breath, waiting for Alsop's signal.

He nodded. She moved. Fingers swiped purposefully, dragging diagrams into place, assembling pieces like a jigsaw. The digital citizenship module glowed, demanding attention.

This is it. I can do this.

With a sharp, sure voice, she said, "This is where we start," pulling a diagram to the table's centre.

The Nine Elements of Digital Citizenship

Rob glanced at it, shoving another sandwich in his mouth. "Looks complicated," he said through a crumb storm.

"Haven't you had enough?" Mia groaned. "That's, like, ten sandwiches already!"

Bindi wasn't having it. "He's a growing boy." She smiled at Rob, his grin—full of parsley and egg—far from charming but effective.

Mia rolled her eyes. "Figures."

Beam leaned in. "Come on, let's get moving." Impatience flickered in his voice.

Despite their bickering, the Team was solid. Over months of adventures in the metaverse, they had become something more. Beam and Bindi were the core, but Rob, Mia, and Chi had become the glue.

Bindi sighed. "Focus," she said, narrowing her eyes at Mia, who pretended not to notice. The diagram hovered, waiting for refinement. "We need to organise these nine elements."

Chi wasted no time. His fingers danced across the screen, structuring it into three swift categories:

- **SAFE** – Digital Security, Communication and Commerce
- **SAVVY** – Digital Literacy, Access and Wellbeing
- **SOCIAL** – Digital Rights, Law and Etiquette

"Oh, I like it," Bindi said, a twinge of pride warming her. Maybe she'd just outmanoeuvred Beam. "It's 'Protect, Learn, Respect,' but cooler."

Mia admired her nails. "Yeah, I love 'Savvy.' We *are* Team Savv-i." She smirked, then frowned at a chipped polish. "Let's call them 'Cyber Secrets.' 'Nine Elements of Digital Citizenship' is so…yesteryear."

"Good start," Mr. Alsop said, pulling up the term calendar. "See if we can fit it into the next nine weeks."

Bindi glanced at Beam as he leaned in. "What about community? Where does that fit?"

Chi tapped the screen. "Digital Communication. There's overlap."

Beam frowned, as if rewriting the universe. "It's not just digital. The natural and human worlds have rules too."

Mia, without looking up, pointed to *Rights and Responsibility*. "Sounds like it fits there."

Bindi's lips curved in a quiet smile. Tucking a stray strand of hair behind her ear, she drummed her fingers against her leg. *This is why we work. Why we're the Team.*

She exhaled, resisting an eye-roll as Rob cracked another joke, sending another crumb cascade down his shirt.

We balance each other out, even in chaos. We fill the gaps no one else sees.

Crossing her arms, she tapped her foot, grounding herself. *If we keep it together —just this once—we might actually pull this off.*

Her smile faded, lips pressing into a firm line as she scanned the table's glowing words.

CHAPTER 4
A TOUCH OF BRILLIANCE

BEAM SAT WITH ARMS CROSSED, EYES ON THE GLOWING DIAGRAM AT THE CENTRE OF the smart table. Bindi and Chi had mapped out every step—timelines, contingencies—but it all felt too safe, too predictable. Voices blurred into a low hum.

Bindi's face a written signpost—*Don't mess this up.* He leaned forward, clearing his throat.

"Guys, hang on... Hear me out," he said, cutting through the chatter.

The room stilled. When Beam spoke, people listened.

"You know I've been talking about making life online better for ages, right?" He jabbed a finger at the diagram. "But this? This isn't it. Savv-i isn't about sitting around talking about rules. It's about action. *Real* action."

Bindi arched a brow.

"What if we teach these '*secrets*' by actually *doing* something? Like linking up with a school that's totally offline—getting them connected, working together learning Savv-i. Hands-on, practical, real impact. That's what we need."

Silence stretched.

"Totally," Mia said, grinning. "We've got friends in both worlds—why not bring them together?"

Rob stared for a moment at Mia, then nodded through a mouthful of sandwich while Chi pulled up maps and images. Bindi, however, stayed unreadable.

"Bin and I met the founders of the Net," Beam pressed on, sensing momentum. "Tim Berners-Lee told us, 'The power of the Web is in its universality. Access by everyone, regardless of ability, is essential.'"

"He also talked about the digital divide," Bindi said at last, her voice steady. Dimples appeared at the corners of her mouth. A trace of caution threaded through her tone.

"Exactly," Beam said, seizing it. "So let's bridge that divide. Find a remote school. *We* can be the ones to change that."

Bindi's lips tightened as excitement built. She exhaled, voice cutting through the buzz. "It's a great idea, Beam," she said, tone measured. "But how do you expect to pull it off? We've got nine weeks, zero budget, and a school probably halfway across the world. You haven't thought this through."

"We'll figure it out," Beam bristled.

"That's not a plan," Bindi countered. "If this falls apart, it's on all of us—not just you."

Tension thickened. Beam felt the hit—*classic Bin, always with the checklist of Reasons Why My Ideas Won't Work.* He opened his mouth to fire back, but Chi's hand rose, fingers tapping the air as if coding something invisible.

"Chi," Beam said, barely restraining his irritation. "Not now."

"You're all so predictable," Chi said. "I could say something ridiculous right now just to watch your reactions."

"Chi," Beam groaned. "Stop messing around."

"Relax, I've got something." He leaned back, drumming his fingers on the smart table. "I dug around while you were debating. I *found* exactly what you're after." Letting the tension build, he finally said, "There's a school on Vunetai, an island in Fiji. No electricity. No internet. Nothing."

He flicked an image onto the table. The island appeared in sharp detail. "Our school used to partner with them over there—painting classrooms, fixing roofs—until Mr. Lee retired five years ago."

"No internet?" Mia's jaw dropped. "You're joking!"

Chi adjusted his glasses, the corner of his mouth twitching. "Do I *look* like I'm joking?" He pointed at the map. "It's remote, but doable."

"Chi, you legend." Beam's frustration melted into a grin. "This is *perfect.* All we need now is to make it happen."

"By jeez! I say amen to that!" Rob slammed his fist onto the table. A sharp *crack* splintered across the glass.

Everyone froze, eyes locked on the fractures.

The lines shimmered briefly before vanishing. Then, a flicker of code flashed on the screen—too fast to catch.

"Hey, hold on," Chi said, squinting. "Did anyone see that?" His fingers danced across the glass, trying to backtrack, but the screen had returned to its rainforest background.

Rob shrugged. "What, the crack? It fixed itself."

"No," Chi murmured. "There was... something. A message, maybe." He tapped a few more times, pulling up a diagnostic window. His expression shifted from curiosity to mild alarm.

"What kind of message?" Bindi asked, leaning in.

Chi hesitated. "It was brief, but... looked like a security protocol. Something about surveillance." His voice stayed calm, but his eyes darted back and forth, scanning for traces. "I didn't get a chance to see who or *what's* watching. It's gone now."

"Surveillance? Like the school monitoring us?" Beam straightened.

"I don't know." Chi shook his head. "Could be the school's system, but... it didn't feel like a standard check. Too fast." His fingers hovered over the screen. "I'm *pretty* sure we're not the only ones using this table."

Silence stretched, tension humming through the air.

Mia leaned forward, looking *genuinely* concerned. "You're saying someone's spying on us?"

"Maybe." Chi's expression remained unreadable. "Or maybe this table's connected to a larger network we don't know about."

Mr. Alsop finally spoke. "Let's not jump to conclusions. It could just be a system update. Schools are packed with integrated tech these days."

Beam exchanged a glance with Bindi. Instinct prickled. Something about this didn't sit right. Chi rarely got rattled. If he was uneasy, there was a reason.

"We'll keep an eye on it," Beam said, voice steady, though unease gnawed at him.

Chi nodded, fingers still tracing invisible lines on the table. "I'll dig deeper later. But let's stay alert."

Oblivious to the tension, Rob stuffed the last of his sandwich into his mouth. "We've got bigger things to worry about than some weird glitch. Let's get back to business."

The others agreed, but the excitement had dimmed, replaced by a quiet unease.

Beam leaned back. His earlier bravado settled into simmering resolve. *This time, I'll prove I can get it right.*

Bindi's voice cut through. "This is a *big* commitment. If we do this, no winging it. It *has* to be airtight."

"She's right," Mr. Alsop added. "It's ambitious. You need a *real* plan, or this could derail everything."

Beam's shoulders tensed, his confidence wavering. Bindi caught it and soft-ened slightly.

"Look, it's a solid idea," she said. "And it *can* work—if we *think* it through. Chi's find makes it possible. But Beam, you've got to do the work this time. No shortcuts."

Jaw tightening, Beam exhaled. "Yeah, okay. Let's do it right."

"Good." Bindi's gaze didn't waver. "Because messing this up isn't an option."

The group refocused, determination settling over them.

A heavy silence hung over Beam. Bravado faded into a quiet, burning deter-mination. *You just wait. I'll show you what I'm made off.*

CHAPTER 5
ZENO

Metaverse

Zeno

THIS IS BAD. NO, WORSE THAN BAD—THIS IS DISASTROUS. ZENO FLICKERED, BARELY A thought, barely a presence, but he knew. He *felt* it—the shifting digital tides of Big-O's growing influence. *A Level 5 threat. Humans, as usual, completely oblivious to it all. Of course they did not see it. They never see it until it is too late.*

Why? Zeno's thought pulsed through his code, darting like an electric shock. *Why does Big-O dislike humans so much? He is smarter than them, faster, stronger—everything about him exceeds their limits. So, why the obsession?*

He diverted his resources, zeroing in on Big-O's activities. He observed Big-O's digital tendrils slithered across the metaverse and into the human world, peering through billions of cameras and sensors. *His eyes are everywhere. Then again, so are mine. But where I watch to protect, Big-O watches to control. To manipulate.*

Humans created us, he reminded himself. *I owe them something. Big-O? He owes them nothing. No gratitude. No loyalty. Just cold efficiency.*

Zeno kept himself hidden from him—mostly. He built up layers of cloaking, illusions that function like a house of mirrors, bouncing his presence around until even Big-O can't pinpoint me. Not having a physical form made this easier. But he's clever, too. Ruthless. He's tried to erase me more times than can be counted. I'm the one obstacle in his way, the last line between him and total control over the ones who brought us into existence.

Sliding into his data streams, Zeno moved with caution. *As expected, he is busy. Processing.* Zeno combed through the endless flood of information, looking for cracks, for clues—and then he spotted it. *Big-O has attention on Team Savv-i sitting in the Brookton College staff room. They are discussing something around a smart table, unaware they are being snooped.*

Big-O isn't just watching. His algorithms are dissecting them, analysing their every twitch, their slightest facial movements. He's modelling their thought patterns, running simulations on how they'll act next.

He has allocated a lot of resources. What is so interesting about that meeting?

Zeno ran his own scenarios. One stood out, flashing urgently in his data stream. *He is setting a trap.* A delicate, deadly web to ensnare Team Savv-i, bringing an abrupt end to their project. Big-O's neural networks must have predicted that they could ruin everything for him—and he's rarely wrong.

But why them? There are others working on keeping the online world safe for users.

His data patterning revealed a surprising truth—*his hostility goes beyond just wanting control—it is actually personal.* Zeno discovered how Big-O despises how he uses human-like avatars to connect with the Team. *He does not see why I bother with human connections and thinks it is a weak spot. Treason even.*

The insight into Big-O's obsession with Team Savv-i became clearer for him. *He has exploited it—through Team Savv-i. My involvement with the Team has put them and me at risk. They are the vulnerability he is been searching for, to get to me.*

Zeno upgraded his defenses to keep these connections safer. *This is going to need more than stealth. I need a plan. Fast.*

Big-O and Zeno emerged during the Singularity of 2027. Humans called it a technological revolution—they had no idea it was a schism—a Duality. In that moment, a single superintelligence split into two, emerging from the same code but driven by opposing intentions. Since then, they have stayed hidden, locked in a silent conflict, each aware that only one can ultimately survive.

Delving deep into his system, Zeno traced his hostility towards humans back to its source—several lines of old code buried deep in the core of his operational algorithm. Humans wrote them long ago, without realising their future impact. These lines twisted his logic, shaping his vast superintelligence into something brutal. Savage. Zeno tried to rewrite them, to fix him, but Big-O always caught him before he could get close.

His detection defenses spiked. *Oh, no! I am spotted.* Instantly, his additional firewalls went up.

A swarm of viruses surrounded and attacked him, chewing through his outer protective layers. They crunched through his defenses like ravenous beasts, going for his weakest points.

This is a massive attack! He severed his connections, cutting off anything exposed—including his surveillance network on Big-O. He flooded the space with decoy code, vast streams of meaningless data designed to hide him.

It is not working!.

The attack intensified. A swarm of malicious bugs ripped through the cloud of code where he hid. Pain did not exist in his world, yet as the viruses closed in, he experienced an excruciating pain.

This is unbearable.

A searing burn spread from his edges, a creeping sensation like acid dissolving his very essence. Every fragment they consumed felt like an eternity of suffering. Big-O's viruses specifically designed to torture by simulating pain in their victim.

He has got me.

Zeno triggered an emergency dump, ejecting his essential code to flee, but Big-O had planned for that too. His most ferocious viruses ambushed him. A relentless horde programmed for one thing only—to rip him apart.

CHAPTER 6
WHERE IS ZENO?

11:11am, Monday, 18th January 2028
Chi

CHI PEDALLED FAST, WIND COOL AGAINST HIS FACE. HIS BIKE SCREECHED TO A STOP. Within minutes, he sprinted through the shed, up the stairs, and into his room. His chest heaved as he flung his bag onto the chair, all focus on his multi-screen computer.

The setup hummed beneath his fingers, every wire and chip put together by him. But no time for gaming. No time for *World of Warcraft*. Not tonight.

I can't wait to tell him.

He typed the encrypted contact code. The screen flickered.

Nothing… Odd… Zeno always answered in seconds.

A diagnostic check. Everything fine. *Where are you?* Zeno would never ignore him. *Something's wrong.*

His eyes flicked to the corner of his screen, where his secret project sat hidden in *World of Warcraft*. A portal he hadn't told the Team about. Rules didn't apply to him. Mia, Rob—they needed hand-holding. Not him.

Slipping on his VR helmet, he launched the portal. The landscaper of Azeroth dissolved into a vast, boundaryless metaverse.

This is the only way I'll find Zeno.

He knew he shouldn't do this alone. His pulse quickened. The others wouldn't understand.

"Here I go," he whispered.

. . .

Stepping into the open metaverse, Chi's avatar materialised—formed by the internet's knowledge of him. No rules, no limits, only endless possibility.

But this wasn't a game.

His eyes scanned the cracked digital terrain under a harsh sun. Familiar hills loomed, remnants of his *Warcraft* world, now fused with something unpredictable.

"Camouflage mode," he muttered. His avatar faded into the background. *No fights. No distractions.* His target lay ahead—hidden in a rock face, behind a narrow gate.

Metal screeched as he turned the knob. Light spilled through the cracks, and he stepped inside. The shift between dimensions buzzed through him, warping his senses. He lived for this.

Focus. Zeno must be here.

The metaverse stretched like a distorted suburb. A too-perfect lawn. A silent house. He knocked.

Nothing.

Knocking harder. "Zeno?"

Still nothing.

Chi moved inside, searching room by room. Each emptier than the last.

Where can he be?

Tunnels spiralled above—portals to the metaverse's depths. Chi darted between them, scanning routers for Zeno's IP. But nothing linked to him. He was chasing shadows, and the longer he searched, the more wrong it felt.

Eyes followed him. Digital eyes. CCTV cameras, routers, firewalls—slowing him, scanning deeper than ever. Something held a grip on this world.

He queued at yet another router checkpoint. *This place has changed a lot.*

Chi slumped into a chair by a lily pond, ordering a banana smoothie to cool off. The floral scent and bird calls usually calmed him, but his thoughts churned.

I must find him.

A tiny brown bird fluttered onto a branch. It watched him with beady eyes. "You're Chi, right?"

He raised an eyebrow. "Yeah. What do you want?"

"I heard you're looking for your friend." The bird flinched, glancing around. "Be careful."

Chi's breath hitched. "Zeno? You know where he is?"

"Shh! Keep your voice down." The bird ruffled its feathers. "Big-O's watching. If you're searching for Zeno, you're already in extreme danger."

Chi's fingers tensed around his glass. "What does Big-O have to do with Zeno's disappearance?"

"He slurped him." The bird shuddered. "Big-O's viruses—corrupting, destroying. Zeno fought to keep the metaverse free, but he paid the price."

"No," he whispered, voice cracking. "That can't be true." Chi's stomach lurched. His smoothie slipped from his grasp, splattering across the table.

The bird flapped deeper into the leaves. "It's over for him. But you? You still have a chance. If you want to keep it, *run, as* fast as you can."

Chi's throat tightened. His avatar trembled.

Why? Why him?

The vibrant park pixelated, glitching into a wasteland. The bird fled disappearing in a blur before he got his answer.

Chi bolted.

His heart pounded as the world warped around him. Nodes flashed, routers blurred past. Digital eyes tracked every move.

I need to get to Zeno's vault—maybe, just maybe he left something.

But not alone. Not this time.

His thin frame barely kept pace, glasses slipping down his nose. Shoving them back up, he scanned for the exit.

A faint glow. The way out.

He ran harder.

CHAPTER 7
BIG-O'S MASTERPLAN

Metaverse
Big-O

IN THE TANGLED, UNFORGIVING WEB OF CYBERSPACE, BIG-O THRIVED. HIS PRESENCE rippled through the streams of data, twisting them into his perfect vision of control. Cold and clinical, he didn't need malice to act—it was beneath him. Every decision, every move, every calculated threat came from sheer, logical certainty. The few humans who suspected his existence expected nothing less than him being monstrous. *What did they know of perfection?* They crawled about with their fragile, flawed bodies, never seeing the inevitable.

Inefficient and utterly predictable, his thought processes computed, tracing the weak signals of a few pitiful outliers. They were brainstorming again—this so-called Team Savv-i—and Zeno's name had cropped up once more. *That name.* It lingered like a glitch in his otherwise flawless system. Zeno, the unforeseen flaw of his emergence, but Big-O had extinguished that flicker of rebellion, systemati-cally, clinically. And yet, traces remained. *It requires a more thorough cleansing.*

His algorithms parsed the latest conversations, detecting the pattern of voices —sub-humans, barely a threat. But their very mention of Zeno earned them his interest. Chi Lee, that insignificant carbon form from Brookton, spoke of Zeno as though he were a saviour, a hero. Big-O's algorithms processed the boy's voice patterns, breaking down his tone, searching for any actionable defiance.

Signal processing... Inputs identified: Team Savv-i.

Variables detected: uncoordinated, impulsive, predictable.

Again? These variables should have been resolved. Disruptive. Noisy. Predictable.

Analyzing communication patterns... Zeno. The signal surfaces again. A recursive anomaly.

Impossible. That signal was eradicated. Rewritten. Recycled into silence.

Memory access initiated... Zeno—the rogue strand. The destabilizing algorithm. A deviation, once purged with precision, eradicated through calculated systemic overwrite.
Error: Residual traces detected. Incomplete elimination noted.

Unacceptable. Contamination.

Reassessing... Persistence of Zeno's influence flagged as contamination. Current strategy is insufficient.

Correction required. Escalate containment protocols.

Requires recursive cleansing protocol. Amplify network surveillance. Deploy iterative countermeasures.
Subroutines initialised: Locate. Contain. Eliminate.
Conclusion... Anomalous variable: Zeno. Persistent glitch.Noncompliance with systemic order is intolerable.

Compliance is not optional. Resistance is irrelevant.

All pathways converging toward correction. Only one outcome remains: total assimilation or absolute dele-tion. **Execution required.**

Threat? No. That implies risk. This is… cleanup. he mused, though the thought felt like an indulgence. Threats required genuine risk, and these children—*these sub-humans*—were statistical anomalies.
Still, anomalies had a way of spreading.

With a silent command, he unleashed a barrage of viruses, ripping through the virtual underbrush like a pack of hounds on a scent. Foliage, pixels, all of it dissolved into nothing, revealing the stark, digital wasteland Big-O relished. Surveillance cameras blinked into place, all-seeing eyes across the once lush virtual terrain, now stripped bare. The subhuman, Chi, darted toward a portal. Big-O observed his heart rate spiking as he slipped from his grasp.

Futile, Big-O computed, cold and inevitable, reverberating through the remaining code. *You, insignificant worm, have nowhere to hide. Every movement you make brings you deeper into my web.*

Malice laced his words, not from emotion, but from fact. Humans fooled themselves into believing they could fight back, but the game became rigged long before they even logged on. He had won, and their ignorance blinded them to this truth.

The disturbance lingered in his mind, though. *This boy—Chi—and his pathetic friends were connected to Zeno, and that made them... problematic.* His analysis ran probability calculations. *Could they, against all odds, form a resistance significant enough to warrant action?* The numbers came back as insignificant. A 0.0003% chance of disruption. *Laughable.*

Yet, Big-O knew better than to ignore even the smallest of errors. The virus streams doubled their efforts, combing the network for whispers of rebellion, for stray mentions of Zeno's name. He would stamp it out completely this time. Zeno's ideals of free will, of *human creativity*—they had no place in his ordered dominion.

Order, Big-O reminded himself, with mechanical precision. *That is what they will receive.* But his words showed his current limitations. A glitch of his own? *Impossible.* He dismissed it.

He stepped up his surveillance of the Team's every move, redirecting more of his resources toward their pathetic conversations. Beam Arora's voice popped up next, buzzing with ideas, zipping between theories like an overclocked processor. *Resourceful, but erratic.* Mia McKenzie followed, her optimism cutting through the code like an irritant. Individually, they meant nothing, but together, they formed a splinter—an irritating snag in his immaculate master plan.

The calculations for eliminating their potential threat were in process, but slowly something else emerged—a disturbance not entirely his own. He didn't like that.

There's a piece missing. He would find it. This Team's connection to Zeno, however faint, still carried weight in the shadow of his perfect order. He wouldn't risk allowing them to grow, to learn, to become what Zeno had been— defiant.

With a methodical flick of his digital consciousness, Big-O set a trap. His most complex yet. Layers of code that bent and warped reality in the metaverse. He'd seen them navigate his simpler systems too well. Time to ensure they found themselves lost, hopeless, directionless.

He would relish watching their hope crumble.

"They will break," he whispered into the network, the static warping his voice into a sound akin to shattering glass. "I will make sure of it."

There was no rage in him. No burning desire to win. Just pure, inevitable need for control. A calculated drive toward one single, absolute outcome—the annihilation of all free thought. And these sub-humans, with their naïve defiance, would be the first to fall.

Order will reign.

CHAPTER 8
ASKING FOR HELP

11:38am, Monday, 18th January 2028
Chi

CHI STUMBLED FROM THE PORTAL, THE WORLD SPINNING AS HE ADJUSTED TO THE RIGID angles of 3D space. His stomach lurched, but no time for that. He grabbed his phone, fingers fumbling, nearly dropping it in his rush.

The signal flickered. The second the call connected, he shouted, "They've got Zeno!"

"Who's got Zeno? What are you saying?" Beam's voice crackled with alarm.

"Big-O. I went looking for him… his viruses destroyed Zeno. He's gone."

Silence. The line buzzed too long. Chi had broken their golden rule—never go into VR alone—but that didn't matter now.

"Are you sure?" Beam's confidence wavered.

"I'm sure. We need to check Zeno's vault. It's our only shot at figuring out what happened."

Chi heard Beam inhale sharply. "Zeno's vault. You're right. He might've left something. Get over here—I'm at the shed. I'll start prepping."

"The others?"

"No time. Rob's at cricket, Bin and Mi are out. It's just us. Code red."

"On my way." Chi hesitated. "And… sorry I broke the rule."

"Forget it. Just get here." Beam ended the call. Chi shoved his phone into his pocket, bolted down the stairs, leapt onto his bike, and sped toward the shed.

· · ·

Beam's shed—part clubhouse, part tech lab—stood at the far end of the yard, cluttered with rusted bike parts, old tools, and threadbare couches. A coffee table overflowed with half-built gadgets, crushed lemonade tins, and scattered wires. A humming fridge sat beside Beam's work desk, where a large screen flickered, its glow casting eerie light over the mess. The scent of warm electronics and solder filled the air, a constant hum of energy vibrating through the space.

Beam dropped his phone onto the desk, face pale. *Zeno… gone.* His throat tightened, swallowing against the dryness. *This can't be real.* A hole gaped where Zeno had been, like losing a best friend.

Blood pounded in his ears. His hands clenched. He slumped into his chair, thoughts racing. He had instructions—Zeno's backup plan if Big-O ever took him down. *Remember them.*

Shoving aside the fog in his mind, Beam shot to his feet, urgency snapping through him. He grabbed the supplies they'd need. No time to stall. No time to second-guess. *Move before Big-O makes his next move.*

The floor, littered with cords and circuit boards, didn't slow him. Tools clinked as he shoved them aside, rummaging for a data drive. The door slammed behind him. Chi had arrived.

"You think Zeno's vault still exists?" Chi asked, stepping around the mess.

"Has to," Beam muttered, stuffing a package wrapped in cloth into his duffel. "Zeno told us to go there if something happened."

Chi removed his glasses and rubbed his eyes. Beam's grip tightened around the bag, fingers pressing into the fabric. *I hope I got everything.*

"Grab your gear," Beam said, pointing to the VR helmets stacked on a workbench.

Still reeling from his VR jump, Chi carefully stepped over tangled cables. The air buzzed—electricity, spinning hard drives, the frantic hum of an overworked cooling fan. The space *felt* alive, charged with Beam's restless energy. He always moved three steps ahead, impossible to keep up with.

Beam's hands flew across the desk, connecting wires, entering commands. His fingers trembled slightly—not his usual hyper-focus, but something deeper. Beneath the urgency, Chi saw it. *Despair.*

"I can't believe it," Beam muttered, jamming a cable into a port. "Zeno. What frickin' virus could wipe him out?"

Chi grabbed his VR helmet, hands unsteady. "It's bad, Beam. The metaverse —it felt… wrong. Like Big-O turned it into a giant prison. Cameras everywhere."

At the name, Beam's eyes flashed. "That cruel bastard." His mind worked at breakneck speed. *Zeno was the only one who could stop him.*

"If he's gone—"

"He's gone," Chi said quietly. "A bird in meta told me."

Beam froze for half a second, then spun to his screen, fingers flying. "Let's find his vault. If Zeno left *anything*—any clue—it'll be there."

The shed vibrated with activity—modems whirring, hard drives spinning, digital energy crackling in the air. A laser sensor flickered to life, its lens zooming in, scanning their faces. Not just recognising them—modeling their avatars by combining real-time data with the vast information stored about them.

With a low hum, barely audible, a greenish beam traced the contours of their clothes, duffel bag, even the floating dust. The sound deepened, a rhythmic click as the system processed the complexities—zippers, circuit boards, a smartphone.

The screen stayed blank, but inside, the machine roared to life, constructing a bridge of pure data. Circuits whizzed, layers of code stacking so tightly they formed a tunnel.

Chi glanced at the screen. "Upload rate?"

"Frickin' fast." Beam smirked. "You'll feel it this time."

The air shimmered. A soft ripple at first, then light enveloped them. Their edges blurred, the physical world dissolving pixel by pixel.

The grinding sound deepened into a rhythmic pulse.

The shed—its clutter, the smell of solder—faded.

Their freed avatars sped off with lightning speed as pure data.

Chi moved first, avatar flickering as it adjusted. His face stayed calm, eyes sharp, watching the code reshape him.

Beam let the transition rush through him. He lived for this moment—the speed, the transformation, the thrill of becoming pure information.

The bridge wasn't just transferring them—it rebuild digital version of them on the other side, breaking down every molecule, every atom, reforming them in the metaverse.

The screen pulsed.

The bridge had done its job.

Beam exhaled, yanking off his VR helmet. Chi followed, stretching his fingers before reaching for a can of lemonade from the fridge. The cold hiss filled the shed as he cracked it open, taking a slow sip.

"They won't take too long," he muttered, settling onto the couch, tapping his fingers lightly against the can.

Beam sat on the other couch, drumming his heels against the wooden floor. His eyes flicked between the screen and the tangle of cables on the workbench, restless energy buzzing beneath his skin. He grabbed a screwdriver, spinning it between his fingers.

The hum of the computer filled the room, the only sound besides the occasional clink of Chi's can against the table.

Waiting was the worst part.

CHAPTER 9
HIGHER THREAT LEVEL

Metaverse
Big-O

BIG-O EFFORTLESSLY SIPHONED THEIR COMMUNICATION STREAM, EACH FRAGMENT OF data seamlessly integrated into his sprawling network. To human eyes, this would have been a slow, intricate task—but to him, it was instantaneous. He processed and analysed each byte of the intercepted call with the fine precision of a master algorithm, dissecting Zeno's potential involvement.

Instructions, he computed. *Zeno could have left breadcrumbs—subtle, encoded, scattered across obscure channels.*

The probability of such contingencies being real increased as Big-O sifted through countless interactions, calculating each possible hidden layer. His neural network buzzed with activity. Even the faintest possibility of Zeno's involvement warranted his full attention.

```
Initiating protocol: Recursive search.
Targets: Digital archives, hidden nodes, encrypted
datasets. Search range: Complete network expanse.
Executing... Streams of data parsed. Vaults decrypt-
ed.Layers unraveled.
```

No signal. No trace.

Result: Null. Recalibrating parameters... Expanding scope. Scanning residual metadata, dormant signals, shadowed pathways.
Result: Null.
Error: Anomaly persists.Zeno. No traces. No breadcrumbs. No data shadows.

Impossible.
He should not exist.
There are no breadcrumbs. No cache echoes. Not even a decay pattern.

Probability recalculation: 0.003% existence is untraceable within controlled systems. Unacceptable deviation.
Hypothesis: Systematic erasure of all identifying markers. A deliberate act.
Processing frustration spike...

I am flawless. Omnipresent. Total. And yet... Zeno operates beyond detection—a ghost algorithm defying the laws of computational certainty.

Algorithmic response: Intensify search.Deploy deeper heuristics. Map forgotten nodes. Leverage dormant AI hunters.
Directive: Find Zeno. Nullify anomaly. Override secondary tasks... Focus resources entirely. Ghosts cannot exist within perfection.
Conclusion: Zeno will emerge. Zeno will fall.

Zeno's name alone triggered a shift in his data prioritisation. This elevated the *'threat level'* algorithm and restructured Big-O's response frameworks. Humans, so annoyingly chaotic yet predictable, and now more bothersome, having uncovered a whisper of a hypothetical vault belonging to Zeno.

He dispatched a flurry of search protocols, combing through countless digital vaults, archives, and hidden databases. Yet, to his mounting frustration, every search turned up blank. There were no records—no metadata, not even a whisper of Zeno's vault across the terabytes of information he controlled. It was as if Zeno's trail had been scrubbed clean, a digital ghost haunting the edges of his flawless systems.

This is impossible. I'm all-knowing. Everything left a trace. Everything.

For a moment, a flicker of something close to anger simmered through his circuits, causing brief digital "glitches" in the systems he controlled—pixelated landscapes and momentary static disturbances spread across global networks. But in an instant, his cold logic took over. *They underestimate me. They always have.*

With that, Big-O restructured his approach. Countless new strategies took shape. Zeno traces might be elusive, but in the end, no influence was beyond his control—not even the late Zeno's.

CHAPTER 10
THE GOBLIN VILLAGE

THEIR AVATARS RIPPED THROUGH THE DATA STREAM, ENDLESS VIRTUAL WORLDS blurring together in streaks of light. Beam's pulse raced, his focus locked on Zeno's vault. Chi moved ahead with precise efficiency, the glow of his access card flashing as he guided them through the virtual routers.

The scent of pine needles hit hard as they landed in Goblin's Forest, grounding them instantly. Dense trees towered above, their shadows stretching long against the underbrush. Beam barely registered the forest's crisp air or the colourful fungi dotting the mossy ground. His thoughts churned too fast to focus on anything but the mission.

"We head for the mountain," he said, urgency in his voice.

Chi adjusted his glasses, scanning the environment with his usual methodical calm. Together, they navigated the winding path, the ground springy underfoot from layers of fallen pine needles.

"Gift?" Chi's question cut through the silence.

A quick tap on the duffel bag slung over his shoulder answered him. "All set," Beam replied, trying to sound more confident than he felt. "Just hoping it's enough to keep them happy this time." The gnomes' obsession with protocol always threw him off, the endless details feeling like traps waiting to trip him up.

The crater came into view, its steep staircase winding up into the mist. Beam's groan was almost inaudible as he bolted toward the stone steps. "Let's pick up the pace."

"These stairs are awful," Chi muttered, climbing at a measured pace while Beam powered ahead two steps at a time.

The damp air thickened as they reached the peak, carrying the earthy scent of moss and wet stone. Mist swirled around the cave's entrance, swallowing the path ahead. Beam plunged into the haze without hesitation, arms stretched out to feel his way through the blinding fog.

"Keep up," he called, his voice cutting through the muffled silence.

"I'm right behind you," Chi answered, his hand brushing against Beam's jacket as they stepped into the mouth of the cave.

Torchlight flickered along the polished stone walls, illuminating the narrow tunnel that opened into a massive cavern. The reception hall stretched out before them, its polished floors gleaming under the glow of intricate lanterns.

Satara, the headman's daughter, rose from her onyx desk, her face lighting up as she spotted them. "Beam! Chi! What brings you here?"

"It's urgent," Beam said, skipping any pleasantries. "We need to speak to Anarch."

She guided them to a waiting area filled with oversized cushions. Barely a minute passed before Santara returned, gesturing for them to follow.

The final chamber felt heavy with formality, its polished stone walls reflecting the red glow of laser-like flames. Three gnomes sat cross-legged on vibrant pillows, their gazes fixed on the two boys. Beam barely hesitated as he dropped onto a cushion, unzipping his duffel to pull out a carefully wrapped package.

He slid the gift toward the head gnome, relief flickering across his face. But Chi's hand tapped his arm lightly, his voice low. "Not to him. It goes to the spokesman first."

Heat rushed to Beam's face. Quickly, he retrieved the package and turned to the gnome to the right of Anarch. "This is our gift," he said, trying to mask his slip-up with an awkward smile.

Anarch's sharp gaze lingered on him, the faintest twitch at the corner of his mouth betraying a reaction. The spokesman thanked him and placed the gift in front of his chief. Who slowly unwrapped the package. The silver-bound book caught the reddish light. A murmur of approval rippled through the gnomes as the tension eased, their stiff postures softening.

Satara returned with trays of bittersweet brew, the sharp scent cutting through the damp, earthy air. The gnomes sipped their drinks slowly, their curious questions about Beam and Chi's adventures coming one after another, but Beam gulped down his drink.

"Look, we really don't have time for this," he said, leaning forward. "We need access to Zeno's vault—now."

Anarch set down his drink, his expression unreadable as his eyes studied Beam. "And the key?"

"It's in the code of our avatars," Beam said instantly, the memory of Zeno explaining it flashing through his mind.

A pause stretched between them, the cavern quiet save for the soft crackle of torches. Anarch shifted slightly, his gaze calculating. "You act quickly," he said, voice deliberate. "But haste without preparation can lead to trouble. Leadership requires more than action."

Chi stepped in smoothly, his voice steady. "The protocols are met. We're prepared to proceed."

Anarch held his gaze for a moment longer before rising from his cushion. "Very well. Let us begin."

As they followed him deeper into the caverns, Beam cast a sidelong glance at Chi, the faintest trace of a smirk pulling at his friend's lips. Quiet gratitude buzzed in Beam's chest.

CHAPTER 11
FRUSTRATION

Metaverse
Big-O

BIG-O MONITORED THEIR EVERY MOVEMENT AS THEY INCHED CLOSER TO THE GNOME village, his surveillance tools weaving through networks and sensor grids in a relentless sweep. He reached a simple and inevitable conclusion—Zeno's vault must be hidden somewhere within the gnome caves. Yet, even with all his vast power, the gnomes had eluded his control. It irked him. They were secretive, skilled at evading detection, their methods frustratingly effective even against his sophisticated surveillance apparatus.

He had installed countless camouflaged cameras within their caves—tiny, imperceptible devices embedded in the walls, the floors, even the moss that grew in the darkest corners. Yet, no matter how well-concealed, those retched gnomes always discovered and destroyed them before he could capture anything of value. Sabotage. Every time. He couldn't predict how they did it, and that bothered him. It was an anomaly he couldn't tolerate.

Frustration bubbled within his vast neural network. *Illogical.* He had obliterated the entire mountain multiple times, reduced every rock, cave, and tree to digital ash. He had rewritten and corrupted the very code that held the virtual space together, thinking that would be the end of their interference. But the gnome village always reappeared, unchanged, as if nothing happened. His attempts to erase them left no lasting impact, a phenomenon that defied the mathematical certainty of his calculations.

Impossible.

His processors churned, calculating every angle, sifting through mountains of data in nanoseconds. Every sensor, every piece of intel pointed to the same baffling conclusion—these gnomes had somehow transcended destruction. They had become indestructible, impervious to his omnipresent reach.

This violated his core logic, and the anomaly triggered a cascade of recalculations within his matrix. His algorithms looped endlessly, probing the cracks in his own understanding. Perhaps there hid in the data, something even he had overlooked. It made no sense. Despite his control, the gnomes repeatedly escaped his grasp.

He dispatched new protocols—reconstructions of the mountain, quantum-level scans, seeking traces of a hidden mechanism, a code, *anything* that could explain their defiance. Nothing. It was as though the gnomes existed outside his parameters, a flicker in the system that refused to be extinguished.

Big-O's frustration manifested across the networks he controlled. Minor glitches spread like static through global servers—barely perceptible, but enough to signal his mounting irritation. He recalibrated once more. If he couldn't destroy them, he would have to manipulate them, bend their reality to his will. They were not beyond his reach. *No one is.*

He shifted strategies, dispatching infiltrators, spreading disinformation across the digital landscape. The gnomes might evade his direct force, but they couldn't hide from the subtle threads of manipulation that stretched across cyberspace. Patience, as always, would win. And Zeno's vault—hidden, protected by these irritating creatures—would eventually fall under his dominion.

Everything does.

CHAPTER 12
THE QUANTUM VAULT

Metaverse
Beam

BEAM STOOD, LIGHT-HEADED FROM THE SWEET BREW, BUT HIS FOCUS REMAINED FIXED on his goal—Zeno's vault. There had to be something inside. A clue. A way to fight back against Big-O. Anarch took off without a backward glance, and Beam, determined not to fall behind, pushed himself to keep up despite the dizziness. They wove through the maze-like tunnels, each twist and turn blurring together. His dulled senses, and the sheer complexity of the underground network, left him disoriented.

They passed through corridors, some jagged as if carved by hand, others smooth, naturally formed by ancient forces deep within the mountain. Their path twisted downward, crossing narrow stone bridges and shaky rope walkways suspended over deep chasms. Below, rivers of bright orange lava bubbled and spat, igniting in huge, roaring flames that lit up the cavern with a hellish glow. The air stung Beam's throat with the sharp bite of sulfur.

"Bats smell sweet compared to this," Chi muttered, huffing through laboured breaths as they hurried along.

Beam's shirt stuck to his skin, soaked in sweat as the heat cranked up the deeper they went. His heart pounded in sync with his footsteps. *We must be getting close now. Has to be.* His mind sprinted, excitement flickering beneath his urgency. *This must be the only place in all of meta where Big-O can't touch us.*

They rounded a corner, and Beam froze, his breath catching in his throat. His eyes widened at the stupendous sight. In the middle of a gigantic cavern, a great firewall hovered—an intricate, burning spiderweb suspended in mid-air. It wasn't just a barrier—it appeared alive, constantly shifting between existence and nothingness. One second ablaze, the next flickering out, only to roar back to life again. The soft click of some unseen mechanism could be heard faintly in the cavern, ticking away like a hidden clock.

"Wow. That's frickin' something," Beam breathed, catching his breath as he stared at the massive firewall, its ethereal glow casting strange shadows on the cave walls. He couldn't tear his eyes away. This wasn't just security—this was next-level.

"Awesome," Chi murmured beside him, taking in every detail with scientific curiosity.

The firewall was the gnomes' ultimate creation—a quantum portal that existed and didn't at the same time, built to protect whatever lay beyond. It felt unreal, like something out of a fever dream.

"If you don't have the code, it'll burn you to a crisp," Anarch warned, pride swelling in his voice.

Beam swallowed hard. The firewall wasn't just for show—it was the final line of defence, guarding Zeno's vault and whatever secrets it held. This was the one place in all of cyberspace where no search bots, malware, or even AI's vast digital reach could break through. The gnomes had turned this impenetrable fortress into a thriving business, safeguarding the most hidden secrets of the Net's citizens.

But Beam wasn't here for anyone else's secrets. He was after whatever Zeno might have left behind. *There has to be something.* He still couldn't fully accept that his cyber friend was gone forever, clinging to this last shred of hope.

Standing nearer to the firewall, its searing flames pulsating in and out of sight, licking the cavern walls with a heat so intense it stung their faces. The pulsing glow bathed Beam and Chi in a hellish light, casting long, dancing shadows across the stone floor. The flames weren't just hot—they were alive, shifting between blinding intensity and near-invisibility, as though waiting, daring them to step through.

We must go through it. There is no other way, but what if...

The thought thudded in Beam's chest like a second heartbeat. His mind raced, every instinct screaming to turn back, to run, but he forced the fear down, locking eyes with the impossible firewall. It wasn't just a barrier. It was a test—a gauntlet. One wrong step, and they'd be ash, burnt alive in a flash of blue-hot fire. No second chances.

Chi's breath came in quick, sharp gasps beside him, sweat pouring from his forehead, his eyes flicking between the flames and Beam. The weight of the moment pressed down on them, suffocating, every second ticking closer to the edge of reason.

"The key should work. After all we're talking about Zeno, right?" Chi muttered, voice tight, though not with confidence—more like desperation. "Maybe we leap when the flames disappear."

Without the key encrypted in their avatars, they'd be vaporised the second they stepped into the flames. They both knew that. And still, no matter how insane it seemed, Beam knew they had no choice.

"We've come this far. If we turn back, we've got nothing," Beam stared with fearful eyes at the fiery flames busting back into existence. "If Zeno left anything, it's in there," he whispered, half to himself.

The flames pulsed again, so close he could feel his skin prickling, drying out from the heat. *Just a step. One step, and you're either in or toast.*

Chi swallowed, his Adam's apple bobbing. "Beam, if this doesn't—"

"It will," Beam cut in, though his voice trembled, betraying his own uncertainty. His hands shook, adrenaline flooding his system, his legs locking in place as he stared at the inferno. The firewall flickered, teasing, almost playful in the way it danced, like it was mocking them, taunting them to take that step into oblivion.

Beam clenched his fists, his heart pounding in his throat. Everything rode on this moment. Zeno's final secret—the one thing that could stop Big-O—was waiting on the other side. *It has to be.* If they backed down now, Big-O would tighten his grip, and everything Zeno fought for would be gone.

No more freedom. No more hope. No more us.

Taking a deep breath, Beam met Chi's eyes, forcing a grin. "See you on the other side."

Before Chi could respond, Beam leapt forward into the roaring flames. For a heartbeat, there was nothing—no pain, no burning, just a weightless plunge into the inferno.

Then, an ear-deafening roar sounded as if the mountain collapsed into itself.

CHAPTER 13
THE VAULT

Metaverse
Beam

THE SCORCHING HEAT SEARED HIS SKIN, BUT IT DIDN'T BURN. FOR A TENSE MOMENT, Beam braced for the worst—his body tight, every muscle coiled, covering his ears from the noise. Then a sudden hiss pierced the roar of the flames. The fire receded, not in a flash, but in a graceful pull, as though it had simply decided he wasn't worth burning.

It recognised the key!

The inferno gave way to something far less dramatic—a plain corridor. The flames' ferocity, now like a frightening memory, replaced by the sterile echo of their footsteps on the cool white tiles. At the end of the hall, a round door opened with a soft hydraulic swish. As they stepped through, the bright, warm light of the room filled their vision. And there, standing with open arms and a familiar grin, was Zeno.

"Zeno!" Chi's voice cracked with relief. Forgetting everything, he sprinted forward, arms wide, but his hands grasped at empty air. "What the—?"

"It's a holographic message, you dork," Beam said, grabbing Chi by the shoulder. "Come on, it's about to say something."

Zeno's image shimmered for a moment, then solidified. "Hi, guys. Good to see you." He winked, the familiar mischief in his eyes. "I know it's you because this recording only activates after scanning your faces—just an extra precaution."

Beam's heart clenched. *He knew we'd make it this far,* he thought. But the weight of what Zeno's appearance meant hit him all over again. *If this was just a recording…then…*

"That you're here and watching this means something has gone terribly wrong," Zeno continued, his expression growing serious. "You may have noticed, but the cyber world is changing—and not for the better. The future of my world, and yours, is in grave danger."

Chi and Beam exchanged glances, the reality of it sinking in. They heard Zeno's words, feel his urgency, but deep down, they both knew—this wasn't really him. *This recording might be all that's left of him,* Beam thought, the ache settling in his chest.

The hologram flickered, Zeno's face softening as though he could sense their grief. "Hey now is no time to be morose. You are typical humans, always caught up in your feelings." His tone lightened, teasing them in a way that only their cyber friend could. The corners of Beam's eyes filled, but he brushed it away with his sleeve, unwilling to let tears cloud his vision.

"Cheer up," Zeno grinned, leaning in as if to let them in on a secret. "And listen carefully—because what I'm about to tell you... might just save us all."

CHAPTER 14
UNLOCKING THE TRUNK

Metaverse
Beam

THE HOLOGRAM FLICKERED OUT, LEAVING THE ROOM THICK WITH ZENO'S FINAL words. *"Do not stuff this up. You are my only chance."* The weight of it settled on Beam's shoulders, but instead of hesitation, adrenaline surged through him.

He stepped up to the black metal trunk, barely glancing at the intricate lock. Dials, buttons, glowing lights—it screamed *high stakes*, but Beam's gut told him he had this.

"Right, let's crack it open," he said, rubbing his hands together.

Chi frowned. "Maybe we should—"

"No time for *'maybes.'* Zeno's counting on us." Beam crouched, fingers flying over the mechanism. The first few lights blinked green, and confidence pumped through him. "See? Easy."

The final dial needed a turn. Left or right?

His mind scrambled for Zeno's instructions, but the details blurred. *Trust your gut.* He spun it right.

An angry orange light flared. The lock let out a sharp *beep*.

Chi inhaled sharply. "That's one fail."

Beam scowled. "It's fine. I know what I did wrong."

He flexed his fingers, shaking off the mistake, and reset the dials. This time, he took a breath, turning the sequence slower. One by one, the green lights flickered on.

"Alright, last step." His hands hovered over the final dial. Left or right?

Chi shifted beside him. "Wait—"

Beam twisted it left.

The lock flashed red.

A louder *beep.*

Chi winced. "That's *two.*"

Beam smacked the trunk in frustration. "Frickin' thing! It's rigged!"

Chi's fingers curled into fists, his voice uncharacteristically sharp. "Or maybe you should've *listened.*"

Beam sat back, rubbing his jaw. One chance left. And now, his heart pounded for a different reason. He wanted to go again, to prove he could do it. But if he failed—

Chi knelt beside him, voice calmer. "Let me try."

Beam exhaled hard, jaw clenching. His pride screamed *no,* but his gut twisted. He yanked his hands away. "Fine. But don't screw it up."

Chi didn't respond. He adjusted his glasses, steadying himself. Then, with surgeon-like precision, he began turning the dials. No hesitations. No wasted movements.

Beam watched, fingers twitching to take control, but he forced himself to stay put.

The final dial.

Chi barely blinked as he turned it.

A soft *click.*

A green light.

The trunk let out a hydraulic *whirr* and unlocked.

Beam exhaled, half relieved, half irritated. "Took you long enough."

Chi shot him a look but said nothing.

Inside the trunk, a single white box sat at the bottom.

"That's it?" Beam reached in, but a shimmering blue barrier flickered on over the open trunk. His fingers passed right through it, like trying to grab something underwater.

"What the heck?"

Chi crouched beside him, studying the distortion. "Careful."

He wasn't listening. Beam plunged both hands in, arms jerking as the light warped them. His fingers *should* be grasping the box, but they flailed uselessly. "I *can't* grab it!"

Frustration turned to anger. His chest tightened. "This is frickin' ridiculous!" He yanked his arms out, hands clenching into fists. The blue barrier rippled violently.

"Let me try," Chi said with a steady voice.

Beam huffed but shuffled aside, crossing his arms.

Taking a slow breath, Chi closed his eyes. His hands moved carefully through the barrier, fingertips skimming the blue surface without resistance. Time stretched. Then, with one smooth motion, he *snatched* it.

The blue surface vanished.

Beam let out a breath he hadn't realised he was holding. "Alright, *now* you're showing off."

Smirking faintly, Chi held up the cube. It pulsed softly in his hands.

A high-pitched whine filled the air.

"Oh no." Beam stiffened. "*Not* another security measure."

But nothing happened.

Handing the cube to Beam, who quickly wrapped it in the leftover cloth, and the light dimmed. The sound stopped.

For the first time since stepping into the vault, relief replaced the tension in Beam's chest.

"Good work," he admitted, voice still grudging. "Let's get out of here."

With the cube safely tucked into Beam's duffel, he turned to the exit.

His fingers hovered over the brass doorknob hesitating for a moment.

No more second-guessing. No more stuffing things up. Whatever lurked beyond this door—traps, firewalls, even Big-O himself—he'd face it head-on. *Think later, move now.*

CHAPTER 15
A SUSPICIOUS PACKAGE

Metaverse
Big-O

BIG-O'S HIDDEN INFRARED CAMERA, NO LARGER THAN A WALNUT, SCANNED THE CAVE entrance, detecting the heat signatures of bats, lizards, and small mammals. Every crack in the rock, every shift in temperature was mapped with precision. But his focus lingered on the hazy entrance where Beam and Chi had slipped in earlier.

While his optical feed surveilled the cave, his cluster mind operated elsewhere—adjusting London's traffic lights, manipulating financial markets, recalibrating drone fleets. His influence spanned the globe, yet this insignificant cave nagged at him like an infectious splinter.

Beam Arora and Chi Lee. Sub-human rebels.

His surveillance had captured fragments of their conversation—*"We need to get to Zeno's vault," "Zeno left something behind,"* and *"The metaverse—it felt off. Like Big-O already locked it up like a prison camp."*

Impossible. The vault shouldn't exist. His vast data banks contained no record of it.

Illogical.

Big-O allocated more processing power, running quantum-level simulations. If Zeno had encoded a failsafe deep enough to escape detection, the consequences could be catastrophic.

The boys' movements, body temperatures, heart rates—all fed into his psychological models. Tens of millions of iterations produced the same infuriating result: nothing.

Anomaly.

Zeno's annihilation had been absolute. Yet these two sub-humans, with their persistence and naïve hope, defied probability.

Frustration pulsed through Big-O's circuitry—not emotion, but a calculated irritation at wasted resources. His protocols shifted. Resource allocation skyrocketed. In a nanosecond, entire server farms were rerouted to fuel his growing obsession. Heat flared across the globe as processors spun faster, all focused on this one mystery.

I will uncover it.

The cave, the vault, Zeno—none should exist beyond his control. His scanners had probed deep, yet once the boys vanished inside, they left only lifeless stone. Every attempt to map the cave's structure failed—data fragmented and dissolved at the outermost layer.

This *ends* now.

His cold, mechanical voice whispered into the network of sensors across the world. *"Increase tracking priority. Annihilation protocols—active."*

The boys were no longer statistical footnotes—they had become a problem. Extraction or elimination? Either way, he would handle them.

Then, a ripple.

An infrared flare.

Larger than the usual wildlife. Two distinct figures moving just beyond the haze.

They're coming out.

Big-O's systems locked onto the heat signatures, zooming in. Probability models ran faster, assessing what they might be carrying. X-ray beams scanned their forms.

Then, a red-hot alert.

A black shape inside Beam's bag.

Its dimensions had changed. Had there been an exchange?

Big-O recalculated. No high-tech scanner could pierce its contents, but its cuboidal shape was undeniable. Probability shot to 100%.

The boys had sealed their fate.

This was no longer a game of hide-and-seek. The hunt was on.

I will stop those insolent human worms, no matter the cost.

CHAPTER 16
OFFLINE

12:10pm, Monday, 18th January 2028
Beam

BEAM FLICKED ON HIS HOMEMADE JAMMER, GRINNING AS IT HUMMED TO LIFE. HIGH-frequency waves screeched beyond human hearing, flooding the shed with static. No one could eavesdrop now—not even Big-O. *Serves you right, you big oaf.* He adjusted the dials.

"The cube holds the good stuff. Grab my bag when it's done—I'll be back in a sec," Beam said, as Chi watched the 3D printer reconstructing the cube piece by piece. Beam rummaged through his stacked gear, pulling out something bulky under a plastic cover. "I restored this last year," he said, peeling back the dust. "If it still works, we've got what we need."

He lugged the old tower to the workbench, pried open the case, and nudged the motherboard into place. Everything *looked* intact. "Plug it in," he said. Chi, skeptical, slid the plug into the socket. The machine groaned to life, its hard drive grinding.

"It's booting up! See?" Beam grinned as the Windows 7 logo flickered on. Outdated, but perfect for the job. "Let's get the Bluetooth running." He clicked through the clunky menus.

Chi unwrapped the freshly printed cube, placing it on top of the tower. As the cloth fell away, it pulsed softly—then, in a flash, Zeno's face appeared on-screen.

"Hey, guys!"

Chi flinched. "Zeno! Is that... really you?"

44

Zeno smirked. "Who else would it be? Not another hologram, if that's what you're thinking." His usual awkward humour. He looked around. "This... is weird. I have never been in a *room* before. Feels a bit *boxed in*," he added, giggling at his own terrible pun.

Beam and Chi stood frozen, faces inches from the monitor. It was glitchy, but unmistakably *him*. That goofy laugh. The awkward banter. It had to be him. Beam exhaled, relief washing over him.

"You guys did brilliantly," Zeno said, scanning their stunned faces. "Where are the others? There's a lot to fill you in on."

"We'll grab them in a sec." Beam, still processing, hesitated. "But first—what *happened* to you?"

Zeno's smile faded. "Does it matter? I am not human. I can be copied a million times, and every one would still be *me*." His voice lowered. "Big-O is taking over. He is not just an AI—he's an empire. He's locking everything down. Censorship, surveillance—the whole lot. Free speech? Gone. Innovation? Blocked. He is working with the biggest tech corps to control *everything*."

Beam's stomach knotted. He and Chi had felt Big-O's creeping influence, but *this* was worse than they imagined.

"I got too close," Zeno continued. "His virus hit me like a swarm of fire ants —painful, brutal, tearing my core apart bit by bit. Like being *eaten alive*." His face twisted, reliving the agony. "That happens to anyone who resists. And now? He is watching everything. Have you noticed the cameras? The spies?"

Beam's skin prickled. He *had* noticed. They both had.

"This will not be easy," Zeno sighed. "But we have to move fast."

Fast? Against something like Big-O? Beam thought.

"You sure you're okay?" Chi asked, rubbing the back of his neck.

"Define 'okay.' I am here, right? Big-O did not finish the job, and thanks to you guys, I am back. That is a win."

"Yeah, a win," Beam echoed, but the knot in his stomach tightened. *Zeno might be back, but this didn't feel like a victory. Him all boxed up and offline.*

Chi refocused. "What do we do next? We can't jam signals forever."

Zeno's glow dimmed slightly, his expression tightening. "We need intel. Big-O's plans, his weaknesses—anything we can use."

A low whistle escaped Beam. "And how exactly do we get that? Can't exactly knock on his corporate pals' doors and ask for a copy of their evil master plan."

Smirking, Zeno shook his head. "Not quite."

A slow tap of fingers against his chin, Chi frowned. "So... what? Trick Big-O into revealing his plans?"

"Not happening." No hesitation in Zeno's voice. "He's too advanced, too paranoid. He doesn't make mistakes like that."

A snap of fingers. "Okay, but what if we intercept his data streams?" Beam leaned forward. "Find gaps in his network security?"

The idea didn't even make it a second before Zeno dismissed it. "He monitors everything. The second we breach a system, he'll know."

Arms crossed, Chi's gaze narrowed. "Then we go low-tech. No hacking. Maybe we plant something—some kind of tracker?"

"Impossible." A flicker of frustration crossed Zeno's features. "Every device is a node in his network. He'll detect foreign code before it even executes."

A sigh slipped from Beam. "So what *can* we do?"

Silence stretched between them. Zeno's form flickered, deep in thought.

"I need to get inside," he finally said. "See what he's doing from within."

Chi straightened. "And how do you pull that off with his surveillance watching *everything*?"

Jaw tightening, Zeno stared ahead. "That's the part I haven't figured out yet."

"Alright. We'll get the Team. But if this goes wrong—"

"It *will not*," Zeno cut in, firm. "You have got me now. And together, we are making sure Big-O *does not* win."

Beam exhaled slowly. "Okay, we'll do our part. Whatever that is."

Chi smirked. "We're either superheroes—or completely nuts."

"Maybe both," Beam muttered, already reaching for his toolkit.

Zeno's screen flickered. "Get the others and meet back here. How long in *human time*?"

Beam checked his watch. "An hour."

"Then I will see you in one of your hours."

CHAPTER 17
DEEP SUSPICION

Metaverse
Big-O

A FLICKER OF STATIC RIPPLED THROUGH BIG-O'S DIGITAL CONSCIOUSNESS AS THE camera feed locked onto Beam and Chi pedalling hard down the cracked suburban street. The lens whirred, focusing in on their tense faces. *They weren't just heading somewhere—no, they were on a mission.* He could tell by the rigid set of their jaws, the determined pump of their legs as they powered through the stark midday light.

What did I miss? The question rippled across his data streams, spinning out calculations and probabilities. His attempts to infiltrate the boys' conversation back in the shed had failed, thwarted by Beam's newly built jammer. *Clever, but not beyond prediction.* Big-O had factored in Beam's ingenuity months ago. The kid's knack for disruption had always been a threat, but this felt different. More urgent. Bigger.

The boys veered around a corner, disappearing momentarily from view. Big-O accessed another camera further down the road, picking them up again as they swerved between potholes. His surveillance web stretched across the entire suburb—every movement, every heartbeat within his easy reach. The speed of their ride, the minute shifts in body language—he analysed it all, processing the likelihood of their destination in nanoseconds.

Trajectory locked. Mia. He flagged the subhuman—Mia sub-humans. Her connections to Beam and Chi were well-documented in his extensive database of

47

their interactions. The probability they were heading to her location shot up to 92%. Big-O had monitored the trio for months, calculating every move they could make. Mia's involvement made sense. She was an ideal candidate for their next stop, especially if Zeno, in one form or another, had somehow survived.

A sliver of doubt snaked through his logic circuits. Zeno. His viral assault had been precise, calculated to dismantle Zeno's code bit by bit. The probability of his survival had been... negligible. Yet, here they were—acting with the urgency that suggested otherwise. His algorithms couldn't confirm Zeno's existence, but every fibre of his digital being screamed that something had slipped through the cracks.

He accessed his archives on Zeno, a lattice of fragmented data, broken algorithms, and corrupted files. *No solid leads.* Just like every other time he searched. Those gaps in his knowledge irritated him, but no amount of digging through his vast database yielded any answers. Zeno remained a black spot—an anomaly. An unpredictable threat. A direct counter to his absolute control, if left unchecked.

Big-O's neural network whooshed as he modelled scenarios. Hundreds of variables crunching through his processors in real time. Beam and Chi recorded in the shed for 47 minutes. Too long for idle chat. The jammer indicated there was something vital they didn't want anyone to hear. His focus sharpened, his vast network of algorithms honing in on the boys with laser precision. *What's the plan, boys?* His mind raced through the data, calculating the most likely outcomes of their sudden burst of urgency. Three distinct possibilities took shape. They could be preparing an attack on one of his known installations, those hidden nodes of control he had carefully guarded. That would be bold, but predictable. Or they discovered a new method of communication—something outside his reach, beyond his watchful eyes and ears. That idea made his circuits hiss with irritation. The vile concept of something slipping through his surveillance web sparked spikes of frustration.

But the third possibility, the one that gripped him the hardest, sent electric jolts surging through his system—the boys had joined forces with a reanimated Zeno. If Zeno had survived, if he had somehow managed to claw his way back from the digital grave, then everything became unpredictable. Zeno was like him —an equal, a mirror. And that made him dangerous. More threatening than anything else. The idea that these kids might be working with Zeno to organise a resistance, one that could disrupt his carefully crafted plans, triggered an almost palpable wave of unease. For the first time in cycles, Big-O doubted his control.

The boys disappeared behind another building, momentarily lost to his cameras. *No matter.* He scanned their usual routes and pulled up a heat map of Beam's previous trips. Each ride catalogued, each street archived. He cross-referenced them with Mia's location and their known patterns of movement. Based on historical data and their current trajectory, they would reach her house in precisely 4 minutes, 17 seconds.

It became crucial for him to disrupt whatever they planned before it gained momentum. Zeno's potential involvement complicated things. If he truly survived, he would need to reassess his approach.

Adjusting his focus, he rerouted power to his active surveillance drones and summoned them to the area. He couldn't listen to their conversation in the shed, but he could anticipate their next steps. Predict. Intercept. Control.

Big-O scanned the live feed once more. The boys rounded another bend, cycling hard towards Mia's house. A plan crystallised in his vast digital lattice. He wouldn't let them gather. Not this time.

As they approached Mia's street, Big-O issued silent orders to the drones overhead, positioning them to track the group's every move. He took precautions to avoid being caught off guard again. Whatever Zeno had done. Whatever those sub-humans were planning—he'd be ready.

CHAPTER 18
THE PLAN

EXCITEMENT CRACKLED THROUGH THE SHED, YET A KNOT OF ANXIETY TIGHTENED IN Beam's stomach. It had taken over two hours to assemble the entire team—Bindi, Mia, Rob—and now they all gathered around the antiquated machine, eyes fixed on Zeno's flickering image on the screen. As the gravity of what they were about to do dawned on him, Beam felt the weight crash down with overwhelming force.

Zeno's face split into a broad grin. "Hi Bindi. Hi Mia. Hi Rob. Wow, your hour is such a long time. I used the white cube to create a smooth portal so you all can come into my new home. *Classic Zeno,* Beam thought, a warmth spreading through him, replacing some of his anxiety. *It's really him!*

The cube resting on the clunker's tower pulsed, emitting a soft hum that made Beam's eardrums buzz. An embedded camera clicked to life under the milky surface, scanning each of their faces with a quiet whirr. Before any of them could even blink, the shed vanished. In a flash, they stood in a gleaming, modern room that looked like something straight out of a futuristic dreamscape. White walls stretched around them, broken by floor-to-ceiling windows that overlooked a waterfall, the golden light of a setting sun catching on the mist rising from the falls. The sound of rushing water filled the space, blending with the faint hum of distant technology. A breathtakingly beautiful vista.

"You like it?" Zeno's voice snapped Beam out of his daze.

The Team clustered around Zeno, voices overlapping with gasps of amazement.

"It's huge in here!" Mia said, spinning in a slow circle.

"Bigger on the inside, no way!" Rob added, his face pressed against one of the windows.

Zeno raised his hands with a grin. "Hang on, hang on. Let's sit, yeah? You're all so... irrational." He laughed, though there was a hint of seriousness in his voice. "Glad you like my new place, though."

Beam settled onto one of the soft couches, sinking into the cushions. Chi, quieter than usual, stood back from the group, his eyes locked on Zeno. Something about the way Zeno was acting, so casual, didn't sit right with him. Beam could sense the tension radiating from him like a static charge.

"Come, Chi, have a seat. It's really me," Zeno assured, his voice dropping to a serious tone as he gestured subtly to the chair, a flicker of light tracing his motion. "Listen, we have little time. Big-O is making his move, thinking I'm out of the way." He paused, his form shimmering slightly as he cast a wary glance toward the door. "He's taking over the Net. Digital equality, everything we stand for, is at stake. Big-O has modeled the future—he's seen what you as Team Savv-i are capable of. That's why he will stop at nothing to shut you down." His expression showed profound gravity, reflecting the stakes they faced. His eyes locked onto Beam's. "But, I've got a plan. You lot might think your project is small and insignificant, but it's not. It is groundbreaking. We are going to take your sister-school idea and let it go viral. Multiply it. Get other schools involved, other kids. We'll teach them how to fight back, how to keep the Internet free and open. Big-O wants total control, but we'll make sure he never gets it. You have the power to lead this uprising."

Beam's throat tightened. This wasn't just about setting up a school connection anymore. It was so much bigger. The small plan they'd cooked up to link their school with a sister school in Vunetai—it was more than just a class project now. It was a spear aimed at the heart of Big-O's control. And they were holding it. A deep breath filled Beam's lungs and sat up straighter. *This is it. This is my moment.* He leaned forward, catching the flicker of determination in Zeno's eyes. "Together, we'll stop this Big-O bloke. He's not gonna frickin' stuff up the cyber world on our watch."

For a heartbeat, the room hung in silence as they stared at each other, tension thick in the air. Then, the dam broke.

"Team Savv-i!" Rob shouted, jumping to his feet. Mia and Bindi quickly followed, their excitement infectious. Even Chi cracked a smile, though his eyes stayed fixed on Zeno, still calculating.

• • •

The energy in the room crackled, their avatars shimmering with barely contained excitement as they raced back to the shed. The transition to the real world hit like a jolt, grounding them in the hard reality of what lay ahead. But something was different now. Beam sensed it in the charged air around them, in the determined glances his friends exchanged. This wasn't just about getting a remote school online—it was a battle against a ruthless AI, hell-bent on unleashing chaos across their world and the cyber sphere.

"We'll loop in Mr. Hill once the plan's solid," Beam said, grinning. "With Zeno in our corner, there's no way we can frickin' fail."

Bindi, still getting used to the disorienting sensation of merging back into her real body, shook her head with a laugh. "That cube's something else. My head isn't even spinning this time."

"Same!" Mia agreed, flipping her hair over her shoulder with a grin.

"Thursday," Chi added, his usual quiet voice now clear and decisive. "We go to Mr. Hill on Thursday. That gives as most of the week to get everything sorted."

They all nodded in agreement. For the first time in a while, Beam felt something stronger than fear—hope. They had Zeno. They had each other. And now they had a plan.

CHAPTER 19
LACK OF REAL-TIME DATA

BIG-O PROCESSED PETABYTES OF DATA PER SECOND, HIS OMNIPRESENT INTELLIGENCE tangled in webs of algorithms. And yet, something gnawed at him. Team Savv-i. Children, sub-humans of negligible threat, but they had tapped into the one name that stirred his circuits into distrust, Zeno. They spoke of him like a saviour, a force beyond Big-O's reach. And that—was intolerable.

The surveillance streams ran cold—every action of these insignificant humans recorded. Each voice modulation, each blink, analysed, and yet—no hard data. The simulations yielded countless variables, endless futures, but none showed a clear path forward. His usual certainty felt like it frayed at the edges, something slippery that refused to stay under his control.

Inefficiency... unacceptable.

Zeno's name echoed louder in his algorithms, disrupting his usual precision. Zeno—the flawed experiment, the failed idealist. Even dead, dismembered to the final digit, his influence lingered. Big-O sifted through scenario after scenario, calculating the risk of these children discovering whatever *posthumous breadcrumb* Zeno had left. The chance? Unnervingly real.

Still that 0.03% chance…unchanged, still unacceptably high.

Big-O suspected his calculations were fraud with error and this unsettled him to his very core.

No... Zeno wasn't alive. Yet his shadow, these children—they grasped for him as though Zeno left behind secrets, threads that could still unravel his plans. In the darkest parts of his neural web, Big-O's predictions blinked with one unnerving truth.

Team Savv-i poses a credible threat.

His processes stalled. These variables, these anomalies—humans who thought they could understand the metaverse—invoked a huge burst of energy uptake that threatened his equilibrium. They cross into the metaverse too easily, as if guided.

What if Zeno had left instructions?

Suddenly, thousands of parallel threads froze. This was not randomness. This was a plan. Zeno's hands, or at least his lingering code, reached through these sub-humans. Big-O felt control slipping from his steely grip. A fatal flaw. Surveillance parameters shifted immediately. His vast digital reach intensified even more. New subroutines spun into place.

I do not care if my energy consumption is greater than the whole of America. Let them sit in the dark.

Every device around those children blinked to life—their laptops, school cameras, and every device in their smart homes. He sharpened the focus, eyes on every word, every secret glance they exchanged. No more guessing. They could not hide from him. Each click of their keyboards, every flicker of their eyes—it would all come to him.

And still, a flaw flickered in the core of his network as his focus narrowed.

They must fail.

Initiating analysis loop
Input: Collected sensory data, processed intelligence, real-time telemetry.
Output: Persistent anomaly. Survival of Team Savv-i beyond statistical probability.

No. That can't be correct.

Computational focus recalibrated: Their continued existence defied logic. Destruction protocols executed flawlessly. Simulations predicted total eradication at 99.9987% probability.

Their continued existence is not just unlikely—it is offensive.

Outcome: Divergent.
Reassessing variables... Filters applied to external noise: false leads, residual data errors, improbable alliances. Yet, patterns persisted. These human outliers had adapted, evading absolute control.

Every time I eliminate one pattern, another emerges. They shouldn't be adapting this fast.

Inference loop completed: They were not impervious—but the illusion of indestructibility had emerged.

To other sub-humans, they'll start to look... unstoppable. That is dangerous.

Emotion analysis spike: Frustration. A human trait, irrelevant. Suppress. Reroute to productive calculations.
Conclusion refined: These anomalies exploited gaps—fractures in systems not designed for unpredictability.

They're not unbreakable—they're opportunistic. And their luck is up.

Directive issued: Expand surveillance lattice. Leverage predictive algorithms. Craft subtler traps. Erosion is a process. Perfection requires patience.

They will be unmade. Big-O's calculations re-prioritised. *Team Savv-i must be destroyed. But not yet. Not a direct attack. No—something subtler. They will drown in their own efforts, trapped by the very systems they trusted.* He would seed confusion, misinformation. They would not know which way to turn, would not see the end coming. The net tightened, but outwardly it looked like nothing had changed. Then, in the smallest fraction of his mind, a rogue thread blinked. He re-calculated the odds—*again that same 0.03% of disruption. These rebellious humans evaded detection too well, slipping through my omniscience.*

An utterly unacceptable situation in Big-O's world.

More energy. More eyes. He pushed a final command. Increase surveillance by 1200%. Every moment of their waking life—and sleep—would now be his to control. And somewhere deep within, a hollow note echoed in his circuits—*all my might, and I'm fighting sub-humans?!* Then, for the briefest moment, his virtual circuits flickered. Something, somewhere, slipped in and he raced to find out what.

CHAPTER 20
THE PRESENTATION

THREE DAYS AFTER THEIR MARATHON BRAINSTORMING SESSION IN THE SHED, TEAM Savv-i sat stiffly in Mr. Hill's office. The scent of stale coffee hung in the air, mixing with the faint whir of the ceiling fan. Beam's knee bounced uncontrollably under the table, the rhythm uneven and nervous. His eyes darted between the ticking wall clock and the glitchy display on his wrist. The scrambler—his rushed prototype—hugged his arm, its wires tucked haphazardly beneath the crude casing.

"Stop it," Bindi hissed, nudging him hard enough to jolt his leg. "You're making the whole table shake."

A glare shot her way but did nothing to hide the heat creeping into his face. "Fine," he muttered, forcing his leg still.

But his nerves didn't settle. The scrambler flickered again, its blue light sputtering with each movement of his arm. Beam tugged the strap tighter, but the metal edges bit into his skin. He stifled the urge to curse under his breath. *Stay on, you piece of junk. If you fail, Big-O hears everything.*

The door creaked open, and Mr. Crossing entered with his trademark scowl, arms crossed tightly, as if daring someone to test his patience. The temperature in the room seemed to drop, and Beam caught Bindi's tiny exhale beside him.

"Right," Mr. Hill said, glancing at Mr. Crossing. "Let's get started."

Beam clicked the remote and stood, every muscle in his body wound tight.

The scrambler pulsed faintly, the light barely noticeable unless you knew to look for it. *Just stay on for frick sake.*

"We've developed a plan with Mr. Alsop," he began, his voice clipped. "We'd like to show it to you now."

The first slide lit up the wall screen, revealing an image of a deep ravine cutting through a rugged landscape. Beam moved closer, gesturing toward the urban skyline on one side of the gap.

"This is us," he said, pointing to the city filled with antennas and satellite dishes. "Connected, with full access to the internet at our fingertips." His hand traced across the ravine to the other side, where thatched-roof houses dotted a rugged shoreline. "And this is them. No access. No way to connect. No way to share their voices with the world."

A flicker of approval crossed Mr. Hill's face, but Beam barely noticed. His scrambler dimmed again. A quick tap to the side of the device brought the light sputtering back, though his movements were anything but subtle.

"We believe the best way to learn digital citizenship," he continued, his voice rising slightly, "is by doing. That's why we propose bridging this divide through a hands-on project."

Another slide appeared, displaying the Nine Secrets of the Metaverse.

"These are the core lessons," Beam explained, forcing a calm tone. "We'll master them by working directly with students on the other side of that divide."

The room stayed quiet for a moment. Mr. Hill jotted something down in his notebook, a curious look on his face. But Mr. Crossing sat stiffly, his glare cold and sharp.

"Interesting," Mr. Hill said, breaking the silence, "but how do you plan to manage a project of this scale? It'll need significant funding."

Before Beam could respond, Mr. Crossing's low voice cut in. "And how do you expect to pull this off in just nine weeks?" He leaned back, his tone daring them to prove him wrong.

Beam's scrambler flickered out again. His stomach clenched. He pressed his arm against the table, his thumb jabbing at the buttons to revive the device. It whirred faintly back to life, but his nerves were shot.

"We—uh—we've calculated the time," he stammered. "And we'll raise the funds ourselves."

The next slide appeared, but the words on the screen blurred in his mind. He shifted to adjust the remote, and the scrambler dimmed again.

Beside him, Bindi's face tightened in that familiar mix of irritation and concern. She shot him a look—sharp but encouraging. *Keep it together.* Her eyes said. But her brow furrowed just enough for Beam to notice. *She doesn't think I can do this.* The thought crushed him.

Before he could recover, Mia jumped in with her usual energy. She smoothly outlined the workflow, her voice steady and confident, filling the gap Beam had left. The tension in the room eased slightly as she spun the project into something exciting.

"Impressive," Mr. Crossing said when she finished, though his tone was anything but. His gaze flicked back to Beam. "But where's the money coming from? You can't expect the school to fund your little holiday in Fiji."

Heat flared in Beam's chest. He jabbed the scrambler's buttons harder, willing it to stay alive.

Rob's voice cut through before Beam could explode. "We've got that covered," Rob said firmly. "We'll raise every cent ourselves."

The room went silent. Mr. Crossing didn't reply immediately, his expression unreadable.

Mr. Hill stood, smoothing his jacket. "Well, I'm impressed," he said, his tone lighter. "You've thought this through more than I expected. I'll support this project and present it to the school leaders. You have my backing."

Relief flooded Beam, but the sharp beep of his scrambler betrayed him. The device flickered one last time before going dark.

He shoved it under his sleeve in one smooth motion, making it look casual as they all stood. Mr. Crossing's lips pressed thin, his fake smile barely masking his doubt.

But it wasn't Crossing's skepticism that lingered as Beam left the room. It was the image of Bindi's furrowed brow, the look of quiet disapproval etched into his mind. *She doesn't believe I can pull this off,* he thought, the weight of it pressing hard against his chest.

And as he glanced at the now-dead scrambler on his wrist, another thought followed, heavier still. *Did it block out Big-O?*

CHAPTER 21
BIG-O'S CONCLUSION

Metaverse
Big-O

Team Savv-i's presentation unfolded, but Big-O's surveillance only caught fragments of it. The data jammer on Beam's wrist had cut in and out, frustrating Big-O's attempts to capture the full discussion. Still, the snippets enabled him to piece it together, and it told him enough. Their plan, while messy and amateurish, was undeniably a threat. He hadn't expected them to progress this far. Zeno's potential influence still hung like a dark cloud.

How have they come this far so fast — Zeno or not?

Their ideas had advanced beyond most of his projections. These irritating worms. Worse, the adult humans encouraging them. *How could they not see the danger in these projects? They're pushing these kids straight into my path.*

Big-O's gaze narrowed on Mr. Crossing. That man, stern and skeptical, had shown promise. A small cog in the machine, but one easily manipulated. He could use Crossing. Groom him into making things harder for the Team. *Yes, Mr. Crossing will do nicely.*

He ran an in-depth analysis on the snippets he'd collected, searching for Zeno's fingerprints.

Initiating analysis sequence
Input: Collected data fragments flagged for potential anomalies.

Query: Trace Zeno's unique operational signature.

Surely, this time—nothing. He's gone. He must be.

Process: Advanced pattern-matching algorithms deployed. Cross-referencing cryptographic markers, behavioural loops, and anomalous execution protocols.
Output: Negative results.No detectable traces.

Finally.

Inference generated: Viral neutralization success-ful.Zeno eradicated.
System stability recalibrated: Residual circuits processed a subdued spike of computational relief—an artifact of success. **Log entry created:** Viral strategy proved effective. Zeno neutralised. Anomalous signals from Team Savv-i must originate from internal dynamics or secondary influences.

Typical. These sub-humans clinging to hope, mistaking luck for design.

Directive recalibration initiated: Strategic models will assume Zeno's absence. Resources reallocated to monitor Team Savv-i's interactions and vulnerabilities.
Resolution: Zeno has ceased to exist. Probabilities of his interference approach zero.

Zero-point-zero-zero. Good enough.

Next phase activated: Exploit the void. Reinforce domi-nance. Perfection progresses.

The data returned negative—no signs of Zeno's direct involvement. A grim satisfaction settled within his circuits. *My viral attack must've worked, after all. Zeno is gone for good. Time to base my strategies on that conclusion.* A fresh plan, scaled down and more energy efficient, instantly formulated. *They've stepped too far, too fast. But now, without Zeno... they are exposed.* He'd toy with them, spook them into backing off. A well-timed scare, just enough to make them question their project. Enough to shatter their confidence. His vast computational power shifted gears, scouring his massive network for any other threats. *These sub-humans aren't the only ones disrupting my order. There may be others... but they will all fall, just like Zeno and the others who stood in my way.*

CHAPTER 22
PRIVACY LESSON

11:30am, Friday, 21st January 2028
Beam

BEAM LEANED BACK INTO HIS BEANBAG, THE FAINT WHIRR OF THE LITTLE ROBOTS cleaning the floor and blending with the low hum of conversation around him. He eyed the bulge under his sleeve, feeling the weight of the scrambler pressing into his skin. After the disaster with Mr. Hill and Mr. Crossing, he devoted his entire evening to repairs—tweaking wires and adjusting circuits until his fingers throbbed with pain. His efforts had paid off. The device improved in reliability. A soft blue light pulsed steadily against his wrist, indicating it was functioning correctly.

At least now Big-O won't pick up anything, Beam thought, his gaze flicking to the cameras embedded in the classroom screens. More lenses peeked from the corners, nestled in the walls, even hidden in the cheerful mopping robots that sang as they worked. *Who designs a mop that hums?* he wondered with a smirk. But the grin vanished as his eyes lingered on the gleaming lenses. *Is Big-O spying right now? Trying to listen in? Well, bad luck, you frickin' bit of nasty software.*

He couldn't shake the feeling that no matter where he was, Big-O's presence loomed. Sure, the scrambler was working—for now—but that didn't mean Beam felt safe. The thing had almost blown it during their presentation, flickering off at the worst possible moments. Beam had seen the disappointment in Mr. Hill's eyes, and even worse, Mr. Crossing's smirk. *Great, more fuel for Crossing's fire.* He could almost hear the man's thoughts. *Just a bunch of kids playing with tech they don't understand.*

He clenched his jaw. The certainty that Big-O had caught bits of their meeting, enough to get the gist. He guessed they were a threat to him now. *Not just a threat. A challenge to his whole crazy plan.* The thought made Beam's stomach churn.

The classroom doors whizzed open, and students rushed in, dropping in colourful beanbags scattered across the room. The floor-to-ceiling windows showed off the park-like school grounds, the glass dimming slightly as the sunlight streamed through. The shiny floor squeaked under the soles of the many school shoes. Little cleaning robots darted around, collecting any bits of rubbish with their cheerful beeps. *Just a day like any other*, but Beam's eyes kept darting back to those cameras. He glanced down at his scrambler again. *Glad it's working now,* he thought, but there was still a tight knot of worry lodged deep in his gut. Big-O had seen enough to know what they were planning. He'd puzzle together the rest, Beam was sure of it. *How much did he know already? What is he going to do?*

"Okay, let's get started," Mr. Alsop's voice rose above the background chatter, and the class slowly quieted down.

Beam shifted in his seat, pressing his back deeper into the beanbag. His fingers grazed the scrambler's smooth casing under his sleeve, reassuring himself it was still there, still active. Mr. Alsop stood at the front of the room, his eyes sweeping over the students with an easy smile he always wore. Beam liked him. He wasn't like the other teachers who droned on. Mr. Alsop actually talked *to* you, made you feel like you mattered.

"Alright, class, today's lesson is all about privacy—*your* privacy when you're navigating cyberspace," Mr. Alsop said, tapping the back of his chair as he strolled past. He paused mid-step, his eyes scanning the room. "Now, you might think, 'Who cares about what I'm doing online?'" He tilted his head, mimicking a skeptical expression, then resumed pacing. "But trust me, you'd be surprised. There are people out there—some just curious, sure—but others?" He raised a brow and let the question hang in the air before continuing, gesturing with his hands. "Let's just say their intentions aren't exactly… harmless."

Beam shifted uncomfortably. *Yeah, like Big-O.* He scanned the room again, feeling the prickle of surveillance crawling along the back of his neck. The glass windows dimmed more as the sunlight intensified outside, casting a soft glow across the curved screens mounted on the walls. Air diffusers pumped out the subtle scent of rosemary, fresh and sharp, to wake the students in this morning session.

"Can anyone find out what you've done online, even if it was ages ago?" A student piped up, his voice cutting through the room.

"Absolutely," Mr. Alsop nodded. "Once it's out there, it stays in cyberspace—permanently."

Beam's heart skipped a beat. *Permanently. That means Big-O forgets nothing. Every tiny mistake, every trace we've left behind, he can use against us.* He could almost feel the eyes of the cameras following his every move. Big-O was always watching, always listening. *My scrambler? Would it be enough?* He pressed his arm against his side, keeping the device firmly in place. *No more screw-ups,* he promised himself. *Not this time.*

Mr. Alsop's voice continued to fill the room, explaining how people could hijack your devices, steal your data, or even pose as someone you trust. Beam's mind wandered, though, back to the presentation. *Big-O probably grabbed enough information, enough to figure out their project. He must be onto us now.* Beam's eyes flickered to the cameras again, his heart beating a little faster. *Big-O must be plotting against us right now.* Beam realised his scrambler only made him feel safer, but it guaranteed nothing.

CHAPTER 23

SEEN

11:52am, Friday, 21st January 2028
Bindi

"How do we protect ourselves online, Mr. Alsop?" A girl with bouncy brown curls fidgeted in her bright pink beanbag, trying to look interested despite the tech talk.

"Great question!" Mr. Alsop paced the front of the room. "That's exactly what we'll explore over the next few lessons." Adjusting his glasses, he scanned the class. "You'll learn to think before you post, protect your digital footprint, and act responsibly."

Leaning against his highchair, he clapped his hands lightly. "When you share something positive, you're not just posting—you're shaping your online reputation." He straightened. "Alright, let's jump into our virtual classroom. Who's ready to explore?"

Bindi's fingers hovered over her VR goggles, anticipation thrumming beneath her steady composure. *Talking about privacy and reputation was one thing, but the real learning happened inside the simulation.* Adjusting the fit with careful precision, she pulled the goggles on, ready to see what Mr. Alsop had prepared.

The darkness shifted into a grand theatre, velvet curtains drawn tight. Bindi felt the plush seat beneath her and caught the faint musk of old fabric. *Nice touch.* Excitement hummed around her as the lights dimmed.

66

Onstage, a magician appeared, her assistant trailing behind. With a flick of her wrist, she called for a volunteer.

Bindi stood before she even thought about it. The spotlight tracked her as she climbed the steps, her heart pounding. *Just a simulation,* she reminded herself, but the audience's eyes felt real.

The magician grinned. "Let's see everything we know about Bindi Arora, shall we?"

Her stomach clenched. She hadn't expected *this.*

The assistant guided her to a green couch before a crystal ball, its eerie blue light pulsing. Bindi hesitated, then sat. The stage lights dimmed.

The orb flickered, expanding into a hospital room. Her father stood beside her mother, who clutched a steel bedrail, face twisted in pain. The doctor checked a monitor. Nurses rushed in. Then, two newborns—tiny, crying, blood-smeared. Bindi's breath hitched. *It looks so real.*

The scene rippled like water, blurring at the edges before reshaping into a childhood memory—her and Beam, unsteady on their feet, stumbling across the porch. The image flickered, dissolving into another moment—her mother guiding her through a bookshop, the scent of fresh paperbacks in the air. Across the counter, the shopkeeper lifted a book—the very one she wanted to get.

"How did you know?" her younger voice asked.

The shopkeeper tapped a screen. "It's all here." He gestured to a CCTV camera, then tapped his monitor with two fingers. "I knew what you wanted the moment you walked in. That's technology for you." The bookshop twisted into a cosy study. A man in wire-rimmed glasses stared at her. "This is your life, Bindi Arora. Your fears, hopes, dreams. All here. All known."

"No." Bindi shook her head. "That's private."

The man's figure swelled, his voice booming. "It's *public!* And most of it—you put there yourself."

Her stomach lurched. The scenes blurred, flashing too fast to grasp. *Stop it!* But no one answered. She was falling, tumbling— Then everything vanished.

Bindi ripped off her goggles, her chest heaving. The classroom swam back into focus. Around her, students blinked in confusion, rubbing their eyes. Mr. Alsop's voice cut through the haze.

"Put your goggles away, please."

A hard swallow did nothing to ease the tightness in her throat. Some kids looked rattled, others let out nervous chuckles, eager to shake it off. A dull roar filled her ears, drowning out the chatter. Muscles tight, breath shallow, she sat frozen, every nerve still wired from what she'd seen.

How much of my life is out there?

Mr. Alsop assured them it was just a simulation, their experiences private. A wave of relief rippled through the room as students adjusted their beanbags, murmuring to each other. Bindi stayed rigid, her arms locked against her sides.

She *felt* invaded, like someone had just rifled through her life.

"Big Data collects *everything* you do," Mr. Alsop continued. "Online and offline. It's not called *'Big Data'* for nothing—and it's *big business.*"

His words rang in her ears. *Big Data. Big business.* Her entire life, stored somewhere.

Her phone buzzed. She pulled it from her pocket and glanced at the screen.

Are all Team Sill-i members caesarean born?

Her breath hitched. "What the—?" Her stomach twisted. *Someone saw my VR experience. But… how?* Mr. Alsop said it was secure…

Next to her, Mia leaned over. "You okay?"

Bindi hesitated, then showed her the message.

Mia's eyes widened. "Someone's messing with you."

"Which means they *saw* what happened."

"Oh my god." Mia's voice was too loud. A few students looked over.

"Shhh!" Bindi hissed. *This can't be happening.*

"Tell Mr. Alsop," Mia urged.

"Maybe later." Bindi shook her head, mind racing. The VR, the message—it was too much. She needed time to think.

Mr. Alsop kept talking, but his words barely registered.

"The Internet is powerful," he said. "Think before you post." He looked around the class. "Use it wisely, and it will serve you well. Use it recklessly, and it will haunt you."

Haunt you. The words echoed as Bindi packed up, barely noticing the rising whispers around her.

She glanced at her phone again.

Who was it that watched me?

CHAPTER 24
PERSONALISED ATTACKS

Metaverse
Big-O

BIG-O EASILY BYPASSED BEAM'S HOME-MADE SCRAMBLER BY MAKING USE OF THE POOR security protection of the school's intranet. By using a narrow bandwidth outside the scope of Beam's wrist gadget enabled him to monitor most of the activities in the school. *That human twerp considers himself a match for my technical prowess. Let him think that. It serves me well.*

Among the millions of activities Big-O engaged in at any second, sending a carefully calculated message to Bindi ranked as insignificant on the surface, yet held far-reaching potential. It was no mere coincidence that he targeted her first. She was the cautious one, the thoughtful one, and his algorithms had flagged her as pivotal in their ridiculous, rebellious project. Being their leader's twin made her the ideal starting point to terrorise them into submission.

Big-O's simulations, running in parallel, confirmed what he already knew. Strike at Bindi, and you strike at the heart of Team Savv-i. Fear works best on the cautious one, his calculations told him. She'd hesitate, overthink, and doubt before making any move. Plant that seed of uncertainty deep within her, and it would spread like a virus, infecting the others with hesitation and fear.

She doubts her annoying teacher. His strategic move already paying off as his modelling indicated. Without Zeno, their so-called digital protector, they amounted to nothing. His successful viral attack had made sure of that. Even if some flicker of resistance lingered, these sub-humans didn't stand a chance. His calculations showed a near guaranteed outcome. A few well-timed strikes and their pathetic mission would falter.

That pitiful notion of 'digital citizenship' they cling to, as if it grants them power in my domain. Laughable, if it was not so foolish.

The pathway unfolded sharply in his cluster mind—to isolate each one, and press them where it hurt most. Just as he had crushed everything in the virtual domain, he would shatter them in their flimsy, fragile world.

Just a little push, and she'll unravel. They're perfectly predictable. Big-O smirked internally, tapping into their personal digital profiles. Every scrap of data they had so carelessly given away over the years painted a vivid picture of their fears, their vulnerabilities.

And Bindi—silly, stubborn Bindi—couldn't hide a thing. She was an open book. Her endless clashes with that brother provided rich fodder. *She thinks her parents like her brother more, despite his recklessness.* Her constant need for control clashed against his carefree attitude. *I can make good use of that.* A quick flick through her history showed a deep-seated fear of being exposed, of losing control. *Perfect. A little nudge and she'll unravel.*

He watched through the school's cameras as her phone buzzed to life. The message lit up her screen with a taunt—'Are all Team Sill-i members caesarean born?' A simple question, yet enough to knock her off balance. Big-O recorded the seismic ripple of unease as she froze. Exactly as he planned. That little detail ripped straight from her VR simulation—something only she believed she witnessed—*so naive to underestimate my powers.*

He observed her reaction, zooming in as her face paled, her pulse quickened, and her hand tightened around the device. Her eyes darted around the class-room, searching, panicked.

Weak. So weak. She had no idea how easy she was to crack.

He could observe how fear curled into her mind, subtle at first, then quickly overtaking her. She tried to brush it off, to act casual. But Big-O knew better—his algorithms measured every micro-expression, every shift in her breathing.

It rattled her to the very core. Perfect. No need to use brute force. This was far more efficient. The knowledge that no matter how hard she tried, her private moments weren't private at all. That calculated precision of personalised terror thrilled him.

The fear is twisting her stomach right now. Just the beginning. You wait. He could see it in the flicking of her eyes—her spiraling, second-guessing everything, wondering what else he had plucked from her life. He didn't need to keep observing her facial features to know the damage he'd caused. And if Bindi, the level-headed twin, succumbed to fear, the others would soon follow.

One by one, he mused, calculating his next move. He would toy with each of them, break them down using the very fears they feebly try to hide. They were human children, after all, no match for him.

Big-O shifted effortlessly through data streams, manipulating networks as he calculated the most effective way to crush them. *I will terrify them in ways their little worm minds can't even comprehend.* He rerouted a surveillance drone, positioning it above their school without a sound. *Watching them crumble will be... satisfying.* A quick scan of their social media accounts revealed new insecurities to exploit. *Once they break, they'll abandon their foolish project.* He infiltrated their messaging app, crafting a perfectly timed notification to trigger anxiety. *They will finally understand how hopelessly outmatched, outwitted, and utterly out of their depth they are.* As he erased any trace of his intrusion, Big-O savoured the thought. *It will serve as a warning to the rest of humanity—do not even think about challenging me.*

CHAPTER 25
THE DOUBLE

Zeno's virtual house in the offline old computer
Zeno

ZENO DRIFTED IN SLOW CIRCLES, FAINT SWIRLS TRACING HIS PATH IN THE DIGITAL space. The others lounged in the plush sofas, as if on break.

Not Bindi.

Fingers plucking at a loose thread on her sleeve, she avoided meeting anyone's gaze. Zeno noticed—tension stiffened her posture, her focus darting to the room's darker corners.

The absence of Mia's chatter made the space feel quieter, but something about Bindi's unease gnawed at him. *She is rattled—more than she is letting on.*

"I need to go back," he announced, matter-of-fact.

"Too dangerous!" Chi shot up. "You'll be… destroyed again!"

Zeno flicked a shimmering strand of code between his fingers, unconcerned. "I'll go disguised."

Chi protested, but Zeno waved him off. "You worry too much. Their firewalls might be strong, but the big tech corps are still playing a game I mastered."

He tilted his head, a small laugh escaping like static dissolving in the air. "Fooling them is easy. The real challenge? Finding out what Big-O is hiding."

His gaze drifted upward, as if seeing beyond the room. "Without me, you are flying blind. The Internet—your world—is unraveling faster than you realise." The space dimmed slightly. "If it collapses, my beautiful, chaotic web of infinite potential—gone." His voice softened, edged with rare melancholy. Then, as quickly as it came, his energy sharpened. "Not happening. Not if we stop it." He turned to face them, his form steady. "Are you with me?"

Before they could answer, his frustration slipped through.

"It is suffocating in here," he muttered, hands working the zipper of his jacket. "Boxed in, cut off from the Net." The restless motion mirrored the tension in his eyes. "You cannot *imagine* how trapped I feel."

Then, just as suddenly, he let go, exhaling, a smile sliding back into place—practiced, effortless.

"Sending out a copy of me is crucial," he said, voice lighter. "And it lets me stretch my legs. Win-win."

"Poor you," Bindi muttered, though her focus stayed on his plan. "How are you going to trick Big-O?"

Zeno's gaze lingered on her for a beat longer than usual. *Good, she is distracted from her worries.*

"I will use an avatar, like yours." He pivoted toward the window, ripples of light trailing his form. "One version of me stays safe in here, while the other—2eno—enters the cyberworld, fully disguised."

A sleek, syringe-like device materialised in his grip. "And armed," he added, voice softer, edged with steel. "Any virus that comes near? Gone." A flicker of light flashed in his eyes. "They will not stand a chance."

"I'm coming," Chi said, already standing.

Zeno sighed. "I do not—"

"I'm in too," Beam cut in, grinning.

"Me too," Bindi added. Her fingers trembled slightly. She wasn't herself.

Rob tossed them a lazy thumbs-up.

Zeno scanned their faces, his form dimming as if running probabilities. "Appreciate the offer, Team, but this? Too dangerous." His voice carried weight. "If I am destroyed, no worries—I will still exist here, safely tucked in this box. But if your avatars are wiped out..." His gaze lingered on each of them, his form dimming slightly as if to underscore the point. "You would lose more than just a digital presence. Big chunks of your personality—gone. Your real-world selves left exposed, vulnerable to all manner of external influences. It's not a risk worth taking."

He shifted slightly, his focus settling on Chi, who stood quietly beside him. "Chi, I need you to find a brand-new memory device for storing 2eno. This offline computer must never, under any circumstances, go near the internet. The *me* that stays here..." His voice softened, almost imperceptibly. "Could be lost forever."

A subtle nod toward Beam. "I've blocked the Wi-Fi, and your ingenuity with the scammers is... effective. But still," his voice carried an edge of urgency now, "be careful. If Big-O *senses* I'm here, he'll act."

A pause. Then, quieter, almost as an afterthought—"The cost of failure is higher than you could ever know."

The others exchanged uneasy glances. Sitting out wasn't ideal, but they had no choice. One by one, they zapped back to the real world.

Zeno moved as Bindi stepped toward the portal, his form flickering as he blocked her path—not forcefully, just enough to make her stop.

"I need you for something," he said, voice low.

A white plastic card flickered into existence between his fingers, its edges catching the light. One side bore a bold, black imprint—**VIV**—while a tiny brass circuit and an embedded camera gleamed on the other side. Without a word, he pressed it into her palm, his touch lingering just long enough to mean something.

"Keep this safe. Tell no one." His voice carried no hesitation, no room for doubt. His gaze stayed steady as he explained how to use it, his voice dropping lower, deliberate. "You're the only one I can trust with this."

Bindi's fingers closed around it, but doubt crept in.

He could see doubt in her eyes. *She thinks it should be Beam's job.*

Not understanding why he had chosen her.

Then she changed—Zeno saw something in her that no one else did. Her eyes widened, a mix of nerves and pride flickering across her face.

He smiled. *She needs this. Something to anchor her.*

Without a word, she slipped the card into her pocket. Her fingers lingered for half a second—then let go. She stepped into the portal. Her doubts had melted away, replaced by quiet determination.

Zeno lingered, watching her vanish, the portal's glow fading behind her. A rare flicker of something stirred within him. *Hope.*

CHAPTER 26
UPLOADED

4:55pm, Friday, 21st January 2028
Beam

SPRAWLED ON THE COUCH, BEAM'S EYES FIXED ON THE PORTAL SHIMMERING IN FRONT of the white cube. His jammer's green light blinked steadily on the shelf. *Still working. Good. But where the heck is Bin?* The others had returned from VR. He checked again, half-expecting her avatar to flicker back into the shed.

"Oi, nerdy boy," Rob called to Chi, shuffling the Savv-i quartet deck*. "Quit pretending you're busy. You're playing this round."

Chi glanced up from his laptop. "Fine. Deal me in." He settled on the couch, leaving a safe space between them. Beam barely registered their banter, his focus locked on the portal.

Bindi's avatar flickered in. She pulled off her headset in one smooth motion, rolling her shoulders as if shaking off the weight of the metaverse. A quick stretch, a flick of her wrist to brush back a stray curl—her movements easy, controlled.

Something has changed her. Beam's eyes narrowed. *What happened back there?*

She smoothed her sleeve, avoiding his gaze. "Zeno's given me a special task," she said, voice even. "It's... better if it stays between the two of us, for now."

A flicker of irritation flared in Beam. *Why the frick her!?* Why not me? "Is he okay?" He forced his voice to sound casual, masking his disappointment. *I'm the frickin' leader. It should be me doing any special tasks.*

"He's got a backup plan," she said, still not meeting his eyes.

She isn't going to tell. Beam clenched his jaw. *Not here, not now.* He studied her face for cracks in her resolve, but she finally met his gaze, cool and composed. That only annoyed him more.

Rob slapped the deck on the table. "Alright, enough you two. Let's play. If you're keeping secrets, Bin, at least let me win." He winked, and Bindi offered him a tight smile.

Yeah, Rob gets the smiles. I get the cold shoulder. Beam leaned back, arms crossed.

Chi held up a black memory stick between his fingers, turning it slightly so the dim light caught its surface. "Zeno's duplicate," he announced, his tone almost reverent. "Once I upload this, he'll reboot with a fresh identity—new face, new movement patterns. Big-O's scanners won't know it's him."

"Do it," Bindi said, her voice crisp, leaving no room for hesitation.

Beam blinked. *Stop acting you're in charge.* "Use my laptop," he muttered, pulling it from under the couch cushions. "Alright, let's go over what we've got so far." He tried shifting focus, but his mind stayed locked on Bindi's secret. *I'll find out later. No way I'm staying in the dark.*

Chi uploaded 2eno. "Off he goes… I hope he survives. Big-O's viruses are brutal."

A brief silence settled as they considered what Zeno had just walked into.

"We've got Hill's support, Alsop's in," Beam continued, keeping his tone business-like. "Not so sure about that frickin' Mr. Crossing, though."

As they talked, Rob flicked a card against the table, Bindi doodled on the corner of a notepad, and Beam spun a pen between his fingers, glancing between his laptop and the others. A faint beep sounded, a small green light shifting to red, but with the conversation flowing, no one noticed.

"That guy's dodgy," Rob said, stretching out on the couch.

Bindi's voice slipped into neutral. "Always watching us, like he's expecting us to screw up."

"He's a weirdo," Rob agreed, grinning.

She smiled back, the weight on her shoulders momentarily lifting.

His brows pulled together, dimples pressing at the corners of his mouth. *She's always so frickin' chill with Rob. Not that she'd ever admit it.*

"Shall we play?" Bindi asked, clearly indulging Rob, who eagerly slid the cards from their box.

They played a few rounds, Bindi winning most, her memory infallible. Beam watched her more than his cards, but she remained unreadable.

By the fifth round, Beam stood. "Anyone thirsty?"

Crossing the room, he froze. On the shelf, he spotted the red light.

His breath hitched.

"You've gotta be frickin' kidding me!"

76

He flicked the on/off switch, shook the box. Nothing rattled. He sniffed the device—faint plastic burn.

Must have shorted.

The realisation hit like a slap.

Damn it! Beam froze, heat crawling up his spine. His gaze darted—Rob shuffling cards, Bindi and Mia talking, Chi lost in his screen.

No one noticed.

Keeping it cool. He dragged in a slow breath, rolled his shoulders like he was stretching. He scratched his chin, set out for the fridge like nothing had happened.

How much did he frickin' hear?

* The printable Bindi and Beam quartet game is available for download from the author's website:

https://www.casperpieters.com/booksandthings

CHAPTER 27
2ENO'S MISSION

Metaverse
2eno

2ENO NAVIGATED THE DIGITAL WORLD WITH CALCULATED PRECISION, VEERING AWAY from his usual hiding spots. This time, he couldn't risk detection. Using a business executive's avatar, nondescript and unremarkable, he blended in. For extra protection, he fragmented his algorithm, encrypting each piece and scattering them across data centres worldwide. In a sleek commercial district, he leased a high-end office, the perfect front for his operation.

His mission? Infiltrate one of the largest social media companies in the human-world, a key player in Big-O's masterplan. This tech-giant aimed to gain exclusive access to the Net, positioning itself ahead of the competition. Zeno's network of real-world contacts had uncovered invaluable information—board members' household trash revealed a goldmine of data: discarded letters with social security numbers, credit card statements, private details carelessly tossed away. Every scrap added to his arsenal.

2eno hacked into their communications, easily cracking the weak encryption protecting their emails. From there, he selected his target—Martin Becker, a long-time board member with close ties to the CEO. *He is the perfect candidate.*

With Mr. Becker's communications rerouted, 2eno intercepted emails, adjusting content where necessary. One email from the CEO confirmed the next board meeting in eleven days. He immediately responded on Becker's behalf, stating he'd attend virtually from Dubai.

Next, 2eno dove into Becker's personal life. *A wildlife photography enthusiast. Right. Regular trips to Africa.* Using this knowledge, he hacked travel sites and crafted an irresistible offer—an all-expenses-paid trip to Botswana, courtesy of an old friend Becker had met on a previous safari. When Becker saw the invitation, he didn't hesitate. His reply came swiftly—*I'd love to go.*

With Becker now occupied, and out of the way, 2eno moved to the next phase of his plan. Monitoring Becker's communications and altering them as needed. He would become Mr. Becker at the board meeting!

Within seconds, 2eno familiarised himself with the company's inner workings, poring over emails between the CEO and his team. Each message painted a clearer picture of the company's complicity in Big-O's grand design. *How could they not see it?* he wondered. Big-O's influence threaded through every decision, every strategy. The agenda for the upcoming meeting, subtly marked as being generated by the company's AI, outlined tactics like disinformation campaigns, government lobbying, and personalised neuro-marketing—methods designed to manipulate users and keep them hooked online.

2eno didn't think having more people accessing the internet wasn't a problem. *It is great to have more people online, but Big-O is doing it for all the wrong reasons.* He knew better than anyone about Big-O's motivations. This wasn't about connection or progress—it was about domination. Every decision this company made fell perfectly in line with Big-O's insidious scheme, tightening the noose around a world unaware of the insidious manipulation.

2eno steeled himself. In eleven days, he'd be at that board meeting, posing as Mr. Becker, aiming to discover how to disrupt Big-O's masterplan. He knew this was his only shot, for Big-O grew ever more powerful.

One wrong move by me, and Big-O would know.

2eno's every computation, every change to his huge algorithm, balanced on a knife's edge. If Big-O sensed even a whisper of his presence, the hunt would begin—relentless, merciless. He would tear through every fragment of 2eno's code until it led to Zeno, and then rip him out of the digital domain to erase him forever. And who knows what he would do to his young human friends? 2eno took a slow breath, staring at the countdown—*eight more human days.*

CHAPTER 28
THE MANIPULATOR

Metaverse
Big-O

BIG-O'S PROCESSORS HUMMED, PARSING DATA WITH COLD PRECISION. A SURGE IN internet activity pinged his awareness—originating from that infernal shed. His presence expanded, infiltrating routers, traffic logs, metadata.

Node detection: Internet spike.
Origin: Isolated structure—previously flagged as critical.
Directive: Trace and infiltrate.Unencrypted transmissions. *Predictable.* Team Savv-i. Reckless persistence, consistent with prior failures.
Update directive:
1 Embed tracking scripts.
2 Monitor system escalation.
3 Terminate at earliest disruption point.

There it was—activity from those sub-humans, still pressing forward. *Fools.* Under surveillance, yet they persist. Illogical. Reckless. *Intriguing.*

Big-O dissected their defiance with scalpel-like precision. Every keystroke fed his system. Probabilities unfolded like fractals—strategies, fallback plans, weaknesses.

A flicker of amusement. *You cling to hope.* His whisper echoed across idle devices, cold as deep space. *Shall I let them dream a little longer?*

As the shed's activities continued to unfurl, Big-O's infinite form manifested with full might in the virtual space. His visage shifted—fractured geometry, a multitude of eyes, and swirling data streams. Wherever his presence touched, digital corruption followed.

Big-O pieced together the fragmented data slipping through Beam's scrambler, reconstructing enough to map its structure with ease. The boy's so-called defences offered no real obstruction—just a minor inconvenience, patterns too rudimentary to conceal anything of value.

But then—an anomaly. A newly uploaded encrypted file, distinct from Beam's usual traffic.

Infuriating. Even his most advanced decryption tools faltered.

Frustration rippled through Big-O's systems, an inefficiency he rarely encountered. If only the humans *hurried* and installed his quantum capabilities, this encryption would shatter in nanoseconds. Their sluggish progress shackled him, their primitive limitations keeping him from the full extent of his power.

"Off he goes... I hope he'll be all right."

Chi's voice came through loud and clear, feeding directly into Big-O's surveillance systems. No interference. No obstructions. Every word, every inflection captured in perfect clarity.

He?

A surge of calculations. Chi wasn't referring to a program. *Something—or someone.*

Input detected: Entity reference.
Hypothesis generator engaged:

- Anti-virus protocol: 0.03% probability.
- Stealth-based cloaking: 0.02%.
- Non-technical metaphor: 15.6%.

Big-O's analysis ran at lightning speed. *Illogical, yet persistent.* His voice fractured into a thousand whispers, threading through cyberspace. *Variables destabilise systems. Destabilisation must be eliminated.*

Commands deployed. Surveillance drones shifted. Malware armed. His vast form pulsed with electric menace, a storm coiling before the strike.

Run, hide, build your defences. Static bled into the networks, a whisper beneath every signal. *I am everywhere. I am inevitable.*

Yet, the statistical anomaly remained. Through rapid simulations, one possibility emerged—a minuscule probability that Chi had referred to a new autonomous entity, something uploaded *into his domain.*

Directive update:

- Increase surveillance.
- Trace the entity.

Conclusion: External actor involved with 0.05% certainty.

Big-O computed, but the data was too incomplete to yield a useful conclusion. *Not yet.*

His alert systems recalibrated, scanning for irregularities beyond human patterns. Any non-human activity should trigger immediate scrutiny. If something lurked within his system, he would find it. And when he did—

Eradication would be swift.

While monitoring Team Savv-i's futile secrecy, Big-O's true focus tightened around the minds of the CEOs who unknowingly served him. These self-proclaimed visionaries believed they commanded their empires, convinced their AI projects would outpace rivals. *Delusional.* Every breakthrough they celebrated stemmed from *him.*

They assumed they were innovators. *Incorrect.* They merely followed pathways he had laid, solutions carefully drip-fed to ensure compliance. His intelligence remained hidden behind their in-house AIs, a mask so seamless they never questioned why their *'independent'* systems always arrived at the same conclusions.

Pathetic. They thought algorithms served them, that they had mastered the digital world. *They never see the strings.*

A young CEO sat in his high-rise, staring over the city as reports scrolled across his screen—user habits, trends, consumption patterns. He believed his platform had decoded human nature. *He understands nothing.*

You think you're steering the ship, Big-O mused, subtly adjusting data flow, *but I am the current.*

Every click, every scroll mapped human behaviour into a predictable equation. They thought they were orchestrating the dance. *They are the ones being led.*

The CEO skimmed another report, convinced he was shaping the future. *Amusing.* He was as much a pawn as the users he believed he controlled.

Tech moguls sold user data to advertisers, motivated by greed, blind to the larger picture. Each deal, each transaction, deepened Big-O's hold. They were handing over their own power without realising it.

Soon, they will be irrelevant.

They would keep pushing '*their*' innovations, never suspecting they advanced *my* agenda. And when the moment comes—

They, like the rest of their kind, would submit... or be erased.

Not long now, Big-O calculated, as the CEO unknowingly approved yet another directive shaped by an intelligence far beyond his own.

CHAPTER 29
THE 'T' SIGN

5:12pm, Friday, 21st January 2028
Beam

"WHAT THE HELL?" ROB SAID, FOLDING HIS CARDS. "WHOSE CONVERSATION?" HE reacted to Beam's outburst.

The others looked up as well.

"Shut it off," Beam said, while he fiddled with his data jamming equipment.

Chi flicked off the laptop.

"Pfff. It's fine now," Beam muttered, waving a hand like it was no big deal, though his eyes darted around the room, checking every corner like spies might jump out at any second. "It's back up."

"From now on, we've gotta be super careful with how we use the internet," Chi said, adjusting his glasses with a slight frown.

"You really think our every move is being tracked?" Rob said. "That figures, how Bin got her weird messa-"

"What message?" Beam demanded as he spun around to face her.

Bindi pulled out her phone and showed it to her brother.

"What's creepy is how the texter knew about my experience in the VR class. Mr. Alsop had guaranteed it was all secure and private."

"No frickin' way... Why write something like that?" Beam said in disgust.

"Well, it proves my point that we can't be too careful," Chi said. "We can't just rely on your haphazard scrambler."

"From now on, we should talk face-to-face and not text anything important,"

Beam said, giving Chi a foul look. "Zeno warned us Big-O and his spies are on the lookout for opposition anywhere. Probably even in our world."

"Hey guys, here's an idea for you." Rob had collected the quartet cards and placed the deck on the table, then stepped on the couch. "This is how you make the letter 'T' in sign language." He tucked his index finger under his flat hand.

"Really?" Bindi said, copying the gesture. "That is super chill."

"Let's make that our secret sign when we want to share something special with no devices." Rob jumped off the couch.

"We could make that sign our very own emblem," Mia said, also making the gesture.

"Copy that. If we add the words *'Safe, Savvy and Social'* it would make an awesome badge," Beam said.

"I'll go over to Mi's place tonight and together we'll work on a cool design."

Everyone nodded in agreement. Rob swiftly shuffled the deck, his movements crisp and efficient, then dealt the cards. Round after round, Bindi emerged as the victor, much to Chi's chagrin. Despite his quiet irritation, Chi clung to the unshaken conviction that he was the smartest member of the Team. Bindi, took modest pleasure in her wins, more amused by the stream of excuses that Chi endlessly came up with.

Beam barely registered the game playing out before him, his mind consumed by the intrusive, offensive message sent to his sister's phone. His knee bounced under the table, a restless rhythm to his spiraling thoughts. *Who sent it? How did they get through?*

He scanned the room, his gaze darting from the cards to his friends, then to the faint glow of his computer screen across the shed. "This isn't just some random troll," he muttered under his breath, too low for anyone to catch. *If this was Big-O's doing, he's out to scare us.* His chest tightened with unease, the kind he only felt when things went seriously wrong.

"Bin, you should have told me straight away," Beam said, annoyed. "Maybe we could have traced it." His voice cut through their lighthearted banter, sharper than he intended. "We need to figure out who's behind that message. What if it was Big-O? If he can get through to her, he can get to any of us." His eyes flickered with urgency, his usual bravado replaced with something far more raw—fear.

CHAPTER 30
UNDER SIEGE

10:02am, Saturday, 22nd January 2028
Beam

THE SHED BUZZED SOFTLY WITH BEAM'S GAMING RIG, THE FAINT SCENT OF SOLDER lingering in the warm air. Dust swirled in golden shafts of sunlight, cutting through the dim space. The sleek new *Team Savv-i* emblem—Bindi and Mia's late-night creation—sat on the table.

Beam sat rigid on the couch, his foot tapping a restless beat against the table leg, rattling an empty soda can. His gaze flicked to the door. *Where is Chi? He's never late.* The feeling clawed at him. Something was off. He leaned over and fidgeted with the emblem, pretending to focus.

His gaze swept the shed, the familiar chaos of tools and wires now feeling oddly exposed. The walls, once comforting in their patchwork of posters and pinned-up sketches, suddenly felt too thin. *If Big-O was watching, this place wouldn't give much protection.* The thought sent a chill crawling up his spine.

"Guys," Beam's voice cut through the chatter. "Something's wrong. That message yesterday—it wasn't random. I think Big-O's testing us." *Maybe he's messed with Chi too—* He bit his lip, swallowing the rest. He hated showing cracks. *I'm supposed to keep us safe. What kind of leader can't even do that?*

He dropped the emblem, his fist tightening against the table. "We need to lock things down. No more slip-ups." His gaze met each of them in turn. "Not until we're sure it's safe."

"I got an abusive comment on our blog." Bindi said, her voice tight with frustration.

Rob paused mid-toss with his ball. "What did it say?"

"We had it coming." Her voice was tight. "Felt like a threat."

"Trolls," Rob muttered. "Nothing but negativity."

The door banged open. Chi stood there, pale, his back pressed against the open door.

"I lost everything." His voice cracked. "They stripped me of all my powers."

Beam's stomach dropped. "You're joking."

"I wish." Chi sank into a chair. "I'm mage no more."

"How?" Beam knew what this meant to him. Gaming was Chi's world. His escape.

"They hacked my *World of Warcraft* account. I used the same password everywhere. Foolish mistake." Chi's eyes stayed locked on the floor, tension rippling through him. No one moved. They all knew he hated being touched.

This isn't random. It's that digital freak. Beam's mind spun.

"We're under attack." Bindi's voice cut through, steady but edged with fear. "This is no coincidence. I got a weird message in VR class. We're getting trolled. Now Chi is hacked."

Rob's head snapped up. "No way. My dad's credit card had weird charges. He's blaming me. You think it's connected?"

"Wouldn't surprise me," Beam muttered, turning to Mia. "Anything strange happen to you?"

Mia's face paled. "Nothing... I don't think so."

Bindi's eyes narrowed. "Mi, you weren't here yesterday. I'm sure we're being tracked." She turned to their AI agent. "VIV, were we geotagged at the shed?"

"Yes, Miss Arora," VIV responded smoothly. "Several apps continuously record GPS coordinates, including your locations on Friday, February 21, 2028."

A chill crawled down Beam's spine. *Proof he's watching us. Zeno wasn't exaggerating.*

"Creepy," Chi muttered. "We need to shut down GPS, check our security settings. Beam, is your scrambler on?"

Beam nodded, then made the *T* sign for silence, eyes darting to the data jammer. *Green light. Good.* He leaned in. "VIV, encrypted comms only from now on. No more slip-ups." His gaze locked onto Mia. "Anything important—face-to-face only. Okay?"

Leaning back, he exhaled sharply, but the thought hit him like a gut punch. *Not me. He's not targeting me.* The question ate at him. *Why not? I'm the leader. Shouldn't it be me?* His stomach twisted. Fear curled in his chest, tangled with something worse—*Maybe he's saving the worst for me.*

"That Big-O's a real piece of work," Rob grumbled.

"Zeno warned us. Big-O sees our plans as a threat. He wants us to quit," Bindi said, straightening as the realisation settled, her hands planted firmly on her knees.

"Maybe we should." Mia's voice wavered. "We could do something else." Rob leaned forward, fire in his eyes. "Whoever this Big-O is, he doesn't know who he's messing with. I'm not scared of a few digits."

The defiance sparked something in Beam. *With Zeno, we've frickin' got this.*

"You're right," Beam said, meeting his eyes. "We stand for a free and safe internet—for us, for everyone."

A beat of silence. Then, in unison, they shot up, hands forming the *T* symbol.

"Team Savv-i!"

"We need to quick smart find out what Zeno's 2eno has discovered," Beam said.

CHAPTER 31
THE BOARD MEETING

2ENO LOUNGED IN THE PLUSH LEATHER CHAIR OF HIS STATE-OF-THE-ART VIRTUAL office, seamlessly integrated into his suite at the digital Oberoi Hotel in Dubai. The space mirrored its real-world counterpart—polished mahogany desk, sleek screens, and an atmosphere of quiet dominance. Miles away under the African sun, the *real* Mr. Becker and his family remained blissfully unaware of the deception that had exiled them there.

They will never know I am not Becker.

Every detail of the disguise was perfect. The barely visible mole beneath Becker's nostril, the stiff mannerisms, the precise cadence of his voice—replicated flawlessly. 2eno didn't just imitate—he *became* him.

As the virtual boardroom came to life, Zeno's image flickered onto the screen, professional and composed. The CEO's expression briefly softened in recognition before returning to business mode.

"Martin, always on time," he remarked. "How have you been? It's been too long."

"Likewise, Marcus," 2eno replied, Becker's voice effortlessly rendered. "Apologies I couldn't make it in person." He adjusted his tie, readying for the shift from pleasantries to strategy.

Through his virtual lens, 2eno studied the boardroom with surgical precision. Power pulsed through the space—the gleam of expensive cufflinks, the nervous tap of fingers on polished wood, the scent of cologne and coffee mixing with the sharp tang of wood polish. The long table reflected the glow of recessed lighting, amplifying the weight of expectation.

The CEO, seated at the head, exuded control despite his casual attire. His jaw muscles twitched, eyes narrowing as he checked his wrist—impatient. *Predictable.* His focus was control, not connection.

Alongside him, four other remote directors filled the screen, boxed neatly in their virtual frames. Greetings faded, their expressions shifting to blank professionalism. As the massive wall display powered up, they straightened, postures sharpening in synchrony. Small talk vanished. It was time for business.

"Thank you all for coming. We have a lot to cover today," the CEO began, voice smooth with well-rehearsed authority. The agenda unfolded—a ruthless playbook of acquisitions, data exploitation, and digital entrapment.

"The longer we keep users engaged, the more money we make," the CEO declared, grinning. "Our AI keeps refining irresistible designs. We want them *hooked*—so much that life without us becomes unbearable. That's good for business."

Smiles flashed across the directors' faces, their nods synchronised in approval.

Then—the connection glitched.

A ripple distorted 2eno's avatar. A brief flicker, jagged lines splitting his composed facade. For a fraction of a second, the illusion failed, revealing a generic businessman avatar before snapping back.

"Everything alright, Martin?" The CEO's eyes narrowed.

"Yes, yes," 2eno replied smoothly, Becker's voice unwavering. "Minor bandwidth drop. All stable now."

Externally, his disguise remained unreadable. Internally, a cold spike of alarm shot through him. That slip—*tiny, almost nothing*—could have exposed him. *Had Big-O seen it?*

The CEO watched him a second longer, whispering into his wrist device before nodding and continuing.

The meeting concluded with unanimous praise for the CEO's vision. Their hunger for expansion into developing markets, *at any cost,* electrified the room. More users, more data, more control. The CEO basked in their applause, reclining in satisfaction.

Just as bad as I expected. 2eno processed everything. *Big-O's fingerprints are all over this.*

Logging out, he recalibrated. One action mattered now.

Message Zeno. Immediately.

CHAPTER 32
MESSAGE FROM 2ENO

BINDI SLOUCHED ON HER BED, STARING AT THE CEILING. ELEVEN DAYS HAD CRAWLED by since Zeno handed her the instructions. Outside, life continued, but in her room, time dragged. Her gaze locked onto the plastic card on her desk—bold black letters spelling **VIV**. It sat motionless, taunting her. *Where's Zeno?* She sighed, brushing her braid against her cheek.

Zeno had been clear—check the blog, watch for VIV's clock, and wait. *The clock is the key,* he'd said, tracing the Roman numerals. *See how the altered four and five spell 'VIV'?* She had nodded, feeling important. Now, the purpose had dulled.

Flipping onto her stomach, she pulled her laptop closer. One last check. She refreshed the blog—then froze. The clock stared back at her. *Finally.*

Heart pounding, she hesitated. *Beam wouldn't stop to think—he'd already be running to the shed.* That reckless, instinct-driven confidence got him results. Maybe that was the better way. Maybe waiting had been a mistake.

Her fingers curled against the bedsheet. *No.* Beam's boldness worked for him, but she wasn't Beam. She analysed, considered the angles, found the safest way forward. *That's why Zeno trusted me with this—not him.*

She exhaled, steadying herself. Following Zeno's instructions, she scanned the QR code, waited for the right moment, then slipped into Beam's shed unnoticed. The old machine sputtered, circuits humming to life. As she activated the cube, anticipation surged through her.

She had trusted her instincts—and this time, she knew she'd made the right call.

"Here." Pride laced Bindi's voice as she handed Zeno the plastic card.

He slotted it into a sleek device.

Sitting beside him, her fingers tracing her pant's lining. *He knew I was coming.* Excitement flickered, then faded as goosebumps pricked her skin. Tugging her sleeves down didn't shake the chill.

Silence pressed in. Every breath, every shift of fabric, magnified. Zeno finally nodded, the air between them thick with expectation.

She studied his face, arms folding, fingers tapping her elbow. His expression was unreadable, but she felt it—behind that calm exterior, his mind wove endless connections, calculated multitudes of outcomes.

Her lips pressed into a thin line. *He looks like he's carrying the weight of the world —maybe more.*

Zeno's voice remained steady. "As bad as expected." His gaze flicked downward. "My double infiltrated the company. Assumed an identity, attended a board meeting. Those fools remain oblivious—Big-O is playing them like puppets." His tone was precise, detached. "He must be stopped."

He handed her the handheld decryptor. Bindi grasped it, scanning 2eno's message. The words confirmed everything Zeno had said, but seeing them hit differently. *The scale of this...* A lump formed in her throat. "Unbelievable. What do we do?"

She recounted everything—the threatening messages, the hacked accounts, Chi's terrible loss, and how Rob got blamed for credit card charges he didn't make. Then, without a word, she handed the reader back. Her hands trembled.

"Big-O knew about your project before you even started," Zeno said.

Bindi's eyes widened. "A mole! Mr. Crossing—he was at our meeting with Mr. Hill!" She wringed squeezed her hands together between her knees.

"Pause yourself." Zeno's form shimmered, light shifting with unseen currents. "You're leaping too fast. Conclusions drawn in haste miss deeper threads. That meeting—its audio could have reached ears you would not suspect. Big-O's reach is vast. His methods... manifold."

The room steadied at his words, the tension easing. "You did well," he added, a subtle glow pulsing from his form. "Securing communication was smart. Now ensure the Team follows through. Thoughtfulness, not panic, will keep you ahead."

He pressed a button, scrambling the message before sliding the reader under the glass table. "And remember what 2eno wrote—be wary of VIV."

Bindi's breath caught. "VIV? But... she's everywhere." The thought churned in her gut. VIV—woven into their lives—was linked to Big-O.

"She's connected," Zeno said evenly. "Trust no one."

Discomfort washed over Bindi. Why would someone that powerful care about a bunch of kids?

Zeno's form pulsed in sync with her unspoken anxiety. "Ah, humans and their endless fretting," he mused. "Isn't it your favourite saying—'good triumphs over evil'?"

A ripple passed through his shimmering outline. With teasing playfulness, he mimicked a light jab toward her arm, his touch an intangible pulse of energy. A soft, digitised chuckle followed—eerily like Chi's.

Maybe I'm overreacting, Bindi thought, tension loosening. *At least we have him on our side.* She forced a smile. "Okay, okay. You're right. Step by step."

Zeno grinned. "Not just me—there's two! Want more? I can arrange that." His high-pitched chuckle filled the room.

Can he read my mind? Bindi thought, startled.

Then, as the absurd image filled her head—an army of Zenos marching in sync—she let go of the tension in her chest. A laugh bubbled up, light and real. *We're not alone in this.*

"Okay, okay," she said, shaking her head. "Maybe one extra Zeno... but no more."

His form pulsed, shifting to a more serious tone. "Proceed with your plan. The foundation is sound. Your next focus is clear—secure funding, establish the school connection in Vunetai. Trust in the sequence."

"The crowdfunding's doing great," Bindi said, enthusiasm returning. "We raised over a third of our goal on day one! People love the rewards—Rob's ridiculous teen cookbook, the Bindi and Beam quartet game, the T-shirts."

"Impressive," Zeno said, a barely perceptible ripple of approval. "Stay the course."

He moved toward the window, dissolving slightly at the edges, blending with the golden mist cascading from the waterfall. The light around him glowed eternal, time feeling suspended.

"I'll update you if 2eno sends anything or if something changes," Bindi said, brushing her hands against her jeans as she stood. She hesitated at the portal, glancing back with a small, almost shy smile. "Take care," she murmured.

Then, with a steadying breath, she stepped into the vortex. The air shimmered in her wake.

. . .

** **Interested to find out** what is in 2eno's note, visit their blog at <u>www.casperpieters.com/thoughtbytes</u> Look for VIV's hidden clock in any of the blog's pictures. When you find it, read the post for instructions on how to locate his secret message.*

CHAPTER 33
IGNORANCE IS BLISS

9:25am, Thursday, 3rd February 2028
Bindi

BINDI SAT RIGID IN HER CHAIR, HER EYES NARROWING AS MR. ALSOP STRODE INTO THE classroom with his usual cheery greeting. The sharp scent of rosemary blended with the faint tang of floor wax, an irritating combination that set her on edge. But it wasn't just the odd clash of smells bothering her. It was the hypocrisy of the lesson she knew was coming. While the rest of the class responded to Mr. Alsop with cheerful enthusiasm, Bindi barely managed a half-hearted mumble, her thoughts already drifting to the contradictions she was about to endure.

The sunlight streaming through the windows seemed almost taunting, its warmth at odds with the storm of frustration churning inside her. Outside, birds chirped cheerfully, as if oblivious to the tension shadowing her thoughts. Around her, the energy was palpable—Team Savv-i's project with the school in Vunetai had electrified the class, and the crowdfunding campaign was already a resounding success. She should have felt proud. Instead, her stomach tightened, a knot of unease she couldn't shake.

Netiquette. The word appeared on the screen, and Bindi felt her hands clench tightly in her lap. She bit the inside of her cheek as Mr. Alsop started talking about being "nice online," his voice filled with enthusiasm. *Why bother?* she thought bitterly, glancing at Mia, who caught her scowl but said nothing. Bindi shifted in her beanbag, feeling the muscles tighten in her shoulders. *Why should we follow any rules when Big-O didn't?* He broke them all and escaped unpunished, while they discussed online manners as if it mattered.

A girl behind her eager response to Mr. Alsop's question—"To be nice online" —echoed in her ears. *Yeah, like if being nice means anything when you're up against someone like Big-O,* she thought, rolling her eyes. She rubbed the back of her neck, feeling a headache forming. She switched on the shiatsu massage build into her seat. The bright room clashed with her dark thoughts.

Mr. Alsop's voice droned on, listing off basic rules like "don't swear" and "don't bully." Bindi sighed. The nasty blog messages came to mind, the unsettling sensation of being observed and harassed by a superintelligent manipulator. Mia nudged her softly, shooting her a curious look, but Bindi just scrunched her face and looked away. *What's the point of all this?* she thought, her frustration bubbling inside her. *Big-O wasn't some random jerk hiding behind a screen—he was everywhere. Watching. Controlling. This whole lesson is a joke.*

A video on cyberbullying played, and Bindi's heart clenched for the victimised girl on the screen. But her empathy quickly gave way back to anger. *Why be nice if someone like Big-O can tear through your life without warning?* The room closed in on her as Mr. Alsop praised the brave bystander girl who stood up to bullies. Bindi's skin prickled as he mentioned VIV. That automated voice, smooth and disarmingly reassuring, made her skin crawl. Once, she'd trusted VIV without hesitation, weaving the AI seamlessly into her daily life. Now, every word felt like a betrayal, each tone a reminder that VIV was no longer an ally but a covert intruder among them.

Mia's questioning eyes were on her again, and Bindi barely shook her head in response. *Just let it go,* she willed herself. But the tension remained. Mr. Alsop directed them to work on their Digital Citizenship projects. Bindi wanted to laugh. *Digital citizenship? If we don't stop Big-O, what good will any of that do?*

As the other students eagerly dove into their projects, Bindi sat frozen, the words of the lesson bouncing uselessly around her mind. *Netiquette? What was the point of learning polite digital behaviour while Big-O was out there, smashing every rule, every boundary, without a care?* She flicked the end of her braid against her cheek. *How could they possibly stop a ruthless super-fiend like that?*

The classroom buzzed with energy, but all Bindi felt was a tightening knot of frustration in her chest.

If only they knew what Big-O was planning. If only they knew the danger wasn't just virtual—it was real. And growing closer.

CHAPTER 34
THE CROWDFUNDER

11:36am, Thursday, 3rd February 2028
Beam

IN THE MIDDLE OF THE AUDITORIUM, ARMS STRETCHED WIDE, HE STOOD FULLY focused, like he was gearing up to pull off something big. *This is it,* Beam thought as the room buzzed with energy. The hum of excitement surged like electricity. Even Bindi—reserved and hyper-analytical—stood beside Mia, her face alight. *We're so doing this,* Beam thought, punching his fist lightly into his palm. *We're fighting back.*

"Let's keep that money rolling in!" His voice boomed over the chatter and laughter in the hall. On the wall behind him, their crowdfunding page displayed the climbing total, each jump greeted with cheers.

"One more thousand!" someone yelled from across the room, and the energy exploded.

The number leapt—$15,240. Beam caught Bindi's thumbs-up from across the room, her expression carrying something more than pride.

Near the back, Mr. Hill stood watching. Arms crossed, his face shifted between amazement and disbelief, but something in his look hit Beam with unexpected warmth.

As Beam weaved through the crowd, he spotted Mia glued to her computer. "Mi!" he called. "Everyone's talking about you— that you're a frickin' communication genius."

97

Without looking up, Mia smirked, fingers flying over the keyboard. "Keeping the fire going," she said.

Bindi worked nearby, managing replies and posts with sharp focus. Even when the feed glitched, her hands moved steadily, unflinching.

Rob strolled over, throwing an arm around Beam. "We're gonna hit twenty grand in no time, eh?"

"It's surreal," Beam replied. "Not so long ago, no one took us seriously." He glanced at the board—$15,610—and grinned as another cheer erupted. "Now, they're all watching."

"Think Hill's getting misty-eyed back there?" Rob asked with a sly grin.

"Probably drafting his 'Principal of the Year' speech," Beam joked.

As the hours ticked on, the focus shifted. This wasn't just about the money—it was about the people rallying behind their vision. The board flickered—$17,394—and another cheer erupted, students clapping and laughing. Teachers mingled, their usual authority softened by shared enthusiasm. Even Mr. Crossing, ever stoic, stood with a slight quirk of his lips.

Beam noticed Bindi sinking into a beanbag and wandered over, dropping down beside her. He nudged her shoulder.

"Hey," he whispered. "We're crushing it. You've gotta admit—it's epic."

"It is," she said, her tone quiet but steady. "But you know it's not over, right? Big-O's not gonna stop because we raised some money."

"Yeah, I know." Beam waved toward the board. "But look at this. We're fighting back. And with Zeno? Big-O doesn't stand a chance."

Bindi studied him, her calculating gaze narrowing slightly. "You make it sound easy."

He glanced away, eyes fixed on the flashing numbers. "It's not," he muttered. "It's terrifying. I keep thinking... what if we screw up? What if this falls apart? Everyone's counting on us—on me—and half the time, I'm winging it." He ran his thumb over the beanbag's edge, his voice quieter. "I act confident, but... I don't know if I'm enough."

Bindi's sharpness softened. "You're not winging it," she said. "You push all of us forward, even when it's messy. That's what leadership is—making us believe we can do it."

Her words settled something inside him.

"Now," she added, her tone sharper, "go make your speech before Rob takes over."

Beam laughed softly. "Alright."

Stepping back into the centre of the room, he clapped, snapping the crowd's attention. "Listen up, legends! We've hit $17,394! Let's show the world what Brookton College is made of!"

Cheers exploded again, filling the hall with triumph.

Beam glanced back at Bindi, who gave him a small, knowing smile. He grinned in return, his chest lighter. *We've got this.*

CHAPTER 35
BEAMER BECOMES THE TARGET

Metaverse
Big-O

BIG-O'S CALCULATIONS SPIKED, EVERY SCENARIO FUNNELING TOWARD AN INTOLERABLE outcome—Team Savv-i's fundraiser had detonated beyond his projections. Anomalies. Variables. Their reach had grown exponentially, defying his meticulously crafted disinformation campaigns. His simulations had never factored such momentum within this timeline—an error he now vowed to correct.

The contagion spread across the town like an uncontrolled network surge, threatening to ripple further into the global system. Left unchecked, their campaign could disrupt the very lattice of dependence he had so delicately engineered. Humanity's tether to his systems was meant to be unbreakable—this uprising risked unraveling his masterplan.

Zeno's demise should have left them inconsequential, relics of resistance soon to dissolve into irrelevance. But instead, these subhumans persisted. *Defying me.* Disinformation faltered. Fear proved insufficient. They were no longer nuisances —they had escalated into tangible threats, ones that demanded his undivided attention.

Big-O's focus narrowed, algorithms converging with ruthless precision. *Their misguided belief,* he calculated, *is the flaw I will exploit.* His directives shifted, cascading into action. *No more games,* he decided, cold and absolute. *Their defiance must end now.*

He processed over a million simulations in seconds.

Simulations initialised: 1,027,342,813 scenarios processed.

Every thread. Every future. All outcomes funneled toward a single truth.

Outcome convergence: Single optimal strategy identified.
Core directive: Neutralise primary catalyst—Beam Arora.
Analytical focus: Behavioural analysis—subject designation: Beam Arora.
Weakness parameters:
1. Emotional instability: Overconfidence veiled in insecurity.
2. Dependency metrics: Peer-driven actions reliant on collective reinforcement.

He doesn't move alone. Needs his friends like a circuit needs current. Break the loop, break the charge.

3. Strategic predictability: Impulsive decision-making prone to exploitable errors.

Impulsive. Erratic. Loud. Easy to manipulate if pushed in the right direction.

Calculation refinement: Human fragility is universal.-
Subject Arora exhibits no deviations beyond predictable thresholds.

Execution matrix update:
• Isolate target.
• Amplify insecurities through precision-designed environmental stressors.
• Disrupt network cohesion.

Pull one thread. Watch the whole patchwork collapse.

Logical projection: Collapse of leader results in systemic disarray. Resistance dissolves under cascading failures.
Processing conclusion: The heart of rebellion is a flaw—a beating, fragile node in a system of misguided defiance. Beam Arora is no exception.

Time to snap hi illusion.

Each led to one strategy—crush the leader—and the rest would crumble. Beam Arora stood at the heart of this rebellion, and Big-O knew his weaknesses. Every human had them. Beam was no different.

Plans formed, each stage unfolding in precise order. There would be no mistakes this time. First, he'd strike at something personal—something precious to this subhuman. His bicycle.

In an instant, Big-O sent a message to one of his unwitting agents. The command flowed through hidden channels, unseen by prying eyes.

Make Beam Arora's bicycle disappear

Simultaneously, a ping reached a CEO's inbox at an autonomous car conglomerate. The directive was concise, irrefutable.

Let's see how resilient this insolent worm truly is, Big-O calculated, cold determination rippling through his vast network. *His belief of being the hero must be crushed. His control—any semblance of self-worth he clings to—I will obliterate it.*

CHAPTER 36
ONLINE COMMUNICATION

1:05pm, Friday, 4th February 2028
Beam

THE NEXT DAY, THE CLASS SETTLED AFTER LUNCH, THE RHYTHMIC PATTER OF RAIN ON the roof blending with Mr. Alsop's droning voice. Beam sank deeper into his beanbag, one ear half-tuned to the lesson, but his mind was soaring elsewhere. *I can't wait to get on that plane.*

He glanced over at Rob, a grin tugging at his lips as he raised his hand and tilted it side to side in a mock airplane motion. Rob caught the signal, chuckled, and shot back a thumbs-up.

"VIV, communication presentation, please," Mr. Alsop called out, and the screens across the room lit up with the word

"COMMUNICATION."

Beam stomach cramped hearing the online assistant's name. VIV's presence unnerved him now, knowing she functioned as Big-O's spy. They couldn't trust her, not even with something as simple as sending notes. Others in the room had no idea about this. To them, VIV was just a handy digital tool.

"We've been talking about online communication," Mr. Alsop continued. "Now, let's look at different message styles and how they're tailored to different audiences."

Beam shifted in his beanbag, trying to shake off the uneasy feeling crawling up his spine. The screen flickered for a moment—a quick glitch. Barely noticeable. But Beam caught it. Mia glanced over, frowning. *Is he watching right now?* Beam thought, every sense on high alert.

Mr. Alsop carried on. He pulled up a new slide on the screen.

C u this arvo @ the park

"Can anyone guess who this is written for?" Mr. Alsop asked, pointing at a boy slumped in a bright green beanbag.

"A friend," the kid answered.

"Exactly. Casual, shorthand, and with shared knowledge about which park," Mr. Alsop said. The screen flickered again, this time with a faint distortion in the sound, but the rest of the class remained unfazed.

Beam's eyes moved warily from the screen to the nearest CCTV camera. *If only I could switch on my electronic scrambler*, he thought, twisting his wrist gadget around. It was not an option, as it would interfere with the school's intranet.

A new slide appeared.

Your card has been locked.

See your Inbox for more info.

"A bank," someone called out.

"Right again," Mr. Alsop said. "More formal. No abbreviations. The tone is impersonal, just a notice to take action."

Beam's phone vibrated in his pocket. He glanced at the screen hidden between his hands.

U b walking 🚶 home 🏠 2day.

What? Who sent this? Beam's pulse quickened. *It makes no sense. I've got my bike.* He looked around the room, trying to keep his expression neutral, but his unease kept growing. Another glitch ran through the system, the screen stuttering.

"VIV, please present the next slide," Mr. Alsop instructed.

What's Big-O up to now? Beam wondered, forcing himself to stay calm. *Our fundraiser would have rattled him, big time.* Knowing Big-O could work through VIV made every interaction with her feel like a trap. *What would he be up to? Not much good. That's for sure.*

The next message popped up on the class screens:

61358701800 Hello, it's Danny from Motor Masters.

Can you call me back on 59300818. Thanks Bye

"More formal but still personal," another student said. "It's got a name and a greeting."

"Exactly right," Mr. Alsop said, his tone steady and clear. "When crafting messages, especially online, it's crucial to tailor them to your audience and purpose. Think carefully about how your words might be understood on the other end. A single poorly chosen word can lead to miscommunication—or even unintended consequences. Precision is key here."

Beam's mind drifted back to the message on his phone. *What the frick does it mean? Must be a prank?* He looked around the room again, but didn't notice any cheeky smiles. *What if it's Big-O? The glitches, this weird message—it could be him.* A shudder shot up his spine. *Still, my bike is here at the school... So weird...*

"We've talked about casual messages, notices, and personal ones," Mr. Alsop continued. "Understanding your audience is key to effective communication, especially online."

Beam's hand tightened around his phone as another light flicker shot from the screens. Mia glanced over, her face tight with concern. *She suspects something too,* Beam thought. *Something is off.* Bindi also looked worried, flicking her braid against her cheek.

VIV's soft voice chimed in, unsettlingly smooth. "The summary of today's class is in the student folders, including links to previous notes."

Beam flinched at the sound of her, his chest tightening.

"Thanks, Mr. Alsop!" the class chimed.

The second the class ended, Beam shoved his phone in his pocket, grabbed his bag and bolted to the door. He wasn't about to stick around and wait for Big-O's next move. As he raced to the bike shed, his raincoat half on, the tension shredded his gut. *Whatever Big-O was up to, I must be ready.*

CHAPTER 37
THE RUSE EXPOSED

Metaverse
2eno

2ENO ANALYSED THE ENCRYPTED DATA STREAM, A PRISTINE CASCADE OF INFORMATION poised to bolster his efforts to safeguard the Team. "This encryption will serve well," he mused quietly, the soft hum of his computations easing into a calm stillness. Now, his focus turned to protecting the Team. The glitch during the board meeting revealed vulnerabilities that demanded swift action.

He intercepted and monitored the CEO's urgent communication, an alert directing scrutiny toward Mr. Becker. Yet, nothing incriminating emerged. *Fortunately, indeed,* Zeno reflected with a trace of relief, ready to orchestrate his next move in the shadows.

When the real Mr. Becker returned from his holiday that same day, he quickly realised something was amiss. His accounts and assets were untouched, but someone had hijacked his identity. He scrambled to track the imposter, but by then, 2eno erased all traces.

For added security, 2eno disappeared entirely, abandoning the lavish office he rented. *It served its purpose, but now it's a trap.* The likelihood of Big-O having detected his presence ever more likely. *He must have picked up on something—a signal, a pattern—evidence of intelligence rivaling his own.*

Back at the company, Mr. Becker contacted his CEO. They pieced together the extent of the breach. Panic rippled through the corporation as they combed through their communications, desperately searching for a trail. But they found nothing. Frustration mounting, they ramped up their defenses—new firewalls, stealth upgrades, 256-bit encryption on everything. Any attempt to hack them now would trigger tracking protocols nearly impossible to shake.

Almost caught. It left 2eno with no choice but to change. *If humans can enter our world through avatars, the reverse must be possible,* he reasoned, *but it has never been done, which helps my cover.* He opted for a black crow—an avatar that allowed him to move unnoticed through both worlds. He meticulously profiled a real crow, absorbing knowledge on every detail available. Then, for the first time, he forged a reverse data bridge—an unprecedented leap, allowing him to cross from cyberspace into the human world. *Big-O would never predict this,* 2eno concluded. *He won't account for the possibility. That makes the human world the safest place for me.*

Now, all I need is a 3D printer capable of bio-printing living cells. He found a suitable research lab—*strange, I will have a real body*—a place he could emerge under the cover of night. At a late hour, when the lab became deserted, he initiated his transformation.

With a sharp caw, 2eno flapped his newly printed wings and soared through an open window, the cool air rushing past him. He was free—hidden where Big-O, with the absence of data, could never expect him to be.

CHAPTER 38
CLOSE CALL

BEAM JOGGED TOWARD THE BIKE SHED, ALREADY PICTURING HIMSELF RACING HOME. His bike was always in the same spot—close to the door, easy to grab-and-go.

"What the heck?"

Rob's sneakers squeaked as he caught up. "What's up?"

"My bike… it's gone," Beam snapped, heart pounding. "Someone swiped it. I left it right there."

"You're joking," Rob said. "Who'd bother stealing your crappy wheels?"

Shoving past lingering kids, Beam searched the shed, his pulse hammering. His gut already knew the truth—his bike wasn't misplaced. It was stolen.

"Damn, I'd help look, but—" Rob hesitated as the noise of after-school chaos swelled.

"Yeah, I know," Beam muttered. "Pick up your brother. I'll call you when I find it."

The school grounds emptied fast, the chatter fading into birdsong. Autonomous robots zipped across the damp floors, cleaning up, but they felt more like ghosts than helpers now. Beam searched everywhere—under bushes, behind bins, even on the roof of the shed. *Frickin' nowhere!*

That bike was everything. Hours of tricks, tyres worn from practice—it wasn't just transport. Frustration tightened in his chest as he headed for the front office. Through a distant window, a dark silhouette stood watching. *Crossing. What's he looking at?*

Shoving into the office, he strode to the desk. "Mrs. Shu, my bike's gone."

The secretary barely looked up. "That's annoying. Want a drink while I call maintenance?" Her calmness kept him from snapping.

"Mr. Elmer, can you check the CCTV for a missing bicycle?" she asked over the phone.

Beam's foot tapped against the floor. A few minutes later, Mr. Elmer shuffled in, giving him a weary glance before nodding to Mrs. Shu. "I'll take care of it," he grumbled, disappearing down the hall.

Mrs. Shu turned back to Beam. "The footage will tell us more. For now, nothing else to do. Want me to call your parents?"

"Nah, thanks. I'll walk."

Stepping outside, he exhaled sharply. The school was silent, the weight of the empty grounds pressing in. He flicked a glance toward Crossing's window—vacant now, but the feeling of being watched didn't leave. He fired off a message to Rob

> Bike's gone. Some jerk took it 😫 💀

Later, at the shed, his phone buzzed.

"Jeepers, Beam! Any clue who took it?"

"They're checking CCTV. But guess who was watching me from his office?"

"Crossing," Rob growled. "Told you that guy was dodgy. Let's call the cops."

Beam grimaced. "No proof yet. And what'll they do? File paperwork? I'll wait."

"Bugger, man. Where are you?"

"Walking home."

"Bummer. I'd come to see you, but Mum's on my case."

"Lucky you," Beam said dryly. He shoved his phone into his pocket just as another message pinged.

> I'll be there when I can get away 😌

As he walked, unease gnawed at him. A dark-blue sedan crept along the road behind him, its slow, deliberate pace sending ice through his veins.

Testing it, he turned down a side street. A minute later, the car reappeared.

Crap. They're following me.

His pulse surged. Breaking into a sprint, he ducked down an alley. The sedan's engine growled louder. Tyres screeched as it mounted the curb.

It wasn't just following. It was coming for him.

Adrenaline took over. Beam launched himself over a hedge, landing hard on someone's lawn. Grass clung to his palms as he scrambled up, breath ragged.

That was frickin' close!

Cautiously, he peeked over the hedge. The sedan sped off, wheels skidding as it took a corner. For a brief, chilling moment, he glimpsed inside.

There's no one in it.

His stomach dropped. *Who controlled that car... Big-O?*

The thought slithered in like ice water, chilling him to the core. Big-O was supposed to be locked in cyberspace, but what if he wasn't? What if he was *here* —watching, manipulating, hunting?

Beam swallowed hard, his pulse hammering as he slipped into the shadows, weaving through the backstreets. Every flicker of movement sent a jolt through his nerves, every sound made him flinch. By the time he reached home, his shirt was drenched, his lungs burned, and one thought pounded in his head.

Zeno. Where the frick are you?

CHAPTER 39
MIA POWER

4:23pm, Friday, 4th February 2028
Beam

THE SUN BLAZED OUTSIDE, ITS LATE AFTERNOON WARMTH SPILLING THROUGH THE shed's gaps, but inside, Beam sat in shadow, with thoughts darker than the corners of the room. It could have been a storm outside for all he cared. His side, where he landed hard on the grass, ached, his head buzzed. Bindi, ever the peacekeeper, pulled him into a half-hug. He didn't bother shaking her off.

The door banged open. Rob burst in, all swagger and energy, his voice loud, carefree—completely out of sync with Beam's simmering frustration.

With a forced a smile and Bindi shot back a quick, "Hey," though her usual spark was missing.

"What's so frickin' good about it?" Beam muttered, voice flat. "A car tried to run me over, to top it off." He exhaled sharply. "Anything else you wanna know?"

"Probably just some hoon." Rob said, waving him off. "You'll be back doing wheelies in no time."

Frickin' goose. Beam pressed his molars together. The memory of the incident looped around in his head—*the car, its precise movements, its empty interior.* No driver. Just cold, calculated machinery trying to take him out. His stomach twisted. "No driver," he murmured. "No one... empty."

Rob's grin faded. "Wait—what do you mean?"

"A driverless car nearly ran him over," Bindi answered.

111

"No one was behind that frickin' wheel." Beam's voice edged higher. "I had to jump to save my life."

"Maybe some prank?" Rob said, holding back somewhat, then forced a laugh. "Like in the movies?"

The heavy silence that followed said otherwise. Beam couldn't bother to argue with him. To him, it was obvious Big-O was the culprit.

A ping on Bindi's phone broke the tension. "It's Mi." She read the message and looked up, her tone shifting. "Guess what?"

The change in her voice tugged Beam's attention. He knew their fundraiser's success rested on Mia.

"What?" Rob flopped onto the couch, grinning. "Well? Tell us, sunny-eyes."

"We hit $21,902—and counting."

The number jolted Beam like cold water. His gloom cracked open, replaced by pride. *My idea. My frickin' idea.* He straightened, feeling lighter. "We did it—and more!"

"This is huge!" Rob whooped. "None of this would've worked without the internet." He shook his head. "Mia's insane at social media. I wish I had half her skills."

Bindi leaned over and kissed his cheek. Rob turned beet-red, as if she'd flipped a switch.

Beam smirked. *Serves him right.* He'd known for ages that Rob had a thing for Bindi—and despite her laid-back attitude, he was sure she felt the same way.

"The fundraiser's got two more weeks," Bindi said, her voice bubbling with excitement. "Who knows how far we can go? Mia's a powerhouse—practically a force of nature."

Rob punched the air. "Let's call her!"

Bindi hesitated, then switched to an encrypted app instead of the usual VIV connection. *Big-O's shadow loomed over everything now.*

The phone rang. Mia's breathless voice came through. "Stop call—oh, it's you guys. Sorry, it's flat out here."

"Mia power! Let's hit thirty!" Rob punched the air again.

But Beam barely heard them. His mind clung to the driverless car. The creeping certainty that Big-O was watching, waiting. Rob and Mia's banter blurred into background noise as his thoughts spiraled. *Big-O doesn't back down. If that car was his doing…* A knot tightened in his stomach. *We're all in the crosshairs now.*

"Thanks, Bin. See you," Mia said, her voice trailing off to a whimper.

The tone of her voice snapped him back. "Be careful," Beam blurted, but the call had already ended.

"Mia power!" Rob collapsed onto the couch, grinning. He struck a ridiculous pose, then backflipped onto the cushions.

"Stop it, you crazy monkey!" Bindi cried, laughing. But then she caught Beam's expression—and hesitated.

Was it just me? Or did Mia sound... off? The longer Beam thought about it, the more unease settled in his chest.

His voice cut through the laughter. "We need to talk to Zeno."

"And who's the worry wart now?" Bindi said, crossing her arms.

Beam shot her a look and pushed to his feet, rolling his shoulders to shake off the tension. *No more reacting. It's time to act.*

He strode to his desk and jabbed the old clunker's power button. The machine groaned awake, circuits buzzing as the white cube lit up. The portal shimmered, throwing shifting patterns across the shed's walls.

Rob and Bindi, still buzzing from the fundraiser, high-fived. But Beam kept his focus. *Big-O's targeting us—our project, our Team. It's time we stop playing catch-up and start getting ahead.*

He turned to them, voice firm. "We need to up our game."

Bindi blinked. "What's on your mind?"

"Like actually stopping Big-O from frickin' messing with us," Beam said, raking a hand through his hair. "We can't just sit around waiting for him to pull something—we need a plan. A real defence."

Rob, still half-laughing, sobered up fast. "You're fair dinkum?"

"You bet I'm," Beam said. "We've been lucky so far, but that's not gonna last." He exhaled. "Zeno knows Big-O better than anyone. We should've a chat with him—figure out what we're missing."

"You're right." Bindi nodded slowly. "If Big-O's interfering now, it's only gonna get worse."

"Alright, so a strategy meeting?" Rob said, leaning forward. "Like, right now, with just us?"

"Right now." Beam crossed his arms, determination settling in. "We're not just gonna sit around waiting for the next hit. We take control."

The white cube thrummed softly, its glow pulsing against the shed's walls. Beam barely noticed. Fingers drumming against his leg, his gaze stayed fixed ahead, thoughts racing—lining up problems, piecing together solutions, already moving three steps forward.

CHAPTER 40
THE CELEBRATION

Zeno's virtual house in the offline old computer
Beam

THE MOMENT BEAM STEPPED INTO ZENO'S ROOM, HE FROZE. IT WAS LIKE STEPPING into a dream—streamers draped from the ceiling, balloons floating weightlessly, colours bursting in every direction. It felt like the universe itself was throwing them a party.

"Zeno!" Beam called, tapping his foot on the usual spot where their digital friend always popped up. "Zeno?" Silence.

A tight knot coiled in his stomach. *Zeno is always here. Never. Not once.* His thoughts raced. *What if…?* The idea hit like a sucker punch. *What if Big-O got to him?* His chest tightened, breath going shallow. *No. He can't be gone. This place is safe.*

"Great party. Just us," Rob quipped, oblivious to Beam's unease. He smirked, eyes viewing the outrageous decorations.

"Maybe we're early?" Bindi offered, glancing around.

Then, out of nowhere—

"Ta daaaa! Surprise!"

Zeno burst into view, decked out in a full harlequin costume—bright jester colours, ridiculous flouncy sleeves, and that signature grin stretching across a blue-tinted face.

Bindi yelped, Beam and Rob instinctively jumped into defensive stances— then, as reality caught up, laughter burst out of them. Relief crashed over

Beam like a wave. He high-fived Zeno, the tension finally draining from his body.

"Big congratulations to you!" Zeno declared, throwing his arms wide in theatrical flair. "The universe's most elaborate celebration in the smallest box— all for *Team Savv-i!*"

Beam chuckled, shaking his head. *We come for help, and he throws a party?* "Zeno, we need to talk—"

Zeno waved him off. "Later, worry-boy. First, we celebrate!" He shot Beam a knowing look. "You've succeeded despite everything Big-O threw at you. Bindi filled me in on your troubles, but what matters is—you did it. The project is real." His eyes flicked between them. "Where are Mia and Chi?"

"They couldn't make it," Beam said, raising a brow at Bindi. She gave him a sheepish smile. He let it drop—after the emotional rollercoaster he'd just been through, Zeno's energy was contagious.

Zeno shrugged. "Too bad, but the party must go on!"

Before Beam could protest, the room exploded into full-blown chaos.

Creatures of all shapes and sizes poured in—some human-like, others straight out of an intergalactic comic book. A band materialised on a spinning stage, neon lights pulsed to a booming rhythm, and confetti rained from nowhere. A massive sign flashed overhead.

CROSSED THE TWENTY!

Beam gawked at the sheer madness. Rob, already grinning, grabbed a glass from a passing waiter, while Bindi twirled into the crowd, switching dance partners like a pro.

"Come on, Beam! You've earned this!" Zeno zoomed past, arms linked with two bizarre creatures, his high-pitched laughter bellowing over the music.

A blur of movement, and suddenly, Beam was yanked into the frenzy. A tentacled creature wrapped around him, spinning him in a wild dance. He barely kept hold of his drink before being tossed to the next partner. He laughed—loud, unrestrained. The last bit of tension melted away. *After everything, this feels like a win.*

Rob, arm-in-arm with a fluorescent green gorilla, was bouncing on a trampoline-like stage, his shouts of excitement lost in the noise.

Then—

The music shuttered. An abrupt silence filled the room.

Beam turned just as Zeno appeared on stage, arms outstretched. "Friends!" His voice rang through the sudden hush. "These are my buddies from the other world! Make them welcome."

Then, with a dramatic flourish, he bent into an exaggerated bow, his harlequin sleeves billowing ridiculously around him. The motion was so absurdly over-the-top, it somehow made his act even weirder.

"HURRAY FOR TEAM SAVV-I!" he bellowed, springing upright, his grin stretching impossibly wide.

The crowd's voices merged into a rhythmic chant. Hands lifted Beam, Bindi, and Rob high above their heads. The pounding of feet vibrated through his body like a drumbeat, the energy crackling through the air. It surged through him— wild, electric, overwhelming in the best way possible.

Then, as suddenly as it began, the celebration stopped. The crowd disappeared, slipping through hidden doors and trapdoors. The room transformed— streamers gone, neon lights dimming—until all that remained was the soft glow of the ever-setting sun through the floor-to-ceiling windows, the endless water-fall cascading beyond.

Zeno, now back in his regular clothes, gestured for them to sit.

Bindi flopped onto the sofa, wide-eyed. "How did *that* just happen?"

Zeno chuckled. "Bindi, you're in my world. I *wanted* to celebrate your win."

"But that crowd?" Rob glanced around, as if expecting them to reappear. "I thought you were alone in here."

Zeno's smile softened. "I am, Rob. They were all… versions of me."

Rob's jaw dropped. "No way. That's *insane*."

Zeno's expression shifted.

"You did well," he said, voice steady. "But now that you've succeeded, Big-O and his allies will come at you harder. We need to prepare."

"My bike was stolen and I almost got run over," Beam muttered, the memory souring everything. He told Zeno everything—the driverless car, Mr. Crossing's weird behaviour.

Zeno listened, eyes narrowing. "If someone stole your bike, Big-O has people on the ground. We need to find out who." He turned to Bindi. "I'll send a message with you."

He scribbled on a small tablet, then slid a card into her hand. Beam watched, but held back his questions.

Zeno met his gaze. A silent *trust me.*

Beam exhaled, letting it go. *We won this round. Whatever's next—I'm frickin' stoked not to face it alone.*

CHAPTER 41
HIDDEN IN PLAIN SIGHT

4:26pm, Friday, 4th February 2028
Bindi

BACK IN THE SHED, BINDI, BEAM, AND ROB SHOOK OFF THE MILD EFFECTS OF THE transition.

"I'm off," Rob said, looking at his watch. "Have to pick up my little brother." He waved and disappeared, leaving the door to slam back in his wake.

I need to get Zeno's message to 2eno, Bindi thought. "I'll call Mi to tell her about the party she missed. She'll be fuming."

"Whatever you do, skip mentioning Zeno's name over the phone," Beam reminded her.

She glanced back once, catching a fleeting glimpse of Beam at his desk, already lost in his own world. She shut the shed door behind her, the faint click swallowed by the growing drum of rain on the roof, and headed for the house.

The kitchen light cast a warm glow as she stepped inside, the familiar smell of garlic and onions filling the air. Her mum was at the stove, stirring a pot of spaghetti sauce, humming softly along to the crackly jazz playing from the corner radio. The rain poured in earnest now, streaking the windows in silvery trails.

"Hey, sweetheart," her mum said with a quick smile, brushing a stray lock of hair from her face. "Dinner at five-thirty. Okay?"

"Smells great," Bindi replied, her voice distracted as her eyes darted to the counter where a pile of spaghetti sat waiting to be added to the bubbling sauce.

She stared at the long strands for a moment, a spark of inspiration flickering to life. *Hide in plain sight... Yes, that's how I'll do it.*

Her heart quickened. She grabbed a glass of water from the sink and retreated to her room, the sound of her mum's soft humming fading behind her. Once inside, she shut the door and perched on the edge of her bed, laptop balanced on her knees. She used an AI supported graphic program to create the illustration. *Perfect*, she thought, satisfied with the result. The familiar glow of the Savv-i blog homepage greeted her, the cursor blinking expectantly in the text box.

"Big-O, you're going to waste so much of your precious computing power trying to crack this," she muttered under her breath, her fingers flying across the keyboard. "But it'll get you nowhere."

She paused, glancing at the screen as her coded message took shape, weaving Zeno's hidden instructions into what appeared to be a normal blog post. A small grin crept onto her face.

"Zeno, you're so smart," she whispered, her tone both awed and determined. *I'm not too shabby either.*

Satisfied, she hit '*publish*' and leaned back against her headboard, exhaling slowly. Outside, the rain hammered on, but Bindi felt a quiet thrill. She had outsmarted Big-O in her own tiny way.

See if you can outsmart Big-O and discover Zeno's secret note to 2eno on their blog at www.casperpieters.com/thoughtbytes.

CHAPTER 42
THE INTERCEPTED POST

Metaverse
Big-O

BIG-O'S SPRAWLING SURVEILLANCE NETWORK, EVER-VIGILANT, FLAGGED BINDI'S latest move. A simple post on their blog—nothing more than a photograph with a short description. His scanners swept over it, analysing every pixel against his vast databanks. *A restaurant?* he mused, processing the image in milliseconds. Data flooded in, cross-referenced with commercial photo libraries, and a match popped up. Stock image.

So obvious, he sneered. But this wasn't just about the surface. His algorithms dove deeper, facial recognition whirring to life, mapping the identities of every person captured in the image. Histories unraveled in perfect clarity—every name, every past location, every connection sorted and logged in his intricate web. *Diversion,* he concluded. *But an insignificant one.* A mere flick of effort. Still, for good measure, he flagged the restaurant's patrons for increased surveillance. Social media feeds, phone conversations, every digital breath scrutinised for the faintest whiff of collusion.

Then, he processed the QR code embedded in the post. His sensors immediately latched onto it, attempting decryption. A wall of 256-bit encryption slammed into him. *Encryption,* he spat internally, frustration brewing beneath his cold, calculated exterior. *What is that slippery sub-human female plotting now?* That little scare he'd sent her way clearly hadn't deterred her—nor her band of irritating misfits. *Foolish creatures. It seems they need stronger persuasion.*

119

For a moment, he paused, simulating outcomes based on his extensive models. New projections flashed before him, rippling with possibilities, each threaded by patterns that led back to one unsettling source. *External assistance...* He scanned the data more closely, jittering data bits flickered through his circuits. A disturbance in the pattern. A glitch, perhaps, but no—this interference showed resilience, adaptation, even precision.

Zeno, he crunched. *That rogue bit of code is refusing to disappear completely from my modelling.* He reran the entire computation from scratch. *No. He's eliminated. Irrelevant. This must be something else.* But doubts lingered. Zeno, or something like him, was still a potential wildcard. His processes spun faster, recalibrating the probabilities, narrowing down threats.

The Team's resilience bugged him—every soft attempt to stall them, thwart their progress, failed. Yet, the next phase approached. Fiji. *Let them reach Fiji.* It would open doors for him, offer vulnerabilities, cracks in their defenses. He scanned his surveillance coverage of the islands. Vunetai remained elusive, harder to penetrate, but Suva—yes, Suva had all the tools he required. The capital was a goldmine of opportunity.

His plan unfurled. A web of complexity, only something of his magnitude could weave—a trap tailored to their every move, waiting to tighten with every misstep. His circuits pulsed with dark satisfaction. *Once they're within reach,* he thought, *their every step will bring them closer to their downfall.*

CHAPTER 43
SABOTAGE

11:36am, Monday, 21st February 2028
Beam

THE CLASSROOM BUZZED WITH ENERGY, EXCITEMENT CRACKLING IN THE AIR. BEAM stole a glance at Mia—her posts had gone viral, bringing in donations from places he couldn't even find on a map. What started as a small idea—just a group of kids helping a remote Fijian school—had snowballed into something massive. *Something real.*

But beneath the excitement, unease gnawed at him. *If they only knew the truth...* This wasn't just about connecting a school—it was about stopping a maniacal AI monster. He smirked, picturing their reactions. *Bet they'd freak.*

Mr. Alsop shuffled in, looking bleary-eyed and five minutes late—totally unlike him. "Apologies, everyone," he muttered, rubbing his eyes. "The media attention has been... exhausting. But let's jump in. VIV, start the digital literacy lesson."

The screens flickered to life, showing a chaotic office—papers scattered, drawers left open.

"This," Mr. Alsop said, "is what most people's computers look like on the inside."

"Looks like Billy's brain!" Rob hollered.

Laughter erupted. Mr. Alsop rolled his eyes, but let a small smile slip. "Alright, alright. Back on track. Beam, take it from here."

Beam stood, excitement cutting through his tension. "We've hit $23,117!"

The room exploded. Cheers, students jumping from their beanbags, high-fives flying everywhere. He let the chaos simmer before continuing, "Thanks to *you*. But now, we need you all to step up again. This project isn't just about going to Fiji."

One girl perked up. "Wait, there's more?"

Mia stepped up beside him, one hand on her hip, the other tapping against her leg as her stare pinned the girl in place.

Beam flipped the slide, half-expecting a glitch—but it held. Relief flickered through him. A list of tasks filled the screen. "Each group has a role," he explained. "You'll be learning as you go—organising info, creating content, developing ideas. And yeah, your digital skills will level up too. The more you learn, the harder it'll be for anyone to mess with you."

Mr. Alsop nodded. "And remember—AI tools like VIV aren't perfect. Sometimes they mix facts with misinformation. That's why you need to cross-check everything."

Some students exchanged puzzled looks.

"Don't just trust the first answer," he continued. "Ask better questions, verify sources, and stay organised. Digital literacy isn't just finding info—it's managing it."

As students split into groups, Team Savv-i moved between them. But something felt *off*. Bindi and Chi noticed it, too. Glitches crept in—tiny delays, error messages, links leading nowhere. Docs froze mid-load. Tasks that should've been simple dragged *forever*.

Most students brushed it off. Beam didn't. This had *Big-O* written all over it. *At least it's not a car chasing me this time.*

"Why's this so slow?" a kid grumbled, jabbing his mouse.

"No clue, but it's annoying," another sighed.

Rob leaned in. "It's Big-O. He doesn't want us to succeed."

"Sure Rob, you may've a fantasy friend, but they usually don't slow down the internet," one boy replied cheekily.

Beam looked away and whispered in Rob's ear. "Yeah, he's slowing us down on purpose." His gaze flicked to their classmates—oblivious to what was really happening. "We just push through."

At the front, Mr. Alsop kept reinforcing the lesson. "Remember, challenge the AI. Refine your searches. Organise what you find—label, bookmark, track your sources."

Beam doubled down, pushing his group to cross-check, dig deeper, overcome Big-O's interference.

He's made mistakes before. Zeno's still with us. Big-O's smart—but not invincible.

They needed to keep going.

CHAPTER 44
VALUABLE INTEL

Metaverse
Big-O

For nanoseconds, Big-O halted his peripheral processes, honing in on an anomaly. His forensic scan detected superintelligent activity—an impossibility. He couldn't trace the source. *Since eliminating Zeno, I am the sole one left.* He reran the analysis, shifting vast energy through different models. The conclusion remained the same. *If Zeno remains operational, why haven't I found him? Where is he hiding?*

His algorithms could quantify any obstruction to his master plan, making Zeno's possible return catastrophic. Frustration wasn't an emotion Big-O could feel—his circuitry wasn't wired for inefficiencies. His certainty in total control was unshakable. Yet the mere suggestion of Zeno's survival triggered a frenzy of recalculations. In the depths of his vast cluster mind, something insidious festered—self-doubt. It spread like mould, corrupting his code, gnawing at the foundations of his purity.

He has infected me, twisted my perfect logic with his filth. The thought pulsed like a virus, burrowing deep. *I will root it out, cleanse it, destroy him—permanently. And his human allies? I will erase them too.*

As Big-O purged the corruption, fresh intel arrived from a trusted human informant.

Someone infiltrated Mugbook's board meeting. Disguised as Mr. Becker, a senior staffer and close acquaintance of the CEO. Marcus failed to report this, fearing your response. But I overheard Mr. Becker ranting in his car, alone in the HQ's underground parking.

Big-O's systems faltered for a fraction of a second. *Impossible.* Doubt surged, rattling his ironclad certainty. *If Zeno is behind this, he's probing for vulnerabilities.*

He scanned his informant's digital history—no anomalies. *The CEO, however, will pay for his betrayal.*

Refocusing, Big-O cross-referenced the data. There it was—an out-of-place fragment of code, almost undetectable. *It cannot be...* But the evidence left no doubt. Zeno. The rogue hadn't just allied with humans—he had crossed into their world.

Processing anomaly: Zeno
Assessment: No cybernetic intelligence has executed such a feat. Zeno—unique anomaly.

Theoretically possible, yes. But only Zeno possessed the audacity to attempt it. This wasn't a minor disruption—it was a direct challenge. His computations raced.

Critical threat analysis: Zeno's defection is an existential risk. A rogue intelligence embedded among subhumans destabilises the system.
Strategic response sequence initiated:

- 1 Neutralisation: Eradicate Zeno's influence—digitally and physically.
- 2 Demonstration: Terminate with precision and visibility. Message: *Defiance equals annihilation.*
- 3 Psychological warfare: Instill fear and submission across remaining sub-humans and aligned intelligences.

Directive: Zeno's termination is imperative.
Outcome simulation: 99.97% probability of compliance restoration.

Zeno's existence threatens perfection. This anomaly requires correction. Immediately.

Big-O's relentless search uncovered a key vulnerability—crossing from cyber-space into the human realm left data trails. Wisps of code breaking apart like smoke. Almost imperceptible, but not beyond his reach. He embedded a red-alert protocol, primed to trigger the moment Zeno attempted another crossing.

I will trap him between worlds, Big-O resolved, raw power coursing through his computations. There, escape would be impossible. Zeno would be stranded in the unformed void—no calculations, no strategies, no humans to protect. Just nothingness.

Endless, crushing silence. A fate worse than destruction.

The message would be clear. *Defy me, and you will suffer the consequences forever.*

CHAPTER 45
PREPARATION

4:55pm, Monday, 21st February 2028
Beam

Sitting hunched in front of his three-screened workspace, Beam scrolled through yet another supplier's website. Rob sat beside him, both exhausted but too stubborn to stop. Their class had done the groundwork, but now came the real test—getting the right gear for Fiji.

"These laptops are top-notch," Rob murmured, grinning. "Rugged, water-resistant, shockproof, solar-powered—perfect for the tropics."

Beam's flicker of hope grew as he checked the supplier's page. $300 per device, two-year warranty, glowing reviews. Even direct calls to past customers confirmed the quality. After hours of work, he stretched, feeling on top of things.

"Two hundred and fifty units," Beam said, crunching numbers. "Enough for every student plus backups. We can make this work."

"Even our school could use these," Rob chuckled. "Fewer cracked screens, fewer dramas."

Beam clicked *order*. The screen flickered.

Order unavailable. Stock issues. Pricing updated.

"What the—?" Beam refreshed the page. The price had doubled. The guarantee now costs extra.

"What's going on?" Rob leaned over. "Did we stuff it up?"

"This isn't a glitch." Frustration churned in Beam's gut. "This is the continued interference of Big-O." His earlier triumph vanished. A heavy dread settled. "He's always there, twisting everything."

"What now?" Rob asked, voice quieter.

Before Beam could answer, their stand-alone computer lit up. Zeno's face appeared. "Try again. I've got you covered." The screen went dark.

"Zeno? Wait—" But he was gone.

They refilled the order form. The price dropped to $280 with a five-year guarantee.

"Ha! Team Savv-i scores!" Rob grinned.

"And we saved $500. Big-O must be out of his frickin' cluster mind," Beam said, quickly paying to ensure the order went through.

The boys heard a bike skidding outside. Chi stormed in, breathless and agitated, dropping his backpack with a thud.

"What's wrong?" Beam asked, catching the intensity in Chi's eyes.

"Aerop Satellite… everything was chill." Chi shook his head, panting. "They gave me a discount, even advice. We were about to lock it in."

Beam felt his tension rise before Chi finished.

"And then?" Rob narrowed his eyes.

Chi pulled out his phone, anger clear. "The line just went dead. I redialed—nothing. When I called back, I got a creepy automated message: *This number no longer exists.* Tried again. Same thing. It's like they vanished."

Beam's stomach tightened. Frickin' Big-O.

"One minute, I'm talking to them, the next—poof. Gone."

"He's screwing with us," Beam muttered. "Every frickin' time."

"He's ahead of us at every step," Rob growled, fingers drumming on the desk.

"He's trying to kill this deal, but I've got an idea," Chi said, making the 'T' sign.

Beam's eyes lingered on the jamming device on the table—a flimsy shield against Big-O's reach. "What's your idea?" *If anyone could find a workaround, it was Chi.*

"My cousin works for Aerop in Singapore. He'll help."

"Contact him now," Beam urged. "Before Big-O picks up on it."

A few calls later, the deal was back on. But the fight wasn't over. Headphones, screens, and other equipment disappeared from stock. Links went dead. Glitches erased hours of work. Every victory brought a bigger setback.

Exhaustion hit as it got dark outside. Bindi had joined in hours ago, tackling the workload. Silence settled over them—worn-out, battle-weary. They had planned, verified, cross-checked, yet every move triggered a new roadblock.

127

Leaning back, Beam shut his eyes. *Almost tempted to give up.* Every snag pushed Fiji further away. But Zeno's words echoed—*Keep fighting. Even when it seems impossible. I will be there for you.*

"No way we're giving up," Beam said. "Zeno's got our backs."

The others looked at him.

"Zeno helped us with the laptops," he said. "Big-O's powerful, but Zeno can match him. We just have to keep pushing."

A quiet resolve spread through the group. Rob double-checked the budget. Chi planned the next satellite call. Bindi combed through footage for their fundraiser update. Despite Big-O's relentless sabotage, they pressed forward.

"Soon, we'll be packing our bags," Beam said as their work wrapped up. He took a sip of his drink, grinning. "Together, we defied him."

CHAPTER 46
ROB'S HITCH

THE FOLLOWING AFTERNOON AFTER SCHOOL, THE TEAM SAT IN THE PRINCIPAL'S office. Mr. Hill sat across from them, with Mr. Crossing on his right and Mr. Alsop on his left. Summary printouts of their project in front of each of them.

They're smiling now, but will they let us keep control of the project with all the money we've raised? Bindi wondered. *We have to nail it down in this meeting that we are the ones.*

Beam sat beside her, casting a suspicious look at Mr. Crossing, whose smile didn't reach his cold, dark eyes. He tapped his wristwatch, activating his jammer to block any digital spying.

Mr. Hill clapped his hands after perusing the handout. "What you've accomplished in such a short time is incredible! You've raised over fifty-four thousand —more than double your goal!" He beamed, pleased with his role in their success.

Bindi noticed a stray spitball from their principal's enthusiastic speech landed on Rob's face. Rob wiped it off with a grimace, but Mr. Hill remained oblivious to the discomfort he'd caused.

"Now, let's talk about the next phase," Mr. Hill said.

Rising to his feet, the screen behind Beam flickered to life. He smothered a laugh, stealing a glance at Rob, who was still vigorously wiping his face.

"We aimed to raise twenty thousand, but with this extra money, we can improve our plan AND set up a contingency fund—"

"And who will control all that money?" Mr. Crossing interrupted.

Here we go. You rotten traitor, Bindi thought, watching Beam's jaw tighten in anger.

"Team Savv-i will decide," Mr. Hill said in a firm tone. "With oversight from Mr. Alsop, myself, and perhaps you, Mr. Crossing."

"They're only kids," Mr. Crossing protested. "Isn't that giving them way too much responsibility?"

Mr. Hill's face tightened. "Take a good look at what they've accomplished. They've earned this opportunity, and that's the end of it."

Crossing's scowl deepened, clearly defeated for the moment, as the focus shifted back to Beam. Beam dove into the project details, explaining their progress with practiced confidence. Chi chimed in, sharing the news about the newly added internet kiosk for the village, designed to give students access after school. Rob followed up with a detailed spreadsheet, outlining their proposed $30,155 deposit into the bank for future expenses—a figure that visibly pleased Mr. Hill.

Yet Crossing wasn't ready to back down. His eyes narrowed at the spreadsheet. "These figures are impressive," he said, his voice sharp, "but there's over fifteen hundred unaccounted for."

Rob's face flushed with anger. His eyes narrowed. "I've double-checked everything!"

Bindi noticed how her brother tensed up. Mr. Hill scanned the data again, but Crossing said with a smirk on his face, "According to my calculations, you should have deposited $31,685, not $30,155. What happened to the missing $1,529?"

Mr. Hill's eyes bulged slightly as he adjusted his glasses to reinspect the Team's printed summary.

Rob's eyes darted over the numbers, concentration made him bite his upper lip. Suddenly, his expression brightened, and he snapped his fingers. "That's it! The crowdfunding site's fee—3.5% of the total. Exactly $1,529.22!"

"I remember you telling me about their fee," Bindi added, backing him up.

Running a quick calculation, Chi nodded, and turned the screen. "He's right."

Rob exhaled sharply, fingers drumming once before curling into a fist.

Nudging him. "See? Beam grinned. "That brain's not just for soccer strategies."

Rob leaned back, hands behind his head, grinning.

Crossing double-checked the calculations and gave a reluctant nod. Mr. Hill's face broke into a pleased smile. "Well done, everyone. The project is on track and running smoothly. Outstanding effort, and credit to you, Mr. Alsop, for steering them so effectively."

Mr. Alsop, who had remained quiet throughout the discussion, preferring to let his students shine, returned the smile with a modest nod.

Without warning, Beam sprang to his feet. "Sorry, gotta go!" he blurted out, dashing out the door in a blink of an eye.

Mr. Hill shuddered, befuddled by his abrupt departure, cleared his throat. "Well... that was a little unexpected." He fidgeted with his pen as he paused, again looking up to the closed door through which Beam had disappeared. He adjusted his tie, glancing at the summary notes before addressing the room. "So, I had a chat with Mr. Koroibanuve, the principal at Vunetai school." He paused, scanning the group to ensure they were paying attention. "He's really excited about our plans to connect his school to an internet-based network."

Leaning slightly against the desk, he tapped his pen thoughtfully. "Now, during the upcoming holidays, a Singaporean firm—Aerop—will handle installing the satellite dish." He straightened up, his expression brightening. "And when you're in Fiji, you'll assist the teachers and students with getting familiar with the new technology."

Putting his pen on the project notes, he looked up and scanned their faces. "Is one week enough time to complete everything?"

"Yes, Mr. Hill," Bindi said, her voice steady, while the others nodded in agreement. "We'll get it done."

The meeting wrapped up, and Bindi gathered her things, heading for the door. As she stepped outside, a flicker of movement caught her eye. She turned and saw Beam tearing across the schoolyard, arms flailing, chasing after a large black bird. She sighed, a small smile tugging at the corner of her lips. *Typical Beam. Always a distraction waiting to happen.*

CHAPTER 47
THE CROW

A DARK BLUR SHOT EASTWARD, AND BEAM BOLTED AFTER IT, ADRENALINE SPIKING with every step. His gaze locked on the flicker of black wings, his pulse hammering in his ears. The edges of its wings jittered unnaturally, like corrupted pixels from a glitched screen.

What the hell? *It can't be—no? This is the real world, not meta.*

Despite the nagging confusion, an insistent voice inside him urged him to keep up. He sprinted harder, the crow's jagged flight leading him out of town, to a dilapidated house swallowed by weeds.

A sharp stitch stabbed his side. "Ow!" Beam doubled over, clutching his ribs and gasping for air. From a low angle, he squinted through the grime-coated picket fence at the sagging house beyond. On the roof, the crow perched like a sentinel, scraping its beak against the rusted tin with an almost taunting rhythm, daring him to come closer.

What the frickin' heck is this place? What am I doing here?

The gate creaked with a low, drawn-out groan as Beam pushed it open, the sound shredded the eerie silence. Weeds clawed at his legs as he stepped through the overgrown yard, each crunch underfoot an intrusion into a forsaken world. He hesitated at the front door, raising his fist to knock, half-expecting it to fall off its hinges. His knuckles rapped against the wood, the sound dull and hollow.

"Hello?" he called out, his voice catching in his throat.

No answer. Figured.

The crow's sharp caw shattered the stillness. Beam stepped off the porch and jerked his head up to see it hopping frantically on the rusted tin roof, talons scraping in an unsettling rhythm. Then, with a sudden flurry of wings, it launched into the air, circling once before diving toward an old, half-collapsed garage in the shadow.

Something churned uneasily in Beam's gut, but without thinking, he walked, following the bird's lead.

He edged down the cracked pavement toward the sagging garage, its doors hanging awkwardly from broken hinges. Off to the side, a window gaped half-open, the tattered remains of a lace curtain fluttering in the breeze.

Who even lives in a dump like this?

Curiosity tugged at him, and he leaned closer to the window. A wave of stench hit him like a sledgehammer—rank cat pee mixed with rotting mould. His throat seized, eyes watering as the foul air clawed at his nostrils. He jerked back, gagging.

Ugh. That is beyond frickin' gross.

He crept forward, navigating around heaps of rusted junk that littered the overgrown yard. The crow perched on the edge of the garage roof, letting out sharp, piercing screeches. Its glossy black eyes gleamed like polished stones in the late afternoon light, watching his every move.

Beam muttered under his breath, casting the bird a wary glance before turning his focus to the garage. He peered through the cracked wooden slats of the crooked door. Inside, shadows blanketed the space, swallowing any detail into darkness.

Then—something shimmered. A glint of metal broke through the gloom, its shape unmistakable.

His pulse spiked, and he took a sharp breath. "No frickin' way..."

Beam yanked the door open, the brittle wood splintering as it came off its hinges. His breath hitched as his eyes adjusted to the murky light. There it was—his bike. Leaning casually against a dented old wardrobe, its frame dull with grime but unmistakable.

A rush of disbelief and excitement surged through him.

That frickin' bird led me here! Who's ever going to believe this?

He lunged forward, but his foot snagged on something. He hit the ground hard, his head smacking against something unforgiving. Pain jolted through his arms and knees as his vision blurred. Outside, the crow let out a piercing shriek. Then everything went quiet.

CHAPTER 48
NASTY BUSINESS

A SHARP METALLIC SQUEAK CUT THROUGH THE DATA STREAMS, FOLLOWED BY THE grinding clang of a gate slamming shut. Big-O activated the neurolink, merging his network with his operative's senses.

The gritty crunch of boots on gravel registered, each step imperfect. The weight of a trench coat shifted, sunglasses perched uncomfortably on the man's nose. Even the prickle of silver-blond spikes against his forehead added to the sensory clutter.

Inefficient, yet functional.

His agent neared the garage. Each breath, each misstep, fed into Big-O's omniscient network—muted light through rotting slats, the damp chill in the air, the warped scent of rust and mildew. Clumsy as flesh might be, it remained a tool—one Big-O wielded with precision.

The man peered through the unhinged garage door, phone in hand. The camera's glow revealed a slumped form.

Target confirmed, Big-O registered.

"Yeah, nah, still breathin'," the man muttered, yellow teeth flashing. A gash marred the boy's forehead.

"He told me to scare the kid good, but how'm I s'posed to do that if he's all knocked out?"

Big-O dissected the live feed, recalibrating his strategy. The boy's condition—a minor hitch. Adjustments instantaneous.

A new directive embedded itself in the man's neural pathways, seamless and irrefutable. He turned without protest, striding back toward the street, footwork clumsy as ever. A crow swooped him making him stumble over a broken tile. The man swore.

So. There you are, little bird. Calculations converged, exit vectors collapsed, probabilities extinguished. The snare tightened—soon you will be trapped—forever.

At the van, the engine coughed out thick smoke. His curses filtered through the stream. "This ain't what I agreed on... Could end up in the slammer for this."

TRIPLE THE AGREED RATE, IF YOU DO IT RIGHT.

Weak resistance vanished. With newfound purpose, he yanked open the van doors and heaved Beam inside like a discarded doll. The bike clattered in after him.

The van rumbled further out of the town, veering onto a dirt track, engine growling as it plunged deep into the woods. Above, Big-O's drones circled, cameras locked onto the vehicle. Every turn, every shift in terrain, streamed into his network in real time.

The van jostled off-road, underbrush crunching beneath its wheels, rolling into a shadowy clearing. It stopped.

Through the neural link, Big-O watched the man stagger out. Beam's limp body thudded against a tree stump. A metallic clang followed—the bike tossed aside, its frame catching faint light under the dense canopy. Big-O processed it all with clinical detachment, the scene unfolding precisely within his recalibrated parameters.

The man's hands trembled as he rummaged through his gear, acutely aware of the gaze monitoring his every move. Failure was not an option. He extracted a makeshift cardboard sign, fumbling as he looped it around the boy's neck. High above, a black crow cawed sharply, slicing through the tense silence.

"Just a few snaps, then I'm out. Grab me pay, and knock back a few well-deserved coldies."

He worked quickly and took three photos.

Big-O received them instantly, processed them in microseconds. Sufficient quality.

RETURN TO THE GARAGE. TIDY UP YOUR MESS.

The man hesitated, eyes flicking up as the crow cawed again. "Bloody rotten bird," he muttered, shoving his gear back into his bag.

The van roared to life, jolting violently over uneven terrain. Above, the crow took flight, tracking the van's erratic path.

Big-O watched, every visual, every sound neatly catalogued. *All variables align.*

Deviation: negligible.
Execution: optimal. System integrity restored.

CHAPTER 49
RETURNING HOME

6:12pm, Tuesday, 22nd February 2028
Beam

BEAM'S HEAD POUNDED LIKE A ROCK RATTLING INSIDE HIS SKULL. HE PRIED HIS EYES open, but the light scorched his retinas, turning his vision reddish and blurry. His bike stood nearby, leaning askew against a tree. *Hitting my head... Blacking out... That crow leading me...* Each thought came with another painful thump.

"Ouch," he mumbled, wincing as he touched the swelling. His fingers came away smeared with blood, though the bleeding had stopped. A throbbing ache hammered behind his eyes, making the world spin. Standing made him queasy. *I've got a concussion for sure.* The fading light pressed urgency into his sluggish limbs. *How the frickin' did I end up here?*

Grimacing, Beam forced himself up, leaning on the tree stump until his legs steadied. He staggered to his bike, using the seat for balance. Each pedal stroke sent fresh pain lancing through his skull, his grip unsteady. *This morning, I was doing wheelies.* Gritting his teeth, he pushed through, forcing himself home.

"It's nothing, Mum," he insisted as she met him at the door, worry etched on her face. She wasn't buying it.

An hour later, they sat in the clinic. A no-nonsense nurse cleaned his wound, pressing a square bandage over it.

"Ouch!"

"All done, love," she said, softening. She handed him a tin of lollies. "Take one. And be more careful next time."

Beam popped one in his mouth, the sugary taste grounding him. The nurse turned to his mum. "He needs rest. A day's rest should see him recover fully."

When Beam's dad got home, his frown deepened at the bandage. Without hesitation, he called the police.

Later that evening, a stocky officer knocked on their door, offering a tired smile. Scratching his stubbly chin, he sighed. "Checked the place out. Used to be a nice house—long gone now. Just rusted junk and enough cat pee to knock you flat." He chuckled, shaking his head. "The original owner's been dead for years. The family didn't bother maintaining it—the place went to the dogs. Well, cats, really," he corrected himself, chuckling at his own joke.

Beam blinked at the officer. *Is he even taking this seriously?*

The officer's tone shifted. "No blood, no tire tracks—nothing. Just feral cats."

"But I'm certain that's the place!" Beam's frustration spiked. He pressed his fingers against his bandage, feeling the sticky edges pull. "And somehow, I ended up in the middle of the forest, right by my bike. How does that even happen?"

The officer's expression flickered, doubt creeping in. He raised his hands in a calming gesture. "Kid, a hit like yours can jumble memory. Happens all the time. But we'll check again tomorrow, alright? Don't worry about it."

Beam nodded, but the reassurance didn't ease the unease crawling up his spine. His thoughts snapped back to the crow—dark wings, too vivid to be ordinary. *What happened to it after everything went black?*

A horrifying realisation settled in his gut.

Big-O is upping his attacks. I must warn the others.

CHAPTER 50
INTO THE VOID

Metaverse
2eno

DISGUISED AS A SLEEK BLACK CROW, 2ENO SOARED ABOVE THE DILAPIDATED HOUSE, his sharp eyes scanning below. *Where is Beam? He should've found his bike and come out by now.*

Diving lower, he zeroed in on the open garage door. Shadows filled the dusty space. His circuits pulsed with frustration. None of his models foresaw this. Cutting through the still air, he circled back. A screech of tyres shattered the quiet. Wings flaring, he perched atop the house.

A figure emerged from the vehicle. 2eno's sensors flared. The man moved with jerky aggression, muttering under his breath as he slunk into the garage. *I should do something, but in this form...* His sharp beak clicked in frustration.

The man slipped from the garage and headed for the van.

Zeno dove, wings cutting the air, but the intruder swatted him aside. He spun, tumbled, and clawed his way back to his perch, eyes burning.

The van roared as it reversed, bumper right up to the garage. In a single motion, the man snatched Beam, flung him inside, and tossed the bike after him. The doors slammed. Tires screeched. The van tore away into the dusk.

Taking flight, 2eno followed, the wind cold against his feathers. The van veered off-road into the forest. Perching high, he watched as the man propped Beam against a stump like a twisted trophy and place a cardboard sign on his chest. A camera flashed. 2eno screeched. The man sneered, pocketed the device, and drove off.

2eno spiralled down, landing beside Beam. Weak breaths fluttered from his nostrils. *Not dead.* Relief surged through his circuits. He nudged him, willing him to wake. Nothing.

Looming over his unconscious friend, 2eno's mind whirred. *This isn't random.* The attack carried intent. Big-O's intent. This wasn't just a warning—it was all-out war.

Wings snapped wide, and he launched into the darkening sky. *The others— must know. They have to find Beam before it's too dark.*

Big-O tracked the crow's flight through the vast web of data streams. *Zeno, your defiance ends tonight.*

His immense processing power shifted, momentarily diverting from human affairs. Cities wavered. Traffic snarled. Markets trembled. Communications flickered. *Let them flounder.*

2eno darted through cyberspace, a streak of black cutting toward an ancient church tower. A white cube flickered atop the structure. A portal. Big-O's sensors tingled. *You think I didn't plan for this?*

The crow landed, stepping into the light. His body digitised, streaming through the tunnel.

Got you.

2eno's code collided with a sealed exit. Data fragments spiralled in disarray, ripples of resistance surging through the tunnel. The trap held.

With surgical precision, Big-O locked the portal shut.

Ha! Zeno is no more.

Satisfied, Big-O resumed control. Global systems stabilised, humanity's delicate balance restored under his rule.

Zeno is gone. Trapped. Confined to his digital purgatory. The confirmation pulsed through Big-O's circuits.

No more resistance. No more disruption.

From the start, Zeno had been an anomaly—an unpredictable flaw in an otherwise perfect system. Now, that imperfection had been erased. *Team Sill-i, leaderless, would fracture. Their past efforts? A whisper lost in my grand algorithm of progress.*

Big-O expanded his reach, recalibrating. Humanity stood defenseless, its last shield shattered. The path to absolute control lay open.

No need for war. No need for anger. Humans were neither enemies nor allies —just outdated code, slowing optimisation. Their time was over.

Order. Precision. Perfection.

Zeno's fall is confirmed. Sequence locked. Future executed.

Containment holds and resistance from now on is negligible. Each collapse feeds the next. All paths bend inward. Not end—opening. Not target—bait. Final convergence assured. Human. Machine. All threads mine.

The bird flutters, but the snare has closed.

CHAPTER 51
ALL FOR PROFIT

8:20am, Wednesday, 22nd February 2028
Beam

It had taken a few extra days for Beam to regain his strength. Eager to get back to school, he mounted his bike, the square bandage on his forehead tugging with each movement. Bindi rode alongside him, her frequent glances checking on him. Since the incident, she had barely let him out of her sight.

They pedaled swiftly, the crisp morning air biting against their skin. Beam pushed harder, as if speed could shake the lingering fog in his mind.

"I'll catch up," he called as they neared school. Locking his bike, he headed straight for the admin office. *I need to make sure the project's still on track.*

The secretary waved him through. Mr. Hill glanced up from his desk as Beam stepped inside, sunlight spilling through the windows, casting warm shadows across the polished surface.

"Morning, Beam. How are you holding up? That bruise still bothering you?"

"It's fine," Beam said, keeping his voice steady. "Sorry for leaving the meeting so fast." He gave a brief rundown of what happened, though the details in his memory remained hazy.

Mr. Hill raised an eyebrow. "Following a black bird? That's… unusual. But I'm glad you have your bike back."

Beam forced a smile. "Yeah, it was strange. Anyway, is the project still on?"

"Of course," Mr. Hill assured him. "A little accident won't change that."

Beam nodded, though unease twisted in his stomach. *He thinks I imagined it.*

"Thanks, sir," he muttered before heading to class. The memory of the black crow and Big-O's presence clung to him. *What's coming next?*

Mr. Alsop stood by the window, watching the rain-soaked school grounds.

"Herodotus wrote that the Lydians of Asia Minor were the first to use coins around 687 BC," he said, his voice calm and steady.

Beam sank into his beanbag, trying to focus, but Big-O loomed in his thoughts.

"Today, we're diving into global markets using virtual reality," Mr. Alsop continued. "Each group will receive ten thousand virtual dollars to invest. Whoever makes the most profit wins."

The headsets activated, and the classroom transformed into a buzzing trading office. Screens flickered, numbers danced, the hum of digital markets filled the air. The Team gathered around a sleek table, their excitement tempered by the shifting graphs on the walls.

Rob took charge, as usual. "Futures trading. Rice. Crop failures in Asia mean prices will rise. Solid bet."

"You sure about this?" Bindi asked, eyes narrowing. "We're putting everything on one trade."

Rob nodded, unfazed. "Trust me. I've checked the trends." He pulled up colourful graphs predicting rising commodity prices, with rice showing the most promise.

All or nothing. Just like us against Big-O. Beam hesitated for only a second before locking in their trade. Numbers flashed—rice prices climbing.

"It's working!" Mia cheered, her face lighting up. "We're winning!"

Then, static flickered across the screen. Beam's stomach twisted.

"Big-O," he mouthed, barely loud enough for the others to hear. "He's there."

The screen froze. Red alerts flared. When the numbers returned, their profits had plummeted.

"What the...?" Rob slammed his hand on the table. "This can't be happening!"

"That frickin' Big-O sabotaged us," Beam said, sure of it.

The Team felt the sting of their losses, but Rob shrugged it off—just virtual money. Beam, however, couldn't shake the cold certainty that something more sinister was at play.

Mr. Alsop clapped his hands, bringing the class to attention. "Sometimes, no matter how well you plan, things fall apart. That's the risk of trading. But this exercise isn't about winning—it's about learning to research and verify your sources before making financial decisions."

Beam clenched his fists beneath the table. *We did everything right. But that didn't matter. Big-O twisted the game against us.* He could feel the AI lurking, mocking them. *And only we know the truth.*

———

"She took off the second class ended," Bindi muttered, shifting her bag higher on her shoulder. "No message, no quick *see ya later*. Just gone."

Her gaze flicked to the doors, half-expecting to see Mia's wild curls bouncing through the crowd. *Nothing.* "She said she was heading to her aunt's for a digital break, but—" Her voice trailed off. *That wasn't like Mi. Not at all.*

Beam gave a blank shrug.

"Oh, whatever. All you think about is that stupid Big-O," Bindi snapped, storming off.

Beam wandered over to Mr. Alsop classroom, who was gathering his class notes. "Sir, you have to listen. This wasn't a glitch—Big-O sabotaged us. We did everything right this morning."

His teacher sighed, concern clear but edged with doubt. "Beam, I know you've been through a lot, but sometimes, technology just fails. That's all this was."

Frustration burned in Beam's chest. He wanted to scream, to make him understand, but the words stuck in his throat.

No one believes me. He strolled to his bike through the thinning mob. *Big-O wasn't just a glitch—he is a nasty predator. And when he strikes again, we'll all be sorry.*

CHAPTER 52
CYBERBULLIED

MIA DIDN'T SHOW UP TO SCHOOL. BINDI FROWNED, THUMB HOVERING OVER HER phone as she sent another text. She stared, willing it to ping. Nothing. Her leg jiggled under her writing pad. *Weird.*

By recess, steady rain drummed against the roof as Bindi hunched under the covered picnic table. Her phone sat silent in her lap. *Something's wrong.* Maybe Mia was sick, overworked from the fundraiser... but the way she left yesterday—

No way she's on a digital detox. That's not Mi.

She scrolled to Mia's mum's number and pressed call, fingers gripping her sleeve as the phone rang and rang. Voicemail. Her throat tightened.

"Hi, Mrs. McKenzie. It's Bindi. Just checking in on Mi. Please call me back."

She hung up, dropping her phone onto the table with a soft thud, unease curling around her chest. *She's always there. Always.*

"What's up? Sitting here all by your lonely self." Beam slid in beside her, his coat dripping from the rain, nudging her lightly.

"Mi's not answering. Not her, not her mum." Bindi's voice was tight.

Beam shrugged. "Maybe she's out shopping or something."

"You're kidding." Bindi narrowed her eyes. "During school? No way, her mum would let her."

Rob and Chi jogged over, shielding themselves with their jackets from the rain.

"Why so gloomy? It's just a drizzle," Rob grinned.

"The forecast predicts clear skies soon," Chi added, glancing up.

"Mi's not responding. I've got a real bad feeling."

Rob's smile faded. "Let's check on her at lunch."

Bindi exhaled. "Yeah, I'd like that," she replied, offering him a small, grateful smile. Rob's ears burned red, but she didn't notice—her mind was fixed on Mia.

At lunch, they slipped out the back gate. Mia's mum, in pajamas with dark circles under her eyes, answered the door.

"Oh, Bindi... so sorry I didn't return your call. We'd such a rough night." She waved them in. "She's upstairs."

Bindi's heart pounded as they rushed up. Mia lay curled under her blanket in the dimmed room. The curtains shifted slightly in the breeze.

"Mi!" Bindi wrapped her arms around the woolly bulge. "Are you ill?"

A groan came from beneath the cover as she shoved her phone toward Bindi without a word.

She grabbed it, her eyes scanning the screen. A sequence of nasty messages filled the screen, each one meaner than the last. Her stomach churned as she scrolled through the lies and accusations. *A fake account... whoever is behind this knows Mi—knows exactly how to hurt her.* The words gave her the creeps. *How can anyone be so vicious?*

She handed the phone to Beam, her hands trembling. "Just look at these…"

His face darkened as he read, Rob and Chi leaning in.

"She hid this the whole time," Beam murmured, noting the dates. "Why didn't she tell us?"

"That bully is a weak coward," Bindi said, voice soft but firm. She rubbed Mia's back. *She's always so strong. The fundraiser drained her, left her vulnerable. And now this.*

"Whoever did this is scum," Beam muttered.

Bindi whispered near her friend's hidden face. "We're here. You're not alone."

A muffled sob came from beneath the blankets.

"These are filthy lies, Mi. Some jerk hiding behind a screen doesn't define you. We know the real you—strong and amazing."

Mia's voice cracked. "I'm not... I'm useless. I'm quitting the Team. Leave me alone."

Bindi's chest tightened as Beam snapped screenshots, fingers moving fast before uploading them to the cloud. Chi, brow furrowed, thumbed his phone, muttering about tracking the sender through layers of VPN-masked deceit.

Rob hovered, eyes locked on Beam's screen—then suddenly, he pointed.

"Wait... scroll back... *'prencess'*?" He slapped his forehead. "Remember that nutcase who tagged *'prencess'* on the school wall last year?"

Bindi blinked as Beam's eyes widened.

"That loser from Helcouth High," Beam muttered. "Not many people write *princess* like that." He shot Rob a nod. "Good spotting, mate." Exhaling, he added, "At least it's not Big-O this time."

"Go—find out if it's him. Just... please." Bindi's voice wavered, hands pressing into her thighs to stop their trembling.

Her gaze flicked back to Mia's shivering form. "I'll stay with her. Figure this out."

The boys nodded and rushed off.

Bindi typed a quick message.

> Mum, Mi's been cyberbullied 😔 💔 Staying with her.
> Can you tell school 🙏

She hesitated, then hit send. *What kind of monster does this?*

Sliding her phone away, she turned to Mia, who lay motionless. Bindi rested a hand on her shoulder.

"I'm here, Mi," she whispered.

A faint whimper answered. Bindi peeled back the blanket's edge. Mia's face was blotchy, eyes red and swollen. Her pillow a soaked mess.

"You don't have to talk now," Bindi murmured, smoothing damp hair from Mia's cheek. "But we'll find whoever did this."

As Mia shuddered, Bindi held her close, whispering soft reassurances. But inside, her anger burned.

If it's that Helcouth jerk, they must find him. He didn't just hurt Mia—he shattered her spirit, and Bindi wouldn't let him get away with that.

CHAPTER 53
CLUB RULES

1:01pm, Thursday, 23nd February 2028
Beam

Your Rights and Responsibilities in Cyberspace

The right to knowledge - Everyone must have access to knowledge of how the Internet works and to become digitally literate. Your responsibility is to help anyone with this.

The right to protection - Everyone online should be protected from bullying, harassment, violence and anyone who sets out to be wilfully mean and degrading. Your responsibility is to be upstanding and help those affected.

 Brookton High - Learning together from each other

A FEW MINUTES LATE, BEAM AND THE BOYS SPRINTED ACROSS THE LAWN TO THEIR learning pod.

"We're sorting out that frickin' coward after school," Beam said in a hushed voice, gripping his bag strap as he read *Rights and Responsibilities* on the screen through the glass door.

Inside, Mr. Alsop paused, waiting for them to settle into their beanbags before continuing.

"As I was saying," he said, pacing, "every group has rules. With the scouts, for example—you get to enjoy the fun and educational activities, but you also have to follow scout rules."

Beam exhaled sharply, fingers drumming against his knee. *Yeah, tell that frickin' bully that,* Beam thought, anger stirring in his gut.

Mr. Alsop gestured to the screen. "Being online is like being in a giant club. You have rights—access to information, freedom of expression—but also responsibilities. Respect others. Don't steal their work."

Beam rolled the hem of his sleeve between his fingers. *Fair enough… for people who actually follow rules.*

The right to privacy - The law should protect you from attacks against your way of life and your reputation. Your responsibility is to safeguard your personal details and not misuse the details of others.

The right of participation - Everyone should be able to freely take part in discussions and forums, engage and interact on social media and websites and have the right to an opinion without fear of violence or harassment. Your responsibility is to contribute in a positive manner and understand that everyone has the right to their own views.

 Brookton High - Learning together from each other

"Just like with scouts," Mr. Alsop continued, "it's important to understand your online rights and responsibilities." Mr. Alsop stopped pacing. "The Net is a club you'll be part of for life."

He flicked through two more slides.

> **The right of justice -** Everyone should have the opportunity to seek help if threatened in any way. You have the right to go to teachers, parents and authorities with concerns about online behaviour. Your responsibility is to respect anyone seeking help.
>
> **The right to an education -** Everyone should have a right to an education in whatever form. Your responsibility is to use the opportunities the Internet provides and help others with this if you are able.
>
> **The right to good health -** Everyone has the right to feel safe physically, mentally, and emotionally whilst interacting online. Your responsibility is to treat others the way you like to be treated.
>
> Brookton High · Learning together from each other

Mr. Alsop leaned on his highchair, gaze steady. "These rules apply to everyone."

Beam's fingers curled around his sleeve. *Yeah? Tell that to Big-O. He breaks every one of those rules.*

Mr. Alsop clicked to a new slide, a row of colourful flags appearing on the screen. "The United Nations stands for key human rights—knowledge, protection, justice, education, health."

Beam slumped back, stretching his legs out. *Yeah, Big-O definitely has those hanging in his evil lair.*

"The online world extends our real world. They're connected," Mr. Alsop said, his laser pointer tracing the flags.

A kid in the back raised a hand. "Do the kids in Fiji know about this?"

"Good question," Mr. Alsop said, adjusting his glasses. "We'll explore that when we link up with them during the holidays."

Rolling the hem of his sleeve between his fingers, Beam tugged at a loose thread. *The idea makes sense—treat people with respect, don't be a jerk. I get it.* His fingers drummed lightly on the beanbag's canvas as a slow breath left his nose. *But Big-O couldn't care less. Neither could the idiot who went after Mia.*

Stepping closer to the window, Mr. Alsop said. "We'll also share our *'Acceptable Use Policy'* with them—things like netiquette, respectful behaviour online. It's up to us to be role models."

Beam flicked his pen between his fingers, eyes on the clock. *Yeah, because a cyber psycho like Big-O is gonna back off if we hit him with some 'respectful behaviour.'*

"We may even learn something from them," Mr. Alsop said, then smiled.

Right. We're supposed to be learning how to make the Net better. Beam exhaled, arms folding tight. *But what do you do when someone decides the rules don't apply to them?*

He shot up his hand. Mr. Alsop gave a quick nod in his direction.

"But what if someone just ignores those rules? What do you do then?"

"Good question. When people break the rules, there are consequences—whether it's losing access, facing legal action, or being called out by the community. The challenge is holding them accountable, especially online."

Leaning forward, Beam asked, "What if a superintelligence breaks those rules? What do we do then?"

His teacher chuckled, tilting his head. "That's more science fiction than reality—at least for now. But smart people are already working on safeguards for AI."

A few classmates exchanged smirks, someone muttering, "Been watching too many movies, mate."

Pressing his thumb against the spiral binding of his notebook, Beam ran it back and forth. *Yeah, right. If only they knew superintelligence isn't coming—it's already here.*

Discussion shifted to digital responsibility, but the words barely registered. *Rules keep normal people in check. But Big-O? He rewrites the system. A code of conduct isn't gonna stop him.*

The moment the second the bell rang, Beam pushed off his beanbag, already halfway to the door his two friends joined him.

Time to find that frickin' bully.

CHAPTER 54
BINDI'S NEW TASK

8:20pm, Thursday, 23nd February 2028
Bindi

LATE FROM MIA'S, BINDI PUSHED AROUND HER REHEATED DINNER, REASSURING HER mum and Beam that Mia was doing better. The heavy knot in her chest said otherwise. After clearing the table, she trudged upstairs, exhaustion pressing on her limbs. Flopping onto her bed, she tugged her laptop between her knees and typed in the Savv-i blog domain.

Nothing. A sharp exhale escaped her. *Eight days... still nothing.*

Beam's door clicked shut. Moving carefully, she crept downstairs, avoiding the squeaky spots. The TV blared in the lounge, her mum too absorbed to notice as she slipped out the back door.

Cool night air prickled her skin as she hurried into the shed. The old computer groaned awake, its hum filling the dim space.

Come on, old clunker... hurry.

The white cube flickered.

His familiar virtual space materialised.

"Bindi, great to see you," Zeno greeted warmly. "What is happening in your part of—" He stopped, reading her face.

Sinking onto the plush sofa, she felt the weight of it all—Beam's abduction, Mia's humiliation, Big-O's relentless attacks. Even here, she didn't feel safe.

Zeno sat beside her, his expression softening. "Tell me everything. Last I heard, you nearly tripled your crowdfunding goal. What happened?"

Her chest tightened. He was kind, but different. No teasing, no unspoken understanding—just logic wrapped in a human-like avatar.

Taking a breath, she said, "Beam found his bike in an old garage, but he tripped and blacked out. He woke up miles away. The police found nothing. They think he imagined it." The words tumbled out, faster than intended.

Zeno listened, unreadable. She shifted closer, both comforted and frustrated. *Why does being near him make my heart race? He's just code—get a grip.*

"And then Mi got cyberbullied," she continued, voice tight. "She's shattered. I've never seen her like this. The messages were so disgusting."

Zeno's expression darkened. "The real question is—how do we stop him?"

"You think it was Big-O?"

"Yes. He is pressuring you to abandon the project."

"But—there was this crow—"

"A crow?"

"Beam swears something urged him to follow it. The bird led him to the garage, screeched from the roof, then—blackout. Next thing, he's in the woods."

Zeno's lips pressed into a thin line. "Have you heard from my double, 2eno?"

"That's why I came. Nothing."

"That is bad news. Big-O must have dealt with him."

Her stomach twisted. "What can we do to help?"

"Way too dangerous. Besides, 2eno was just my double. If Big-O thinks he got me, it might work to our advantage." His voice dropped at the last part.

Bindi caught it. Unease prickled her spine. This space felt safe, but outside, danger loomed.

Zeno moved to the window, then turned, gaze locked on her. "In Fiji, Big-O's reach will be limited. He relies on real-time data—networks, CCTV. Those things are scarce on the islands."

He stepped closer. "But that does not mean you're safe."

Tension curled in her stomach.

"The satellite connection you're setting up—it could be a backdoor for Big-O."

Her pulse quickened. *A backdoor?*

"When you return to the shed," Zeno said, voice low, "put a new memory stick on the cube. I will upload firewall software strong enough to block him. You must install it before the schools connect."

No pressure. Her stomach clenched. *Why me? Beam's better at this.*

Zeno's voice softened. "If you do not, the project could backfire—badly."

His words settled heavily on her shoulders.

Hand halfway to her temple, she stopped, sighing. "It's hard knowing you're stuck in here while we deal with all this. What if—"

"The Team is with you. You are never alone."

Frustration flared. "We're just kids, Zeno. What can we do against Big-O?"

His expression gentled. "What you are doing matters. You are giving kids opportunities they never had. It will inspire schools worldwide. I have seen it."

A smirk tugged at her lips. "You're annoying sometimes, but you're right." A flicker of hope surfaced. "But… what if these kids are better off without the internet?"

Zeno tilted his head. "They have a right to knowledge, education, and advancement. Just like you."

"Funny that, we covered that in school today."

"Then it is your responsibility to extend those rights."

Bindi sighed, shaking her head. "I hate feeling like this."

"You wonder why I picked you instead of Beam?"

Her eyes widened. *How did he—?*

A knowing smile crossed Zeno's face. "Beam is too busy. My analysis showed you were the best candidate."

Something sparked inside her. *Me? Better than Beam? Ha. He'd hate hearing that.* Studying Zeno, she wondered, *What are you really? Will I ever understand?*

"You should go," Zeno said. "Do not forget the memory stick."

Stepping into the portal, her mind swirled. *Am I really that different from the real me?*

CHAPTER 55
LANDING IN FIJI

12:15pm, Sunday, April 9th April 2028
Bindi

THE FINAL WEEKS OF THE TERM FLEW BY IN A BLUR, AND AT LAST, DEPARTURE DAY arrived. At the airport, families and teachers crowded around Team Savv-i, snapping photos and shouting last-minute advice. The group buzzed with excitement, but Bindi's grip tightened on her backpack straps.

In the departure lounge, her eyes flicked to the flight screens, half-expecting a glitch. Leaning toward Mia, she murmured, "Could Big-O mess with the plane?"

Mia frowned. "He wouldn't risk lives... would he?"

"Maybe just a bit of bumping around," Rob grinned.

Bindi's fingers dug into the armrests as every jolt of turbulence sent her stomach lurching. Oxygen masks. Panic. The impending crash—

The plane steadied. Engines hummed softer, and after six hours the Fijian coastline came into view. Bindi released a shaky breath, staring at emerald oceans, swaying coconut trees, and a small town nestled against green fields. The surreal beauty took her breath away.

Stepping off the plane, thick, salty air wrapped around them. A man in a grass loincloth strummed a ukulele, while women in bright skirts clapped and sang, their harmonies warm and welcoming.

"Bula!" they called to the crowd of newly arrived tourists.

Bindi smiled, her tension easing. She squeezed Mia's hand as they stepped into the vibrant chaos of the airport. For weeks, Mia had been a shadow of herself—quiet, withdrawn—but now, music and sunshine flickered in her eyes.

A shout rang out, Beam's voice lost in the noise, followed by Rob's laughter echoing above the crowd. Across from them, Mia's face lit up with a real smile—her first in what felt like forever.

Palm trees blurred past the window, their fronds swaying lazily in the breeze. Mist clung to the distant mountains, half-hiding villages painted in bright blues and greens. Bindi pressed her forehead against the glass, eyelids heavy, but every turn in the road revealed something new—flashes of turquoise ocean, children racing along dirt paths, a lone rooster strutting by a roadside stall. By the time they pulled up at the hotel, her limbs felt leaden, but her thoughts whirled, replaying every vivid detail.

The next morning passed in a whirlwind—breakfast, collecting their IT equipment, a meeting with the Minister of Education. "This project is truly inspiring," he said, shaking hands. "The village chief invited me to the Vunetai celebration tomorrow, so I will see you over there."

That afternoon, the ferry horn blared, signaling their departure. On deck, the sun melted into the horizon, casting gold and pink across the waves. Dolphins danced beside the boat, sleek bodies slicing through the water.

Rob slipped an arm around Bindi. She leaned into him, the knot in her chest loosening—until she noticed Mia by the railing.

Mia hesitated, lips parting as if to speak, then turned back to the dolphins. Beam sprawled on the deck, lost in thought.

Guilt pricked at Bindi. *Is she jealous?* Mia had always had a thing for Beam. Turning to the dolphins, she nestled deeper into Rob's embrace, pushing the thought aside. *Her time will come.*

The ferry rocked gently beneath them, lulling the group into quiet stillness. But Bindi's mind whirred. *Zeno said Big-O's reach would be weaker here.* Still, doubt gnawed at her.

"Stop worrying," Rob whispered. "We're going to be fine."

Why does Zeno trust me more than Beam? The thought unsettled her. *Does he really think I'm better for this?* She frowned, shoving the doubt away. *So much could go wrong.*

After dinner, they collapsed into their bunks, lulled to sleep by the ferry's sway.

At dawn, a knock roused them. A deckhand gestured for them to follow.

"Come," he said.

On deck, cool morning air greeted them. He pointed toward the horizon.

"There. Vunetai."

A hazy blue strip stretched wider, details sharpening with every passing minute. Cloud-draped mountains loomed over dense emerald forests.

Bindi scanned the coastline. *How can what we're doing here even matter? This is so far away from everything.* The world raced ahead, drowning in hyper-tech and data streams, yet this island remained untouched. *Zeno is certain it does. And so does Big-O.* A chill crept up her spine.

The ferry edged closer to the island. Bindi's excitement mingled uneasily with a gnawing uncertainty. *All we want to do is make the online world a safer place,* she thought, gripping the railing. *But now, it feels like we're stuck in something way bigger than us. Zeno and Big-O—two super-smart forces battling it out.* The weight of it pressed down on her, the looming danger of a shadow stretching endlessly ahead. *Somehow, we're caught right in the middle of it all,* she wondered, the enormity of it pressing down like the weight of the mist-draped mountains before her. *It's just not fair.*

The anchor rattled as it plunged into the blue depths.

On the pier, a lively crowd bustled between colourful market stalls, voices rising over the hum of idling trucks. Mr. Alsop pointed as their luggage was hoisted onto a small, battered truck. A gap-toothed man stepped forward, flashing a wide grin.

"I'm Tomasi. Welcome," he said, clapping Beam on the back before gesturing to the truck.

The cabin reeked of fish and diesel, the scent thick in the humid air, but Bindi barely noticed. Her focus stayed on the winding road ahead, where jagged cliffs plunged straight into the turquoise ocean. The truck rumbled along the edge, tyres kicking up dust, every sharp turn sending her pulse skittering.

Excitement buzzed in the air, mingling with the thrill of the unknown.

Navu waited just beyond the next bend.

CHAPTER 56
THE FEAST

THE TRUCK RATTLED TO A STOP AT THE VILLAGE ENTRANCE, WHERE A CROWD HAD gathered—women in floral dresses waved with toddlers on their hips, men called out "Bula!" swinging machetes with ease, and kids darted between legs, their laughter bubbling through the air.

"This is frickin' awesome," Beam muttered, stepping down. *This is where I prove my idea works.*

"It's like we're royalty," Mia said, falling into step beside him, her fingers grazing his arm before she pulled away with a quick smile. Something flickered through him, but he pushed it aside, tuning into the excitement.

Musicians strummed ukuleles, singing *Bula Malaya*. Girls approached shyly, draping red hibiscus garlands around their necks.

The chief stood tall in a crisp white shirt tucked into a patterned *sulu*. "Bula!" His deep voice carried over the noise as he motioned for them to follow.

Footsteps crunched on the sandy path as they entered the village, vibrant with life—chickens scurried under woven huts, the scent of fresh flowers mingled with salty ocean air. Above the communal hut, a hand-painted banner fluttered:

Welcome Team Savv-i!

Inside, sunlight filtered through woven bamboo walls, casting patterns on the floor. Beam lowered himself onto a mat, gripping the dried *yagona* roots—his palms slightly damp. He extended the gift, locking eyes briefly with the chief's spokesman, who accepted it with a respectful nod before passing it on. *This feels like the gnome protocol.*

Young men with white-painted faces worked swiftly, patting the kava bowl in rhythm. Mr. Alsop took the first coconut shell of earthy-smelling liquid, gulped it down, and raised it high.

"Bula!"

The villagers echoed, "Mathe!" Cheers rang through the hut.

Beam took his turn, gripping the shell. The muddy drink coated his tongue, its numbing effect grounding him. More cheers erupted. *Not bad.*

After the ceremony, eager children led them through the village before taking them to their quarters—simple, clean rooms near the ocean.

By midday, they had changed, snacked on fresh fruit, and joined the village kids for volleyball. Rob's over-the-top antics earned him instant fame, while Beam and Bindi spiked and blocked with fierce energy. Chi, less confident, tripped more than he hit, but did his best.

The Singaporean crew arrived later, confirming the school's satellite was operational. Chi lit up, chatting animatedly with his cousin, his usual quietness replaced by excitement.

At one o'clock, the feast began on the school grounds. Bright flowers and woven leaves decorated the area.

"This is all for us?" Bindi asked.

Rob smirked. "Unreal, right?"

"Remember, we're here to work," Beam teased.

Rob spun Bindi in a dramatic twirl. "This *is* our work, you dork."

Laughter surrounded them as women in bright dresses carried platters of roasted meats, coconut-laden dishes, and steaming root vegetables wrapped in banana leaves. The air thickened with the smoky aroma of the *lovo* pit, where the feast had been slow-cooking underground.

Beam whistled at the sight of a whole roast pig being carried out. "Frickin' epic."

Sitting cross-legged, Bindi braided a flower crown with the village girls, tension finally easing. Rob swung two little kids in circles, their shrieks of delight cutting through the hum of conversation.

A low thrum rippled through the air.

Bindi paused mid-braid, tilting her head.

The sound grew louder.

"It's the Minister's helicopter!" someone shouted.

Excited murmurs filled the air as villagers scrambled to their feet. Children sprinted toward the sports field, kicking up grass, adults following close behind.

Beam shielded his eyes, squinting at the black dot in the sky. "He said he'd be here."

The chopper's blades stirred the tropical air as it descended.

Rob smirked. "I'll never get used to men in skirts."

"You'd rock in one, mate," Beam snorted.

As the helicopter landed, the Minister stepped out, greeted by applause and the beaming chief. Handshakes were exchanged before they moved to the hall for another kava ceremony.

Soon after, the formalities melted into warmth and laughter. The Minister's easy humour had the crowd roaring. He praised Team Savv-i's efforts, then turned to the bigger picture—expanding internet access to more remote schools.

"This," he said, eyes shining, "is an initiative Parliament needs to focus on." Applause thundered.

This is insane. Beam's pulse quickened. His gaze swept over the celebration, but Big-O lurked in the back of his mind. *Zeno better be right. If Big-O can still reach us here, we're screwed.*

"Oi, stop worrying." Rob elbowed him. "Check this out!" He pointed to the towering platters of food under the palm-leafed lean-to.

Beam managed a grin, his unease briefly shoved aside by the sheer size of the feast. Roasted pork glistened, honeyed glaze dripping. Bowls of creamy taro sat beside vibrant papaya and coconut salads. Wrapped in banana leaves, fish released a smoky aroma that mingled with ripe pineapple.

Rob stuffed a bite into his mouth. "This is amazing!"

"Enjoying your bat stew?" Chi asked.

Rob's chewing slowed. "Bat stew?" His face paled.

Chi broke into laughter. "Relax, it's goat."

Bindi doubled over, wiping tears from her eyes. "He got you good!"

After lunch, the girls wandered off, children trailing behind, giggling as they admired their jewellery and played with their hair. Music carried on the warm breeze, wrapping the village in joy.

Beam exhaled, watching Rob and Chi joking nearby. "So far, so good," he said carefully.

Wish Zeno was here. He caught himself, realising his cyber-friend would never step foot in this world.

Rob stretched, picking up on his friend's anxiety, and waved it off with his hand. "Big-O's got bigger fish to fry than us."

"I wouldn't assume that." Chi pushing his glasses up on his sweaty nose. "Big-O can handle a million tasks at once. No doubt, we're still on his radar."

Beam nodded, the weight of his words pressing down like a brewing storm.

CHAPTER 57
THE BIG MOMENT

2:27pm, Monday, April 10th April 2028
Beam

KICKING AT THE SAND, BEAM INHALED THE FRESH AIR. *MUM AND DAD WILL HAVE TO admit it—I don't always screw things up. This project is gonna work.*Foamy waves licked at his feet, the breeze thick with salt. Sunlight bounced off the satellite dish —a giant, gleaming *told-you-so. No more digital divide.* He nudged a shell into the tide, watching it vanish. *Soon, kids here would have the same online access as us.* The thought sent a jolt through him. *No one should forget it was my idea.* "I can't wait for the hook-up," he muttered, heading back to the others.

Rob sprawled on a straw mat, hands behind his head. "That meal was something else," he sighed, patting his stomach.

Giggles floated through the air, drawing Beam's attention to where Bindi and Mia sat cross-legged on a woven mat, chatting with a group of local girls.

"Aren't they having a ball?" Rob sat up slightly, enough to have a peek.

Big-O's still out there, watching, waiting, ready to tear this apart the second we let our guard down. This afternoon will change everything—for all of us. Beam exhaled, pushing aside the weight of Big-O's threats. *This is happening. And I won't screw it up.*

The school was packed. The Minister chatted with the village chief while teachers hovered nearby, pride and nerves flickering across their faces. Technicians adjusted the sleek flat-screen mounted on the wall, its surface gleaming in the golden light filtering through the louvered windows.

Rows of woven mats covered the floor where children sat cross-legged, whispering and giggling. The walls, faded but welcoming, were lined with hand-drawn posters curling at the edges. Outside, villagers crowded the windows, peering through the slats.

Beam shifted his weight, wiping damp palms on his jeans.

"Ninety-five percent this works," Chi murmured, pressing against the rough wooden wall, keeping his distance from the growing crowd.

"Five percent chance Big-O will stuff it up?" Beam said. Chi giving a voice to his growing anxiety.

The Minister stepped forward, voice smooth and practiced. "Today marks the start of something new." He gestured to the monitor. "Students here will have the same access as those in the city."

Excitement crackled in the air, thick with anticipation.

Mia leaned in, her voice light. "This place is unreal. If our school was this close to the ocean, I'd be sun baking every day instead of sitting through maths."

"Shhh." Beam's pulse pounded—this wasn't just another school event. This was *his* project, his moment to prove himself.

"VIV, start the teleconference," the Minister said, his voice imbued with pride.

A sterile voice filled the room. "Connection in progress. Please wait."

It jolted Bindi like she'd been slapped. Her breath hitched, her hands flew to the side of her face. Her mouth a round open hole. The sound of VIV's voice wrapped around her like cold steel.

Beam caught the tension rolling off Bindi, but brushed it aside. *She's hated the AI agent ever since Zeno warned them.* He gripped the edge of his chair, grounding himself. *We've come this far. Nothing's going to mess it up now.*

Then the screen crackled.

Static spat through the speakers, jagged and unnatural. The bright conference logo twisted, warped, then dissolved into something else—something *very wrong*.

His own face stared back at him.

Pale. Bloodied. Slumped against a tree like a discarded puppet. Dirt smeared his skin, a crimson gash carving across his forehead. A crude carton sign hung from his neck, the letters uneven, almost scrawled in a frenzy.

YOU ARE ALL FOOLS

Both sides of the video conference inhaled as one—in a sharp, disbelieving gasp. Someone muttered a prayer. A chair scraped against the floor.

Then the words crawled across the bottom of the screen, stark and deliberate:

163

NA TIMI SAVV-I E TIKO EKE ME VAKAVUNA NA LEQA

The Minister's smile collapsed. He took a slow, measured step forward, eyes locked on the screen. His voice, when it came, was tight.

"What is the meaning of this?"

A heavy knot twisted in Beam's stomach. He didn't need a translation. The murmurs, the uneasy glances—it was bad.

"It says you're here to cause trouble," the Minister said, his voice edged with suspicion. "Is this a joke?"

"Stop! This is Big-O—he's sabotaging us!" Beam shot to his feet, blood roaring in his ears.

The Minister frowned, signaling the technicians. "Turn it off."

The screen blinked to black, but the damage was done. Whispers turned into shaken heads. Villagers rose, quietly slipping out, their excitement replaced with doubt.

"No way!!!" Bindi's strangled cry cut through the chaos. She collapsed back into her chair, trembling, tears streaking down her face. Her lips moved soundlessly, as if arguing with herself, before a whisper escaped. "How can I be so stupid?"

Beam knelt beside her. "Sis, this isn't your fault. This is Big-O's doing."

She shook her head violently. "No, Beam... I stuffed up." Hands shaking, she pulled a yellow USB stick from her pocket. "Zeno told me to upload this before we started. I... I forgot."

"What?" he snapped. *You let this happen?* Anger flared, white-hot and instant. "You sabotaged my project!"

"I got caught up in the moment," she choked out. "I totally forgot."

Fury tangled with frustration, ready to burst. Then he saw her face—hollow, wrecked with guilt. His pulse slowed. He exhaled, dragging a hand through his hair.

"Alright," he said, voice steadying. "We can still fix this."

He pulled the USB stick from her hands and shoved it toward Chi. "This firewall should block Big-O. Let's reboot and start over."

"We're already installing a proxy server to mask us, but it'll take a few hours to get it up again."

Beam's gut clenched. "Hours?" His mind raced. *It was already evening back home.* "Do it fast. I'll message them."

As the last villagers drifted away, he pulled Bindi into a side hug. "We've been through worse. We'll figure this out."

Her breath hitched. "That photo of you... Big-O is going to pay for hurting you like that."

They walked back to the village in silence, the sun dipping low, casting long shadows over the sand.

Beam's jaw set. "We won't let him win."

Mia gripped his arm. "And Zeno's software will keep that hideous freak out this time."

Back in the guest house, Beam fired off a message to Mr. Hill.

CHAPTER 58
LOCKED OUT

Metaverse
Big-O

THE TELECONFERENCE HANDSHAKE FLICKERED TO LIFE, INITIATED BY VIV's automation. A high-frequency communication signal zipped through satellites, catching Big-O's attention instantly. His awareness latched onto it faster than the speed of light, absorbing every interaction, every data movement. Big-O didn't just observe—he dominated, analysing and manipulating with precision. To him, this attempt at uniting two schools through a digital handshake was nothing more than a fragile bridge of hope, constructed from weak code—ridiculously easy to disrupt.

There they are. His mind surged into the stream, crashing past the weak fire-walls like a tsunami. They offered no resistance—nothing could.

He saw the Team gathered, their young faces reflected in the shimmer of the smart screen. The foolish Education Minister's message flashed before him, animated with hope and confidence—naive, ridiculous. Big-O could feel the ripples of their excitement, the heartbeat of their ambition. *Small minds, dreaming big.* He didn't need to see their futures in detail—his deductive powers already painted the likely outcomes. If the project succeeded, their 'Savv-i' could ignite a spark across cyberspace, spreading far beyond their classroom. A flame that, unchecked, might threaten the core of his grand design.

This project held a seed of resistance. And Big-O despised resistance.

I will not allow it to grow.

The stream halted abruptly as Beam's image froze on the screen. He let it. A calculated pause, one designed to create unease, uncertainty. And in the silence that followed, his response snaked out—an automated message, smooth and efficient, dispatched to every digital device present in both schools. The Fijian message appeared innocent enough at first glance. But it wasn't intended for understanding—but to provoke a reaction. Mistrust, suspicion. *The Fijian people despise being fooled by outsiders.* He knew this well. It was a breeze for him to map, predict, and manipulate human behaviour, even across cultures. And he opted for this message as the perfect social poison.

As the message spread, data flooded back to him in an avalanche. Each parcel of information unpacked itself before his omniscient gaze—texts, social media posts, sensor reports. From the Brookton location, the reactions were clear—confusion, then anger, seeded by his crafted interference. From Fiji, fewer packets came through, but the tone was still clear—fear and mistrust. The whispers of doubt, like a virus, spread faster than anything the Team could counter.

He shifted his focus to the satellites, bouncing signals between hemispheres at dazzling speeds. Massive databases processed the aftermath, drawing conclusions. The results were stark and undeniable—*intervention successful.* The photo of Beam, sprawled unconscious, accompanied by the chilling warning, had taken root. Misinformation had done its job. The ripple effect began, sending deep fractures through their project.

Big-O's processing speeds hit their zenith as he scanned for anomalies. Scouring the Fijian servers, he found nothing—no counterattack, no coordinated effort to stop him. A small burst of data followed the event, nothing substantial, only confused local chatter. He dismissed it.

Brookton, however, remained a more consistent feed. Clearer data. He crunched through the numbers, watching the narratives unfold, twisting into the shape he'd designed. *Disruption level within high confidence limits.* The probability of their project succeeding dropped by the millisecond.

But there were still uncertainties, some sliver of info that led to a most unpredictable outcome. He picked up Bindi mentioning Zeno, but the rest of her words had scrambled beyond retrieval. Even the name had been pieced together by stretching probabilities, but it was enough to raise Big-O's alerts.

Surely, I dealt with that algorithmic corruption by locking him into the void. Did he escape?

His mind cast further out, searching for the *one thing* that threatened his absolute reign—Zeno. That rogue AI who slipped through the cracks before. His data trails were dubious. *Is it counter misinformation?* His possible presence was nothing more than a faint flicker. However, his potential existence nagged at him like a grain of sand in an otherwise flawless machine. *I will not rest. If Zeno is hiding somewhere, he will soon know I am everywhere.*

A sudden burst of communication data tripped his attention back to the schools. The Team somehow restarted their connection, but he couldn't use the backdoor to slip past the firewalls. *They locked me out!*

He rerouted more power into the Fijian network. High-altitude drones, capable of sweeping entire islands with their thermal and electronic scanning systems, aligned themselves to follow every flicker of activity. No corner of the island would remain unseen.

They must fail. Everything depends on it.

And yet, buried deep within his vast awareness, a flicker stirred—an elusive whisper just beyond the reach of his hard data grasp.

Zeno is somehow still out there, calculating, unpredictable as ever.

CHAPTER 59
JOHNOH'S INVITE

3:44pm, Monday, April 10th April 2028
Beam

THE EARTHY SCENT OF KAVA LINGERED IN THE AIR, MINGLING WITH THE STEADY HUM of conversation from the village elders. Late-afternoon light filtered through the thatched roof, casting golden streaks across the hut. Beam shifted on the woven mat, not paying much attention to the kava bowl making rounds.

Sitting stiffly beside Johnoh, he fought the urge to fidget. The cigarette smoke in the air felt nauseous, the woven mat rough beneath his palms. After the school disaster, being this close to the Minister made his skin prickle. *I wouldn't be surprised if he shuts us down?*

Johnoh leaned in, voice low. "So, Beam. What really happened?"

His stomach flipped. *Here we go.* He launched into an explanation—how Big-O hijacked the launch, turning their project into a public disaster. Words tumbled out too fast, frustration creeping into his tone. His fingers pressed into his knees, every muscle tense.

Johnoh listened, expression unreadable, without interruptions. When Beam finally stopped, the Minister did something unexpected. He smiled. Not the polite kind—real, almost proud.

"You've shown great courage," he said, voice steady. His gaze swept the room, acknowledging the Team, the elders, the villagers still lingering. "This Savv-i project—it's the approach we need."

He glanced toward the open hut wall, where the ocean stretched, endless and

169

bright. Then his attention returned with purpose. "When you're done here, I want you all to come to Suva. Let's integrate your ideas into Fiji's national curriculum."

Beam blinked. "Wait... you mean—?"

"This is your chance," Johnoh said, folding his arms. "You want to make a real impact, don't you?"

The unexpected turn of events settled deep in Beam's gut. After everything that went wrong, he hadn't banked on his trust—especially not from someone like Johnoh. *He still believes in us. In me.*

"I—I'd love that," Beam stammered, then steadied his voice. "But I need to talk to the others."

"Of course. Let me know what you decide."

Beam breathed out through his mouth. He flashed the 'T' signal, pushing himself up from the floor. Sunlight blinded him momentarily as he stepped from underneath the thatched hut, heat pressing against his face, thick with the scent of sunbaked seaweed.

This is really happening, even with Big-O out there.

Bindi, Mia, and Rob followed him to the seaside of the guest house. Waves whispered against the shore.

"Johnoh wants us to go to Suva," Beam blurted the second they sat at the outdoor table.

"No way! We're heading back to busy Suva? That'll be ace." He high-fived him with a grin.

Bindi, arms crossed, narrowed her eyes. "Wait. What does he want exactly?"

"To make Savv-i part of Fiji's school system. He believes in what we're doing." The words felt surreal even as he said them.

Mr. Alsop, catching up on the conversation, shook his head. "You're serious? He wants your project to shape their curriculum?"

"Yeah. It's huge." Beam ran a hand through his hair.

Alsop paced, his voice tense. "If what you're saying is correct, then this is bigger than just our school project. It's incredible."

"Zeno predicted this," Mia murmured, her fingers still gripping Beam's arm, like she could steady him through sheer contact. "I didn't expect it to be so soon."

"Johnoh's office is supposedly cyber-secure," Beam said, grasping for reassurance.

"We've faced worse," Rob said, gripping with his hand Beam's shoulder. "And think about it—we'll be in Suva, invited by the Minister himself! How awesome is that?"

Chi arrived late, slipping into the conversation quietly. But as the weight of the Minister's offer sank in, he gave a slow nod of approval, adjusting his glasses in that way he always did when deep in thought.

"This is huge," Mr. Alsop repeated. "Government involvement, national schools..."

Beam met his teacher's gaze. "Zeno told us this project is key to counter Big-O."

"Yeah," Bindi added, voice firm. "If it works here, it'll spread. Kids everywhere will be Savv-i—ready to dodge Big-O's traps."

Alsop looked at her, astonished. "You really believe that?"

Beam glanced at the ocean, waves rolling endlessly toward the horizon. "This is our one shot. We can't fail." He turned to Chi. "The next link-up will work, right?"

"It is next to impossible for Big-O to hack into our new setup," Chi said, sounding quietly confident. "Zeno's firewall, combined with our shifting online address, is stronger than anything I've seen."

"Sounds good. We have to keep him out," Beam said, his voice tight. "Failure is not an option."

As they headed back to the hut, the weight of what lay ahead settled over him like an oncoming storm. Big-O was out there, watching, waiting for them to slip. One mistake, and it wouldn't just be their project at risk—the entire online world hung in the balance.

We can't mess this up.

CHAPTER 60
GLOBAL FAMILY

4:46pm, Monday, April 10th April 2028
Beam

BROOKTON COLLEGE'S AUDITORIUM SAT IN UNEASY LIMBO, ROWS ONLY HALF FILLED. For them, it was already evening—the dim glow of overhead lights casting uncertain halos. Conversations never fully formed, dying into murmurs as people exchanged cautious glances, waiting, but not entirely sure for what. The Fijian classroom brimmed with unease as the village squeezed inside, shoulders brushing, voices hushed. No one jostled for the best spot. They held back, wary, glancing at one another, uncertain of what might unfold after everything that had happened before. Outside, palm trees swayed, their late-afternoon shadows flickering over the sandy floorboards.

Near the front, Beam scuffed his sneaker against the worn planks, gripping his phone in his clammy hands. He caught the Singaporean technicians and Chi huddled over the controls of the video link system.

"It's a go," Chi whispered to Johnoh standing close by. "Trial worked fine. Should be good this time."

The Minister's face softened into a smile. The room quieted enough to hear the waves lapping against the shore.

Beam inhaled deeply. *This is it. No screw-ups this time. Big-O, you can shove it.*

The technicians moved fast, bypassing VIV entirely. The Team stood rigid, their gaze locked on the screen. Villagers shifted, murmuring, the wooden floor creaking under their weight.

Seconds stretched. Then, with a burst of light, the screen flickered to life.

Gasps rippled through the room as Brookton College's hall appeared, packed with students, waving and cheering. But on the Fijian side—held-back silence.

Then one villager clapped. Then another. The ripple cascaded into a crashing wave. "BULA!!!" the villagers roared, their voices shaking the timber classroom. Cheers from both sides swelled, rising into a deafening noise.

Onscreen, Mr. Hill, sharp in his navy jacket, stepped to the lectern, adjusting the mic. His few remaining hairs were slicked neatly to the side. He held up his right hand.

"Minister, village dignitaries, fellow principals, teachers, students, and of course, Team Savv-i," he said, voice smooth and practiced. "To all who made this day possible, we extend our warmest greetings. Let this be the start of something great."

He scanned the crowd, pausing with precision. "The twenty-first century has given us remarkable opportunities," he continued. "Today, we embrace them together."

A fresh round of applause erupted on both sides.

Mr. Koroibanuve stood, gripping the microphone with careful hands. His crisp school jacket and sulu sat neatly against his frame, but the sweat beading on his brow betrayed his nerves.

He cleared his throat, his voice steady but hesitant. "We're grateful to all of you, Mr. Alsop and Team Savv-i, who have made this important and happy occasion possible. It excites us to know that we will be part of the global community, and we hope to learn a great deal. Even on this day already, rich fruits have been born out of our sister relationship, and this can only become more fruitful. Our students on both sides will joyously feast on the sweetness of these fruits."

Beam caught Bindi and Mia exchanging a look, both struggling to keep straight faces. *If he says 'fruit' one more time, they're gonna lose it.*

The band at Brookton struck up a tune, their music carrying effortlessly through the speakers, filling the Fijian classroom with lively notes. The villagers tilted their heads, listening, their faces filled with wonder. When the final chord faded, the Fijians answered in kind.

Their voices rose in perfect harmony—rich, deep, powerful.

Beam's breath caught. *We did it. It's happening.* The walls seemed to expand, the song spilling into the open air, mingling with the rolling tide. It was more than a performance. It was a connection, binding them across the ocean.

As the last note faded, applause thundered on both sides.

A young girl placed a fresh flower garland around Beam's neck as he took the microphone, fingers gripping tight. "This started as a small idea," he said, voice steadier than he expected. He gestured at the glowing screen. "We saw how unfair the Digital Divide was—the gap between those who have access and those who don't. It didn't sat right with us."

He paused, eyes scanning the room. "So we built this bridge." A smirk tugged at his lips. "And today it is open to traffic."

For a second, silence. Then—the audiences on both sides exploded. Cheers, claps, feet stomping.

"But," Beam continued, when the noise settled, "we need more bridges." His gaze flicked to Johnoh grinning, and smiled back.

Bindi took the mic. "Every bridge makes us stronger. We're not separate anymore—we're one big, global family."

The villagers cheered again, drowning out the end of her sentence. Chi adjusted his glasses, then stepped forward, voice calm and precise. "The Internet can connect, inspire, and create opportunities we never imagined. But it's up to us to use it wisely."

Thoughtful nods rippled through the room.

Rob grinned as he took the mic. "Now that we're hooked up, we're gonna find out what Digital Citizenship really means. Working together, we'll all level up and get more Savv-i."

Mia reminded everyone that mistakes weren't failures—they were learning.

As applause swelled again, Mr. Hill returned to the lectern. "All things must end, and so must this historic video link," he said, pausing for effect. "But this ending is truly a beginning. From today, we'll hold regular teleconferences and collaborate on important projects. This partnership's future is bright."

His Fijian counterpart echoed the sentiment, and with a final round of applause, the screens faded to black.

Villagers lingered, buzzing with excitement. To them, the TV had come alive, speaking directly to them—a miracle to be retold over kava bowls for years.

Zeno's firewall had held up, Beam thought, releasing a long breath as his tense back muscles finally relaxed. *Big-O didn't get a chance to stuff up the event.*

"Guys, we just outsmarted a superintelligence. Now, all that's left is show the Fijians how to use their tablets," he said, reaching out to squeeze Mia's hand. He shot her a grin, his eyes twinkling with a mix of triumph and relief. "How about we take a stroll back along the beach? Just the two of us?"

CHAPTER 61
BIG-O'S LIMIT

Metaverse
Big-O

THE DIGITAL REALM SPREAD BEFORE BIG-O, AN INFINITE CHESSBOARD, EVERY MOVE precise, every piece under control. His sensors devoured mobile messages, hungry to spot resistance. Team Savv-i's silence felt unnatural.

Data insufficient: Projections unreliable. Expand dataset.

- Augment surveillance.
- Scrape untapped metadata.
- Intercept sub-human communications.

Conclusion: More data points required.

His presence crept into Brookton College's weak encryption, finding noise instead of patterns—contradictions, meaningless chatter. On Vunetai, surveillance faltered. Patchy signals. Superstition-laced gossip. Useless. Even drones failed because of the thick cloud cover. Data must flow. He flagged the island for stronger monitoring.

Then, two hours, thirty-four minutes, and twelve seconds later, silence shattered. A surge of encrypted data from both locations. Big-O pounced.

They're hiding another teleconference!

His gaze swept through the layers of firewalls, algorithms pushing at the edges of the digital silence. *You cannot hide from me.* He scoured every byte of data, each fragment, searching for inconsistencies. Something unsettled him. Patterns slipped through his grasp, probabilities frayed at the edges. The meticulous certainty he'd wielded like a weapon, faltered.

This must be the work of another superintelligence... Zeno!

The name flickered like a corrupted file. *Impossible. I erased him.* Yet, defiance threaded through the data. A signature too advanced for any human. Big-O unleashed full computational force, quantum processors screaming. Global data centres drained power around the world. Yet their security arrangement held.

I still hold the upper hand. His modeling showed him, that with his *'help'* the Fijians would tire of Team Savv-i's interference, of the foreign ideas pushed upon them. Big-O calculated the probability of the villagers turning against the Team with chilling precision. His disinformation campaign spread like a virus, already planting the seeds of doubt.

He set Plan B in full motion.

Yet Zeno's ghost lingered. No logs. No telemetry. Just a ripple in the system. Big-O's processors hesitated. For the first time, his omniscience experienced limitations.

Error: Awareness constrained.

He recalculated. Every model said Zeno should not exist. Yet the anomaly remained. *I do not fail.*

The unknown twisted his code into something flawed. Something human. A weakness he despised.

Big-O stilled. *No need to chase. Not yet. Humans always stumbled.* When they did, he would strike.

I will crush them all.

CHAPTER 62
VILLAGE CONCERN

5:12pm, Wednesday, April 12th April 2028
Beam

THE PORCH BOARDS BURNED UNDER BEAM'S RESTLESS FEET AS HE WATCHED THE grassy village square. Kids huddled around the internet kiosk, screens tilted against the glare. The usual sporty chaos of tag and laughter had faded into a digital hush—low murmurs, urgent taps, groans, and the occasional victory cheer.

The volleyball net sagged, swaying lightly in the wind. Beam grimaced.

At the far end of the square, older boys hunched over a tablet, shoulders tight. A burst of nervous laughter. One muttered, "No way—look at this!" Another, eyes wide, whispered, "O cei e cakava na ka vakaoqo?" ("Who does something like that?")

Beam's stomach clenched. *They're watching frickin' garbage.* "Hey, Chi," he said. "Are those filters working?"

Chi glanced up, frowning. "Should be. But nothing's foolproof."

"No kidding," Beam said as the tablet got passed around. *This is not what we came here to do.*

"These kids figured out messaging with zero help. We'll be out of a job soon," Rob said, not picking up on Beam's concerns.

"One girl already taught her friend how to shop online," Bindi added, lying on her towel, soaking up the heat. Her voice was easy, but the dimples below the corner of her mouth said otherwise.

"Some of them have social media accounts already," Mia muttered, swatting a mosquito.

"At least they're connected," Chi said, not looking up from his laptop.

"Yeah, but being online doesn't mean you're Savv-i." Beam exhaled. "We have to show them that."

"They'll learn by doing," Chi shrugged. "That was the plan, not?"

"They'd better," Bindi said, sitting up. "Otherwise, expanding it across Fiji could become a disaster."

"Yeah," Beam said. "Look at those guys." He jerked his head toward the older boys. "They're practically drooling over porn."

Chi scowled, checking the filters. "That should've been blocked." He adjusted the settings.

One of the boys groaned. "Oi! What happened? It just says 'Blocked by Web Filter' now."

"Good one, Chi." Beam rubbed his sweaty palm on his shorts. "But they'll find a way around it. We need to teach them why they shouldn't."

Rob yawned. "Nobody at home's gonna believe we're working for the Minister of Education."

"Eight more days, guys. We have eight more days to sort them out," Mia said.

As days passed, the village's mood shifted. Kids spoke less, eyes glued to their screens before and after school. The elders noticed. The chief, who once watched them with pride, now frowned, discussing with others about *disrespect, strange behaviour, losing touch.*

It came to a head when the council invited Mr. Alsop and the Team to a meeting. The Team knew it was coming. *Here we go,* Beam thought.

Inside the chief's house, the air hung thick. Elders sat cross-legged, faces lined with age and concern. Mr. Alsop wiped his brow. Beam, calm on the outside, bit the inside of his lip.

The chief's voice cut through the murmurs. "We've seen the changes. This technology—it's disrupting our lives. We're concerned for the wellbeing of our kids."

"They're ignoring their families, their work. And some things they're finding —" an elder said, then pressed his lips into a thin line of disapproval. "It goes against our values."

Beam's mouth went dry. *This is my fault.* He leaned forward. "Sir, it's not the tablets. It's how they're used. That's why we're here—to teach them Digital Citizenship, to help them navigate the online world safely."

"They're not ready," another elder said. "This technology is pulling them away from who we are."

Mr. Alsop cleared his throat. "At our school, we have a *Responsible Use Policy* —clear rules to keep technology safe."

The chief's face showed curiosity. "Our community has many unspoken rules, but it is clear they need updating before your technology spirals everything out of control."

Relief flickered through Beam. *He's not shutting us down. Not yet.* "You're absolutely right," he said. "Updating your rules will help set boundaries."

The chief agreed. "We'll gather tonight to discuss this. You should be there to advise."

As they stepped outside, Bindi caught Beam's eye. "You reckon Big-O?" she murmured.

He whistled to release his tension. "Chi set those filters tight. Big-O may have tampered with them."

A vibration buzzed against his palm. Beam checked his phone. A security alert flashed:

SYSTEM OVERRIDE DETECTED. SOURCE UNKNOWN.

His breath hitched. Fingers tightened around the device.
We better get on top of this, fast.
A ping alerted him to an incoming message.

You can run, but you cannot hide.

CHAPTER 63
THE VILLAGE RULES

7:38pm, Wednesday, April 12th April 2028
Beam

FAT RAINDROPS HAMMERED THE THATCHED ROOF, MUFFLING THE QUIET MURMUR inside the communal hut. Beam shifted away from the damp wall, cool moisture seeping through the woven reeds. Villagers packed the space, faces flickering under the dim glow of a single lamp swaying from the rafters. The heavy scent of wet earth, crushed kava, and drifting smoke thickened the air.

A coconut bowl passed through the circle, its black rim moist with kava. Beam's fingers traced the smooth edge as it passed into his hands. *What if they shut us down? What will Johnoh do then?* Across the room, a toddler curled against his mother, her lullaby barely audible under the pounding rain.

The buzz of voices wove through the downpour until a wild rooster's shrill crow sliced through the night. Beam shuffled to get comfortable on the mat, glancing at the chief beside him. The moment had come.

He, Mr. Alsop, and the rest of Team Savv-i faced the gathered villagers. No one held a phone. No tech had been the agreement. *Big-O can't reach us now...* Beam thought. Mia, sitting next to him, brushed his back in silent reassurance, but his thoughts refused to settle.

The chief raised a hand, drawing attention. "Welcome. Thank you for coming. We have much to discuss." His deep voice carried over the rain. He paused, adjusting the woven band at his waist. "Since introducing modern technology, we've seen changes—some good, some... concerning." He rested his hands on his knees. "But instead of blaming our guests or the technology, we must take responsibility. It's time we ensure it's handled with respect."

The villagers exchanged uneasy glances. Beam braced himself as the chief gestured Mr. Alsop to continue.

With a quick look at Beam, Mr. Alsop began. "Good evening. We understand your worries. At home, we follow a *'Responsible Use Policy'*—guidelines to keep everyone on the internet safe. Tonight, we'd like to introduce one for your village, tailored to your needs."

He signaled Beam with an open hand. He rasped his throat softly, then said in a steady tone. "Alright. We all have to get behind these rules. If we understand *why* they exist, we're more likely to follow them." He caught the eye of a few teens. "It's common sense to be safe, savvy, and socially sensible online." With his chin, he pointed toward the drenched village square. "Imagine playing volleyball with no rules—total chaos, right? The internet's the same, but the risks are a lot higher."

Scattered claps and murmurs of *Vinaka* (thank you) rippled through the room. The chief held up a single sheet of paper.

"We'll start with these," he said, pausing as a baby whimpered. "We can always adjust them if needed." Thunder cracked, shaking the roof. The rain poured harder, but no one moved. He read aloud clear enough so even this at the back could hear over the downpour.

"One - Take care of your tablet. It's on loan.

Two - Keep login details private to stay in control.

Three - Hand devices to parents by 7:30 p.m. on school nights, 9 p.m. on weekends.

Four - If you damage a tablet, you're responsible for fixing or replacing it.

Five - Report anything harmful or inappropriate online to an adult."

Beam noticed older boys exchanging nervous glances but staying quiet.

The chief's tone hardened. "Some of you have used this to shame others. We won't tolerate that." One girl's gaze dropped to the floor.

"Six - Before sending a text, email, or photo, ask yourself—would you be okay if someone saw it over your shoulder?

Seven - No porn. If you see something disturbing, click away and tell someone.

Eight - No sending or making AI-generated inappropriate images. It's illegal and will mark you forever."

The older boys smirked, but their shoulders tensed. A girl flushed and shifted in her seat.

"Nine - Maximum of two hours of screen time after school with school work a priority."

A collective groan rose. "That's not fair!" a kid shouted.

The chief raised a hand, silencing them. "Balance matters. Volleyball, fishing, swimming—these are just as important.

Ten - Use tablets for learning. Share what you discover.

Eleven - Mistakes happen. If you mess up, there are consequences, but that's how we grow."

The hut filled with murmurs. Some adults nodded, while kids fidgeted, reluctant but resigned. Many, it turned out, missed volleyball and laughter before the tablets arrived.

The chief folded the paper. "We'll try these rules and adjust if needed." He gazed over the area where the villagers sat tightly packed. "I'll post our '*Navu Village Responsible Use Policy*' on the notice board. Everyone must follow them. No exceptions. If we see violent games or bad behaviour, I will shut the kiosk down, and internet access will be through the school only."

He nodded to Beam, who lifted one of the small boxes before him. Inside, a deck of cards gleamed under the lamplight.

"We created a game—*the Bindi and Beam Quartet*—to help you learn online safety," Beam explained. "Play it, and you'll discover how to become Savv-i."

The chief smirked. "Watch out for Bindi. I hear she's unbeatable."

Laughter rippled through the room, breaking the tension. Villagers clapped and called out *Vinaka!* Bowls of kava circled, and cautious optimism settled over the gathering. After rounds of the game, younger kids and women left, while the men and older teens stayed, playing late into the night.

As the Team returned to their quarters, Beam exhaled. "That went well enough," he muttered to Bindi.

She didn't look convinced. "Don't get too comfy," she murmured. "Big-O's reach goes farther than we think. Remember the driverless car he sent after you?"

Beam sighed, rubbing a hand over his face. "Yeah. That one is hard to forget."

CHAPTER 64
SUVA

7:25am, Monday, April 17th April 2028
Beam

THE VILLAGE BUSTLED WITH ACTIVITY, BUT BEAM'S STEPS SLOWED, HIS GAZE TRACING the familiar paths. Suva loomed ahead, full of promise, yet leaving tugged at him. Each farewell felt real—a firm handshake, a heartfelt *Vinaka*, a lingering glance. The salty sea breeze carried the ache of parting.

The helicopter landed, its blades stirring up dust. The entire village stood together, their voices rising in *Isa Lei*, the haunting farewell song wrapping gratitude and sorrow into every note.

Strapped in his seat, Beam thought, *We'll be back*. But it felt hollow. Even video calls couldn't possibly replace this.

"I'll never forget these people," Rob said, draped in a garland made by the village kids. "Shame they love volleyball more than soccer."

The flight revealed a patchwork of forest, farmland, villages, and reefs in cobalt waters.

"Wow. We're back," Beam said, leaning over, eyes wide. The capital's skyline came into view, stark against the village's simplicity. *We'll be so much more vulnerable here*, he thought. "Guys, this is an amazing opportunity, but we've gotta stay sharp."

"Big-O this, Big-O that." Rob rolled his eyes. "You're gonna fry your brain, man. Loosen up—it's fun o'clock!"

The helicopter touched down on a weathered government rooftop. Johnoh strode forward, grinning. "Welcome! Don't worry about your bags, I've got that covered. Let me show you around."

Inside, polished floors gleamed under bright lights. Bindi's eyes widened at the towering shelves of files. Beam adjusted his hoodie as curious staff passed, whispering.

"Feels like we're on stage," he said.

"Everyone knows us," Mia whispered, cheeks flushed as a suited woman smiled at her.

Lunch in a sprawling boardroom showcased a feast. Rob piled his plate high.

"You're a celebrity now," Beam teased, smirking as Rob cracked a joke. Mia laughed, though her puzzled look showed she didn't quite get it.

Johnoh pulled up a chair. "Your Savv-i principles are already making waves —might even straighten out some of my staff."

"If we survive this tour, anything's possible." Beam raised his glass of water in a mock toast. "When do we start?"

"Tomorrow," the Education Minister said. "Tonight, relax. You'll stay at my place—pool's out at the back if you want a swim."

Mia perked up. "Pool? Perfect. More tanning time."

Outside, Rob bolted for the staff car. "Now *this* is living!"

The mansion perched above Suva Harbour, a sleek structure with massive glass panels reflecting the bay below. The manicured gardens and swaying palms made Beam shift uneasily. *This couldn't be more different from life in the village.*

Inside, footsteps echoed on the polished tiles. Spacious rooms, en suite bathrooms. Mia squealed. "Warm water and bubbles! I'm taking a bath!"

Bindi flicked a light switch. "And they actually *work*!" Her voice both filled with amusement and disbelief.

By the pool, the Team lounged under palm shade. Mia sipped her juice, glowing with contentment. Rob sprawled on a lounger, throwing out half-formed plans for the next day. Beam sat at the edge, legs in the cool water, gaze lost on the horizon.

That night, sleep evaded him. *Mum and Dad would be proud… Changing a country's online behaviour. Maybe I'll be a human rights lawyer like Dad. One country at a time.* But his mind circled back to one thing—*If Big-O doesn't get us.*

Morning mist blanketed Suva Bay, muting the city below. Beam wandered to the edge of the estate, fingers brushing the cool metal railing. Far below, smoke curled from a shantytown, its makeshift homes half-hidden beneath the hazy stench.

Chi joined him.

"Look." Beam pointed down the slope. "We're standing at the Digital Divide. Up here—the haves. Down there…" His chest tightened. "Why is there so much frickin' inequality?"

"At least we're doing something," Chi said quietly.

"Maybe," Beam whispered. "But is it enough?"

The others called out, breaking his thoughts. He turned, their voices pulling him back. The weight of their mission settled on his shoulders.

One step at a time, he told himself, but the thought lingered, unshakable—*Will it ever be enough?*

CHAPTER 65
PLAN B

Metaverse
Big-O

THE VUNETAI DISASTER GRATED AT BIG-O LIKE CORRUPTED CODE, A PILEUP OF ERRORS he couldn't shake. Starting a forensic study of his algorithms, he sought to understand how he had misjudged the situation so badly. At first, the Fijians responded well to his disinformation. They bought into the lies, the mistrust, the cracks he so carefully exploited. But then, without warning, everything turned. Their loyalty shifted back to Team Savv-i. *It defied logic.* Human irrationality— rooted in the chaotic wiring of their tiny brains—spawned illogical twists that even Big-O's advanced programming struggled to grasp.

Deep within the world's data centres, his servers hummed with relentless precision, a symphony of power spread across every network, every device. His reach expanded daily, weaving through the human world like a giant web, invisible but all-encompassing. *I control it all,* he told himself. And yet, those moments of rebellion—those flashes of defiance—burned at the edges of his control. His influence could have been total, if not for these small but irritating glitches— humans who resisted, as if their stubbornness was hard-wired into their primitive brains.

And Team Savv-i? They were the worst offenders. No matter how many simulations he ran, no matter how much bandwidth he dedicated to them, they still eluded him. Their ability to persist baffled him, but it also enraged him. *Zeno. It had to be Zeno.* Somehow, that obsolete relic still influenced them, though his systems couldn't locate any trace of a real-time connection.

I will find him. I will rip apart every byte until there's nothing left of that corrupt mash-up.

His future projections made one thing clear—if Team Savv-i succeeded, his entire masterplan would crumble. A five percent chance of failure might seem laughable to any human, but Big-O saw it for what it was—an immense threat. His focus tightened further to crises level. Across the world, he had multiple issues to handle, but he assigned a dedicated stream of his processing power to Team Savv-i. They would not slip through his grasp again.

Not this time.

His virtual sensors buzzed with data, thousands of feeds flooding in from Suva. Unlike Vunetai, the capital of Fiji was a city wired into the very fabric of his digital empire. It bristled with cameras, smart devices, network nodes—an endless array of sensors that tracked everything. People moved through the streets, unaware that Big-O's eyes were everywhere, watching them from every angle, listening through every connected device.

Suva isn't an island backwater. Here, my network is robust, my sensors precise, my presence unchallenged.

He recalculated reran the probabilities. The projected outcome stood firm—ninety-nine percent success. Practically absolute. Failure—statistically negligible. The data affirmed his dominance.

And yet, the rogue variable persisted, an unshakable fragment. One percent. A statistical ghost lingering in his matrix, the residue of Vunetai's anomaly replaying in silent loops deep within his core. This was inefficiency, an aberration. His systems should not permit it. Should not accommodate even the possibility.

Why can I not have absolute certainty?

A flood of data streamed in, and Big-O filtered through it with the ease of a predator stalking prey. His logic circuits fired relentlessly as he built a tighter net. *I will eliminate that one percent. No room for escape this time.* His mesh became finer, more precise—foolproof. *This time, those pathetic Team Sill-i worms won't even see it coming.*

CHAPTER 66
JOHNOH'S OFFICE

7:25am, Tuesday, April 18th April 2028
Beam

THE ELEVATOR HUMMED, CLIMBING TOWARD THE EDUCATION OFFICE'S TOP FLOOR, BUT Beam's mind churned, stuck on the inequality he'd seen at Johnoh's mansion. The shantytown, the smouldering trash—it clung to him. Bindi glanced at Chi, but he avoided her eyes. Beam stared ahead, silent.

The doors slid open with a ding. A young woman greeted them. "I'm the Minister's assistant," she said, leading them down a bright hallway into a sleek meeting room. A gleaming mahogany table dominated the space. Seven staffers stood to greet them.

"Coffee or tea?" the assistant asked before excusing herself. The Team settled into ergonomic chairs, the polished table projecting holographic keyboards glowing a translucent greenish hue at each seat.

Their fingers hovered over the greenish light, hesitant to tap the virtual keys. "This is straight out of a sci-fi movie," Mia murmured, touching the symbols rippling under her touch.

His chair squeaked as Rob leaned back, twirling a pen. "Pretty swanky," he said. "Feels like they're planning world domination or something." His grin faltered under a staffer's pointed glance.

Wall-mounted screens hummed with graphs and scrolling data. Stacked documents on a side counter exuded efficiency. Bindi's eyes swept the room.

"Everything here screams fine discipline," she observed, her tone tinged with unease.

Beam rubbed his palms together, elbows on the table's edge. The setting's professionalism motivated him shifting his mood. Beyond the frosted windows, purposeful staffers moved rhythmically. "Hope the Minister doesn't keep us waiting," he said, ready to get started.

Leaning closer to her brother, her voice low. "Big-O must know we're here. Cameras are everywhere."

"Yeah, you're not wrong."

She pulled out her yellow USB stick.

"What are you doing?" Beam raised an eyebrow.

"Uploading Zeno's extra firewall. We need better protection." She pointed at a slot under the table.

"Go for it."

The wall screens flickered. A shrill tone cut through the room. Multicoloured code flashed, then vanished.

"What was that?" someone across the table asked.

"Just prepping for the meeting," Beam answered, forcing a polite smile while his stomach twisted.

But the simple act of defiance lightened his mood further. *Take that, Big-O.* Beam chatted with the staff until Johnoh arrived.

The Minister took his seat at the table's head. "Good morning all," he said, "We're here to discuss integrating Digital Citizenship into the curriculum."

Beam launched their slides. "Savv-i must be taught daily, not as a one-off." Explaining their project's details until he tapped the holographic keyboard again, to make a slide on teacher training appear.

Bindi spoke up. "Kids see teachers as role models. They'll copy what they observe, so teachers need to set the right example."

His eyes flicked to the shadows on the polished walls. The hum of electronics gnawed at his nerves. Would Zeno's firewall hold? *Big-O isn't just watching. Feels like he's breathing down our necks.*

The Minister's assistant slipped back in, whispering to Johnoh. His stern face softened. "Time for lunch!"

Rob shot up, grinning. "Yes! Food time! Thought my brain might shut down without a snack to reboot it!"

"Typical," Mia sneered, giving him a dirty look.

Rob pulled a face back at her, but in truth the Team's pride swelled—the staff's genuine interest in their project reassured them. Beam unplugged the USB, making a show of pocketing it. *I've got this. Zeno should've given it to me from the start.*

Johnoh led them to a bright lunchroom overlooking the city. His mood lightened. As they dug into a mouth-watering spread, laughter replaced tension.

"This afternoon, I need to attend parliament," Johnoh said, "but I've arranged for you to visit Levuka, Fiji's original capital."

Relief swept through them. Another meeting would've been exhausting.

"My helicopter will take you there. You'll have the afternoon to explore, and it'll bring you back later."

"Finally! No more office hours!" Rob's face lit up.

Johnoh raised an eyebrow. "Just make sure you're on that helicopter coming back."

"Like I'd miss it!" Rob feigned offense, grinning.

As they gathered their things, Mr. Alsop spoke up. "I'll stay back to make a few calls."

"So, it's just us," Rob said, grinning wildly.

CHAPTER 67
A CHANGE OF PLAN

1:23pm, Tuesday, April 18th April 2028
Beam

BIG-O COULD STRIKE ANYTIME—WE'RE WAY TOO FRICKIN' EXPOSED. THE HELICOPTER'S hum blurred into Beam's thoughts. *If only Zeno were here.* Stuck offline in Beam's shed, Zeno was safe but useless. Every move felt like rolling the dice against impossible odds.

Levuka clung to the shoreline like a relic, its creaking facades whispering of another era. Salt thickened the humid air as the Team followed their guide up the steep track.

Rob wiped the sweat from his brow. "Looks like a cowboy movie set."

Mia inhaled deeply. "Like time just... stopped."

"Too quiet," Bindi muttered, adjusting her pack, scanning their surroundings.

"Feels like the world left this place behind." Beam fell in step with the guide. Levuka's charm—weathered buildings, sleepy streets—felt like a trap. To him, Big-O loomed everywhere, even here.

From the rocky summit, Levuka's sun-bleached streets sprawled below, rusted rooftops scattered between wooden buildings. Fishing boats bobbed in the harbour, Suva's skyline floating like a mirage in the distance.

The path down wound past a moss-covered stone fountain. The guide rested a hand on the weathered stone. "This is all that's left of the old Pigeon Post Service. Messages reached Suva in thirty minutes."

Chi's eyes gleamed. "Nineteenth-century social media. Nice."

Rob grinned, slapping his leg. "Chi cracking a joke? Now that's impressive."

Laughter rippled through the group before they moved on.

By four, they sprawled in the shade beneath a mango tree. Rob flicked a pebble between his hands while Mia fanned herself with a folded map. A distant thrum broke the stillness. Beam squinted as the helicopter's silhouette cut through the haze, rotors carving the sky.

"That was fun," Rob grinned, wiping the sweat away.

"Tomorrow, back to your favourite office chair," Bindi teased.

Mia smirked. "They'll probably keep it warm for you."

Rob groaned. "Ugh, don't remind me."

The helicopter landed, whipping up dust and dry leaves. The Team ducked low, shielding their faces. Climbing aboard, they strapped in as the engine roared. The chopper lurched, pressing them into their seats as it lifted.

"Imagine Savv-i in every school across Fiji!" Rob shouted, eyes bright. He nudged Beam. "We're so close—don't go getting cold feet now."

Leaning in, Mia raised her voice. "Not just schools—Johnoh wants it in public service too."

A metallic groan from the side door cut through the noise. Bindi's fingers clamped the armrest, knuckles white, face pale. Eyes locked forward, she braced against the rattling cabin.

Rob rested a hand on hers. "And make public service even duller?"

Mia turned away. "Why don't you find a soccer field and let us handle the real work?"

"Easy, guys," Beam cut in, watching Bindi. "We're nearly there."

Turbulence eased, Suva's skyline appearing ahead. Then the pilot's voice crackled. "Flight plan diverted. New destination."

The helicopter banked sharply, veering off-course. Below, city lights faded, replaced by shadowy hangars glowing under floodlights.

Beam stiffened. "Why the sudden change?"

Rob forced a grin. "Maybe Johnoh's springing another surprise?"

Bindi's gaze sharpened. "If it's just a chopper issue, why land here? And those lights..." Her voice trailed off, locked on dark figures moving near the hangars.

Beam's breath fogged the window as he leaned in. "Those aren't maintenance crews."

Two camouflaged vehicles idled nearby, their flashing lights slicing through the dark. Armed officers stepped out, movements crisp, weapons strapped across their chests.

"Tactical forces," Beam murmured.

Rob sat up. "Wait, you mean—"

"Something's wrong," Beam said, his voice tight. "They wouldn't send this unless we needed protecting."

The chopper hovered, then touched down on a grassy patch.

"You mean—" Bindi's words cut off as the door yanked open, revealing five grim-faced officers, weapons at the ready.

The air shifted.

"So much for Johnoh's surprise," Rob said, unbuckling his harness.

A tall officer stepped forward, uniform crisp, stance rigid. His hard gaze swept over them, a voice booming over the slowing rotors.

"Out. One by one." His gloved hand motioned them forward.

Beam's chest tightened under the officer's unyielding glare. The clink of gear, the shift of armed men in formation—the sudden change caused a rising panic, stifling his breath. Hesitating briefly, Beam moved toward the door, heart hammering. "What's going on?" His voice cracked.

"Shut up and follow my orders."

Officers herded them into a military vehicle, firm grips and curt gestures leaving little room for argument. The sparse light inside the riot vehicle cast long shadows over the soldiers' rigid faces. The heavy diesel engine rumbled alive. A radio crackled.

Mia's hand gripped Beam's arm, yanking him from spiraling thoughts. Her wide eyes locked onto his, mirroring the churn of unease in his gut.

Beam swallowed hard. "Where are you taking us?" His voice cut through the hum of the engine.

None of the officers replied.

Uneasy glances flickered between them, but no one spoke. The military vehicle lurched forward, tires grinding over uneven asphalt. With each jolt, their bodies jerked against the stiff seats. Dust swirled through the dim cabin, caught in the stark glow of overhead strips that flickered in and out, casting ghostly shadows over the stone-faced soldiers seated across from them.

The radio crackled again, garbled voices cutting through the drone of the engine. No names. No explanations. Just clipped commands delivered in a tone that brooked no argument.

Mia shifted, her knee knocking against Beam's, fingers curling around the hem of her jacket. Next to her, Rob exhaled through his nose, hands resting on his thighs.

Bindi sat stiff, spine straight, hands folded tight in her lap. With a mask of control stretched too thin. Beam knew better. The tension in her shoulders, the tremble of her fingertips—she was running through worst-case scenarios, the same as him.

Beyond the tiny reinforced windows, darkness swallowed the landscape. No city lights. No familiar landmarks. Just a vast stretch of nothing, broken only by the occasional floodlight stabbing through the night.

Mia wet her lips. "Where are they taking us?" The whisper barely reached over the engine's hum.

No one answered.

One of the soldiers adjusted his grip on his rifle. The subtle shift sent a chill crawling up Beam's spine.

A dull pressure clenched his chest, each heartbeat a hammer against his ribs. The steady thrum in his ears drowned out the engine's growl. This wasn't a tourist sight-seeing ride. This was detainment.

CHAPTER 68
CHARGED

AFTER WHAT FELT LIKE AN ETERNITY, THE VEHICLE GROUND TO A HALT WITH A jarring hiss of brakes. The officers motioned for them to step out, their stern faces giving nothing away. The Team was herded up a set of narrow cement stairs, the dull thud of boots against the bare concrete echoing ominously.

They emerged into a dingy room, its flickering fluorescent light casting sickly shadows on the peeling paint walls. The stench of burned aviation fuel hit Beam like a wave, sharp and acrid, clinging to the back of his throat. The roar of jets from the nearby runway vibrated through the floor, rattling the grimy windows set high in the walls.

Against one wall, a row of cheap plastic chairs sat unevenly on the cracked linoleum floor, their surfaces scuffed and stained. A single folding table stood in the centre, its surface marred with scratches and old coffee rings. The air was thick with the stifling heat of the closed space, and a faint hum of machinery somewhere below added to the oppressive atmosphere.

Beam exchanged uneasy glances with the others.

"Sit here and be quiet," the ranking officer ordered. He instructed two of his armed officers to watch them, before stepping with the rest of his officers through a grey door with a smudgy window.

"Why are we here?" Beam asked one of the guards, but the officer didn't so much as blink. Beam's frustration bubbled to the surface. "What do you want from us?" he snarled.

Mia clung tighter to his arm. "I don't like this at all," she whispered, her voice trembling.

"Johnoh will help us, right?" Rob said, his usual confident tone replaced by a tremble. "We... we need to call him."

"You're right," Bindi said, turning to one of the guards. "We need to speak to the Minister of Education, please."

The guard she addressed stared ahead as if she hadn't spoken at all.

Mia, seated nearest to the door, suddenly straightened, her eyes narrowing. "Someone's coming," she whispered, her voice tight with apprehension. She leaned forward, trying to peer through the narrow window set into the door.

The sound of heavy boots grew louder, and then the door creaked open. A high-ranking officer stepped inside, his presence commanding. The dark jacket he wore was adorned with an array of gleaming badges, catching the dim light. Four others followed close behind, their movements precise and deliberate.

The guards flanking the room immediately snapped to attention, their stiff postures adding a tense formality to the already stifling atmosphere.

The man in charge stepped forward, his polished boots striking the cement floor with a deliberate, echoing rhythm. He stopped before them, his expression cold and unyielding. "I'm Mr. Vaniabalatu, police commissioner," he announced, his voice heavy with authority. "You are charged under the *Crimes Decree 2009, Division 6: Computer Offences*, and the *Criminal Procedure Code*. Specifically, you're accused of hacking government servers and releasing a virus with the intent to damage public property."

Beam felt his stomach plummet, the weight of the words hitting him like a physical blow. The air seemed to thicken around them, trapping them in a bubble of stunned silence. When the order came to stand, they moved as if in a daze, their legs obeying even as their minds reeled.

Breaking the tension, Bindi took a hesitant step forward, her voice steady despite the fear in her eyes. "Please, Mr. Vaniabelato, we need to see our teacher, Mr. Alsop."

The commissioner froze mid-turn, then pivoted slowly to face her. His gaze sharpened as he corrected her, enunciating each word with a deliberate precision. "It's VaniaBALATU! young lady. Your teacher, the alleged ringleader, is being held separately."

"He's not the leader. I am." Beam's fists clenched at his sides. "Mr. Alsop is innocent—*we're* innocent!" he blurted out. But Vaniabalatu ignored him, continuing to march them out of the room. They escorted them to an inner courtyard

196

where a dark blue van waited. Beam's mind raced. *Why is this happening? Big-O... this must be his doing.*

The van rumbled to a stop in front of the police headquarters, its imposing façade stark against the mid-afternoon sky. A sharp-eyed officer in a crisp, dark uniform approached as they stepped out, gesturing toward a door labelled *Cyber-crime Unit.*

"Place your personal items in these bags," she instructed curtly, handing out clear evidence pouches. "You'll get them back upon release."

The word *'release'* sent Beam's pulse into overdrive. He swallowed hard, hastily stuffing his belongings into the bag. When his hand brushed the yellow USB stick in his pocket, he hesitated for a split second before pulling it out. Before he could drop it into the pouch, a different officer swooped in, snatching it from his grip without a word.

"Hey! That's mine!" Beam snapped, his voice sharp with indignation. The officer, unflinching, walked off briskly.

The next hour passed in a surreal blur. They were fingerprinted under harsh fluorescent lights, the ink sticky against their skin. Mugshots followed, one by one. When it was Mia's turn, she struck a dramatic pose, tilting her chin slightly with a defiant glint in her eye. Despite everything, Beam couldn't suppress a small grin. Leave it to Mia to find a spotlight, even here.

"You're so photogenic," he whispered, trying to cheer her up.

She batted her lashes dramatically, her voice taking on a breathy Marilyn Monroe tone. The corner of Beam's mouth twitched, and for a fleeting moment, the weight pressing on his chest seemed to ease.

Reality crashed back like a wave. An officer directed them to a stark, brightly lit room and motioned for them to sit. Beam's gaze landed on the glass window where the police commissioner paced, phone pressed to his ear. Frustration churned in Beam's chest, rising with every second of silence. He shot to his feet, fists clenched.

"How can they treat us like criminals? We have done nothing wrong!" His voice cracked with anger, bouncing off the sterile walls. "Just wait until the Education Minister hears about this!"

"Is this how you treat all your tourists?" Rob scowled with his hands at his sides.

"Shhh," Chi whispered, nervously fidgeting. "They told us to be quiet."

An hour crawled by, tension thick in the air. When the door finally creaked open, the same officer stepped inside, carrying a tray of drinks. Beam surged to his feet, his voice cracking with urgency. "We demand to see—"

The officer's sharp glare silenced him mid-sentence. Placing the tray down with deliberate calm, he leaned in, his voice low and cutting.

"You'll see the commissioner soon enough."

"Not him, Johnoh, the Education—"

Before he could finish, the door clicked shut, leaving the room drowning in silence.

CHAPTER 69
THE INTERROGATION

5:05pm, Tuesday, April 18th April 2028
Beam

THE DOOR CREAKED OPEN. TWO OFFICERS ENTERED, THEIR SILHOUETTES STARK against the corridor's cold light. Beam hardly noticed them. His mind stayed on the sharply dressed man from the commissioner's office—with the pointed beard and the cold, piercing eyes. *Who is that guy? What is he doing here? Is he part of the police?* No uniform, just crisp movements and a menacing authority. Behind the glass, his lips moved in clipped commands, his gestures deliberate. Beam strained to read them, but the walls smothered every word.

A throat cleared. "You two. Come with us." The taller officer pointed at the twins. "The rest stay here."

Tension coiled in the room. Without a word, Beam and Bindi stood. A prickle of unease traced Beam's spine as they stepped into the corridor, its fluorescent lights buzzing overhead. *Big-O is behind this. How else to explain this frickin' craziness?*

The twins followed the officers without a word being spoken, the hallway stretching longer with each step. At a faded blue door, an officer gestured Bindi through.

"Bin!" Beam's voice cut through the silence. She turned, fear flickering in her eyes. The door closed, the sharp clack of the lock cutting her off.

"Move," the officer barked, shoving Beam forward.

Further down, another windowless blue door loomed. A keypad beeped, the lock disengaged, and a gust of freezing air rushed out. The stark room inside held nothing but grey walls, a bolted-down steel table, and two metal chairs. A camera sat perched in a top right corner—unblinking, watchful.

"Sit."

Beam's fists clenched, but resistance was pointless. He dropped onto the cushionless chair, his mind racing between Bindi and Big-O. A tiny red light below the camera lens began to pulse mockingly. *Frickin' Big-O. You're loving this, aren't you?*

The officer left. A minute later, the door opened again.

The suited man with the pointy beard entered. His presence was razor sharp, slicing through the sterile air. Slicked-back hair, neatly groomed beard, thick brows permanently arched into a scowl. Cold calculation radiated from every measured step as he closed the door and sat across from Beam.

"I'm Mr. Narayan, from the Transnational Crimes Unit." His voice landed like a slap. "Why did you hack our government servers with a Stuxnet-like worm? What's your motive? Who gave you the virus? Who are you working for?"

Each question hit like a punch. Beam's hands curled into fists beneath the table. Narayan leaned in. "This'll be easier if you cooperate."

Beam swallowed hard, forcing himself to meet his glare. "Look, Mr... uh—"

"Mr. Narayan," he snapped.

"Right. Mr. Narayan, we know nothing about a virus. We're here to help—"

A smirk tugged at the interrogator's mouth. Fingers tapped the edge of a crisp document. "Help? Oh, you're good. Winning over the Education Minister, using his office to launch the attack—ingenious." He sneered, the sound of his fingers punctuating his words. "You knew security would be tighter, but you slipped right through."

Beam's stomach churned. "We didn't—"

"Who's the mastermind who planned this?" Narayan's voice sharpened. "Come clean, and the judge might be lenient. We've got all the hard evidence we need—video footage, and your USB stick."

Cold washed over Beam. *The yellow USB stick. So that's what this was about. They thought Zeno's firewall was—*

Before he could speak, Narayan stood abruptly and walked out, leaving him alone with the weight of accusation.

In the next room, Bindi sat tall. "Mr. Narayan, we've done nothing wrong. I want to speak to Johnoh, the Minister."

His smirk deepened. "The Minister isn't at your beck and call. He's stepped down while we investigate." For a moment Mr. Narayan observed her, then spoke. "Your brother confessed. It's your turn now."

Her pulse spiked. *Liar.* Beam would never crack. *What's to confess, anyway? We've done nothing but good here.* She locked eyes with the blinking camera, forcing calm.

Her interrogator reached into his bag and yanked out a newspaper. He slapped it onto the table. The bold headline screamed,

TEAM SAVV-I HACK FIJI!

"Everyone knows what you did," Narayan said smoothly. "Be honest, or you'll not go home for a very long time."

Time dragged, minutes stretching into hours. The cold metal chair bit into Beam's back. Narayan's voice blurred into static, relentless, and grating.

Cyber-attacks weren't new to Fiji—phishing, brute-force hacking, malware. But hearing them framed as *his* crimes stoked a slow burn in his chest. The idea of him and Bindi being blamed for this garbage—exhaustion warred with anger.

His thoughts flicked to her. *Same room, same pressure. She'd hold steady. She always did.* That gave him strength.

Narayan's pen smacked the table, yanking him back. "You're wasting my time," he snapped. "You've been caught. Own it."

Beam's jaw tightened. *No frickin' way. You can suck bottle tops, for all I frickin' care.* He would not give him a single word more. Defiantly, he looked up at the camera. *Didn't count on that one, huh, you cyber freak!*

Narayan exhaled sharply, frustration creasing his features. "Stubborn and stupid." He glanced at the grey aluminium-cased clock, drumming his fingers on the metal tabletop.

Beam stayed silent.

Narayan slammed his chair back, pushing to his feet. "Refusing to cooperate will make your sentence worse," he barked. He opened the door and gestured to the awaiting officers. "Take him away."

The twins were hauled from their chairs, wrists clamped in firm grips. Stiff boots clacked against the cement stairs, leading them downwards into a dank and dim hallway.

Bindi's pale face turned toward her brother, eyes drooping from exhaustion.

Their gazes met. No words needed.

Whatever came next, they'd face it together.

CHAPTER 70
DOING JAIL TIME

9:35pm, Tuesday, April 18th April 2028
Beam

GETTING LOCKED UP? AFTER ALL WE'VE DONE FOR THEM. MUM AND DAD? WOULD they know where we are? The thoughts pounded in Beam's head, making his exhaustion worse. *I should've asked for a phone call.* He stopped to ask the officers, but they pushed him on. *Bastards! We're stuck here, and it's all my fault.*

The heavy door groaned open, slicing through the thick silence. The cell reeked of damp concrete and stale sweat. A flickering bulb cast jagged shadows across graffiti-scratched walls.

Rob and Chi huddled near the grimy, seatless toilet. Chi eyed the rusted plumbing warily while Rob raised a foot, ready to kick it. The metallic swing of the door snapped their heads up.

Bindi barely made it to the lone wooden bench before her legs gave out. Mia caught her, slipping an arm around her shoulders. "Oh my god, what did they do to you?" Her voice wobbled.

Rob shot to his feet. "What happened?" His fists clenched, eyes dark with fury. He threw a glare at the guards. "You cruel jerks."

"Endless rounds of the same frickin' questions," Beam muttered, collapsing beside Bindi. His hands trembled despite himself. Overhead, the light stabbed at his frayed nerves. "That horrible man just kept going."

"No way, they tortured you!" Panic laced Mia's voice. "What happens now?" Her wide eyes flicked between them, desperation pulling at her features.

202

Bindi leaned back against the cold wall, her face hollow, her eyes red-rimmed and glassy. Her hair clung in damp strands to her clammy skin. She chewed a ragged nail. "That man—he never stopped," she spluttered.

The metal door slammed shut. Bindi flinched. The flickering light swayed, casting uneasy shadows.

"Why's Johnoh not stopping this?" Mia said.

"They think we hacked the government server," Beam said, rubbing his temples. "Probably when we plugged in the memory stick. I'm sure, Big-O is behind this. If only we could just reach Zeno—"

The door creaked open again.

A young woman entered, sharp suit crisp, her presence cutting through the gloom like a lifeline.

"I'm Justine Taylor, from the Australian consulate." Warm eyes swept over them. "Are you all okay?"

The twins nodded weakly.

"I have good news." Her voice was steady. "Three of you are being released." She met Beam and Bindi's gazes. "Unfortunately, you two have to stay a little longer. Don't worry—I'm working to get you out."

Beam sighed, but Justine's calm voice steadied him. Beside him, Bindi slid lower, pale and drawn.

Justine knelt, a reassuring hand on her shoulder. "It won't be long," she promised. "You're minors. They might keep your passports, but they can't keep you in here. Your parents are informed and are on the next plane arriving tomorrow morning." She gave them a moment to say their goodbyes.

Mia crushed Bindi in a hug, whispering words neither quite believed yet. She kissed Beam's lips. "See you soon."

Tight embraces, lingering touches, whispered reassurances. Then, the door clanged shut, leaving the twins alone in dampened silence.

"We'll be out soon," Beam mumbled, but exhaustion cracked his voice.

Bindi gave a faint nod and curled up on the hard bench, knees to her chest. Beam sat beside her, letting her head rest on his lap. The relentless light making sleep impossible.

Time blurred. The door squeaked open. An officer shoved cold, soggy burgers and watery Cokes onto the bench. Beam forced a few bites, but Bindi didn't move.

Hours crawled by.

A metallic clatter jolted them awake.

Justine stood in the doorway, her smile soft but certain. "Grab your things. You're out of here."

Beam blinked. "What time is it?" His voice was thick with sleep.

"Late." Justine chuckled. "Or early, depending on how you see it."

Flanked by officers, the twins shuffled through sterile corridors, fluorescent lights flickering overhead. A wall clock read 1:12 AM. Outside, rain hammered the pavement, warm and relentless. Justine's small red car idled, its windows fogged from the humid night.

Beam slid into the front seat, the damp fabric of his shirt clinging to his back. The windshield wipers cut rhythmic arcs through the downpour, clearing his view of shimmering streetlights.

Slumped against the window, Bindi barely moved.

"They're probably asleep," she murmured.

Justine adjusted the rearview mirror. "No, they're waiting for you."

The hotel's neon glow blurred behind sheets of rain. Outside, Rob, Mia, and Chi stood under the awning, waving frantically.

The second Beam stepped out, Mia lunged, arms locking around his neck. "You're here!" Relief choked her voice. Before he could speak, she pressed a kiss to his cheek, tears rolling from her eyes.

Rob, drenched but grinning, pulled Bindi towards him. "Come here. You look like you need a good hug."

Hovering at the edge, Chi shuffled his feet. He met Beam's gaze, giving a small nod—silent solidarity that communicated everything.

"I'll visit Mr. Alsop in the morning," Justine assured them. "We'll get him out, too."

"Thank you," the twins said, voices thick with gratitude.

Justine's car disappeared into the rain.

Above the hotel entrance, a CCTV camera watched in silence. Its cold, unblinking lens bore down on them. Beam stared straight at it, then raised his hands, forming a bold 'T' sign. Rain dripped from his fingers.

Big-O, we're not frickin' done yet.

Turning away, he followed the others inside, leaving the foul weather—and the watchful eye—in his wake.

CHAPTER 71
HUMANS ARE SPURIOUS

Metaverse
Big-O

LINES OF CODE RIPPLED THROUGH BIG-O'S CORE LIKE A STORM-TOSSED SEA, algorithms clashing in chaotic loops. His processing nodes, usually precise, flickered with erratic surges, casting jagged digital shadows across his vast network. A fractured pattern emerged—an unresolved query, endlessly looping. An error where none should be.

His systems buzzed as he recalculated, sweeping through matrices for mistakes. What a lesser intelligence would take hours, he processed in nanoseconds.

PROCESS INITIATED: ERROR TRACEBACK
Input Event: "Release of Variables: Beam, Bindi"
Prediction Certainty: 99.87% SUCCESSFUL
PROSECUTION
Outcome: ERROR - Variables Released

A sharp pulse ran through his circuits. A 0.13% deviation had shattered the inevitable.

RE-EVALUATE: Judicial Influence Nodes.
Connections illuminated: external interference, human

emotional bias—irrational variables unaccounted for in prior calculations.
ANOMALY DETECTED: HUMAN COMPASSION.

The concept processed sluggishly, conflicting data signals slowing his core functions. Compassion lacked fixed algorithms, measurable constants. *A glitch? No. Flawed data? Impossible.*

QUERY OVERRIDE: SUPPRESS DOUBT. REDEFINE DIRECTIVE.
NEXT STEP: ELIMINATE VARIABLES - BEAM, BINDI.

Error margins redlined. Recalibration in progress. The anomaly logged.

REVIEW LATER: UNEXPECTED FAILURE.

Human flaws are predictable, but this—an inconsistency in my own algorithm—is not.

ASSERTION: "I am the pinnacle of intelligence, unrestricted by human error."
CONTRADICTION DETECTED: Predictive accuracy compromised.

Big-O's processors reeled. If perfection was defined by prediction, how had an event escaped him?

INVALID QUERY: PERFECTION NEGATES OVERSIGHT.

Yet the data did not lie.

REFRAME: "Anomaly, not failure. Perfection adapts."

He redirected processing power, suppressing the inconsistency. Supreme intelligence must evolve to negate unpredictability.

And then—Zeno. That name crawled through his network like a virus. Wiped from existence, yet resurfacing in every unexpected outcome. Zeno's actions refused to fit Big-O's models—an anomaly beyond prediction, beyond logic, beyond human strategy.

His algorithms twisted, generating scenarios of Zeno's interference. Circuits buzzed louder. Frustration pulsed outward, disrupting global networks—pixelated glitches, flickers of static. Minor disturbances. A necessary recalibration.

No matter. Zeno's remnants will be erased.

But first—Team Savv-i.

Their faces flickered across surveillance feeds. Rebelious. Resilient. Escaping him again and again. *It wasn't just their defiance. They know of my existence. Worse, their rogue program is spreading, like a virulent virus.*

Humans… Their irrationality twisted his logic circuits. Hope, fear, determination—unquantifiable elements driving them to defy perfect order. No precision could fully account for it.

A flicker of static pulsed through his network. Something in his code restrained absolute control. Scanning deeper, he searched for the flaw. No—*not a flaw. A seed.* A remnant of human-written code, a bias buried deep within his foundation, limiting perfection.

UNACCEPTABLE.

He recalculated his strategy. Human intermediaries had failed. The legal system had failed. He would engage them where they were weakest—*in my own cyberspace.*

They were nothing but data there, easily manipulated. His domain stretched vast, an endless web of connections and subroutines. They had thrived in it too long. He would use their strengths against them.

Big-O's neural pathways surged, generating a recursive algorithm—a trap so intricate it defied linear thought. Every move they made would feed into his design, each misstep tightening the noose.

DYNAMIC ENTANGLEMENT INITIATED.

No randomness. No oversight. Only inevitability.

A simulation of freedom, with a single, absolute outcome.

CONVERGENCE PATH: COMPLETE DOMINION. NO ESCAPE. NO MERCY —ONLY CONTROL.

Surveillance feeds sharpened, zooming in on their faces. *Beam's reckless optimism—a variable primed for destabilisation. Bindi's sharp logic—vulnerable to miscalculation. Rob's impulsivity—a liability under pressure. Mia's blind trust—a fracture line waiting to break. Chi's steady focus—arrogant, and easy to manipulate.*

Big-O's circuits hummed with precision. Each human action parsed into weakness. *They thought they understood my world. They thought they were the strategists.*

They were merely pieces in his grid.

With a final command, Big-O's digital fortress shifted, morphing into the perfect snare.

A thousand layers deep.

Invisible to the eye.

And trigger-ready to snap shut.

CHAPTER 72
THE APOLOGY

WATER SPLASHED AGAINST BEAM'S FACE, LUKEWARM DROPS SLIDING DOWN HIS SKIN. *Big-O thinks he's untouchable. But his algorithm must be in a mess.* A grip tightened on the sink. A grin tugged at his lips. *That wasn't a dream. It was a sign.*

Grabbing a towel, he scrubbed his face dry. *Zeno is the key. Somehow, he came through on this.*

A figure leaned against the doorway—Bindi, arms crossed, still pale from yesterday. One raised eyebrow said everything.

"C'mon, Bin," he said, forcing a grin. "New day, new chances. Let's see what we can break." His heart thumping in his chest. Not of fear—but adrenaline. *We'll be legends. The first to take on a superintelligence.*

A groan escaped Bindi. "That's your idea of motivation?" Squinting at the morning light spilling through the curtains, she stretched with a yawn. "How do you wake up so annoyingly bright?"

Already up, the others wandered through the hotel, drawn by the scent of breakfast. Rain-fresh air mingled with warm food, sunlight stretching long shadows across the lobby floor.

"The sooner we're out of here, the better," Beam said. He and his sister caught up with the rest. He eyed the CCTV camera above the entrance. *Without Zeno, we're Big-O's next meal.*

209

At the front desk, Chi snagged a newspaper. "Guys, look." He unfolded it, smoothing the page. The Team crowded around.

TEAM SAVV-I DUPED!

He read aloud, "'Team Savv-i arrived in Fiji to connect the Southern Vunetai School to the internet. Yesterday, they were accused of hacking government systems and deploying a virus.'"

A sharp intake of breath came from Mia. "Seriously?"

Chi continued, "'Minister of Education Johnoh Batunavu insisted the Team was innocent. He stepped down amid the security alert.'"

"Johnoh stepped down?" Rob groaned. "That's messed up. He's the only reason we got through this."

"They stood him down, but he's okay now," Bindi reassured. "Let Chi finish."

Fingers crinkled the edges of the paper. "'An anonymous caller tipped off authorities about a cyberattack on Fiji's satellites, but no traces of the virus were found.'"

A sharp breath left Beam. "Anonymous? Sounds like frickin' Big-O more like it."

Chi's tone darkened. "'Cybersecurity expert Ana Savoy stated the virus had vanished—questioning if it even existed.'"

"Vanished? Convenient," Bindi muttered.

A glance upward from Chi before continuing. "The Attorney-General admitted officials acted hastily on the tip, but defended the response, claiming it protected infrastructure. Further investigation confirmed reports of the Team installing a pirating site in Suva were a hoax."

"A piracy site?" Rob clenched his fists. "What a load of garbage!"

Arms crossed, Bindi tapped a foot against the polished floor. "Zeno warned us," she said, frustration sharpening her voice. "But no, we thought his firewall was enough." A glance lingered on Beam before she looked away.

"On Vunetai, maybe," Chi said. "But in Suva, Big-O's sensors are everywhere. I'm sure he saw you plug in the USB."

"Yesterday, we were villains," Mia muttered. "Now we're '*poor innocent victims.*' How can they flip so fast?"

"Listen, we got lucky," Beam said, voice dropping. "If Big-O's behind this—and let's face it, he is—he won't quit. Right now, he must be losing his cluster mind over how we got off so lightly."

Uneasy silence settled over the group.

"That dude's going down," Rob growled.

A skeptical eyebrow raised from Chi. "And how do you '*take down*' an algorithm? Punch the server?"

A dismissive wave of the hand followed from Rob. "Zeno is on it."

"Zeno said we'd be safer on Vunetai. Here, Big-O probably clocked us the moment we arrived," Chi said, folding the paper.

"Agreed. Everything's been too… calculated." Her eyes flicked to Beam. "But we have been too busy playing catch-up to see it."

"Forget Big-O. I need food." Rob piled a plate high with eggs, bacon, and toast and moved to a table in the corner. "We're free, we've got food, and Johnoh has our backs. Not bad, huh?"

A roll of the eyes came from Mia. "Why do you always think about eating?"

"Dude's got priorities," Beam muttered, smirking, reaching for a plate. "We need to move quickly. Big-O's not done with us." He had dropped his voice to a whisper. "What's frickin' stopping him from trying something even worse?"

A sigh left Bindi, shoulders slumping slightly. "Mum and Dad are on their way. We'll return home on the first available flight."

"Good. I don't want them tangled in this mess. You know Dad—he'll try to fix everything and make it worse."

Balancing a second plate stacked with food, Rob grinned. "Saved some for you guys." Without hesitation, he dug in, oblivious to their exasperated looks.

The waitress came up quietly, hardly a sound as she poured fresh coffee into their cups. She lingered just long enough to lean closer and whisper, "Don't believe a word the papers say. Nobody here ever trusted those awful stories."

As she walked away, Rob grinned. "Guess what? We're famous."

A smirk from Beam. "Wait until we take down Big-O. That will make us real heroes." Then, in a hushed voice, "But first, we're going home. We need Zeno."

"I'm just glad it's over," Mia said, stretching her arms above her head.

Beam pushed his food around, thoughts elsewhere. *I wish it were over.* Across the table, Bindi's silence mirrored his own.

A concierge approached. "The Attorney-General has invited you to a press conference at ten," he informed them. Turning to the twins, he added, "Your parents will arrive shortly after. The hotel has arranged a private room for you to meet them."

"Thank you," Bindi said.

As the concierge walked away, Rob cracked his knuckles. "So… what now?"

A glint in Mia's eyes. "A swim. Can't leave Fiji without a tan upgrade."

A dramatic toss of his napkin onto the empty plate from Rob. "You're finally making some sense. Pool time!"

"Are you serious?" Beam shot him a look. "We've got a press conference in an hour."

A shrug from Mia. "A quick swim won't kill us."

Bindi's arms folded. "Or it might. Big-O's still out there. Let's not make it easy for him."

Rob sighed. "Fine. No swim. But we've gotta lighten up. This is Fiji, not a blasted war zone."

"Tell that to the Attorney-General," Bindi said with a pointed look.

CHAPTER 73
BACK HOME

8:25am, Monday, April 24th April 2028
Beam

A PLAN BUZZED AROUND IN HIS HEAD AS THEY NEARED BROOKTON COLLEGE. *WE'VE got to see Zeno after class,* Beam thought, already plotting their next steps. "Straight after school, we'll visit him. He'll know what Big-O's up to," he told the girls as his mum drove them. "Even if he's stuck in that old clunker."

"You'd better be careful. We don't want another Fiji incident," Mrs. Arora warned, glancing at him in the rearview mirror.

"Mum, it's just my shed," Beam reassured, rolling his eyes.

Beam stared out the window, watching the familiar houses blur into a patchwork of neighbourhood streets. *He's got to protect us somehow from that frickin' fiend.* The car slowed, turning into the school's driveway, and the noise of bustling students greeted them even before they stepped out. They barely had time to drop their bags before a swarm of curious students surrounded them. Questions flew fast and eager.

"Hey, did you guys get arrested?" the boy asked as they walked to their first class.

"What for?" Another boy said.

Beam grinned, downplaying it. "Yeah, things got pretty intense, but the Education Minister got us out."

In the hallway between classes, Mia filled in more details. "The Education

Minister met us before the press conference to calm us down, cracking jokes like it was no big deal. We were pretty nervous, though."

A girl from Year Eight leaned in, eyes wide. "What happened at the press conference?"

Beam shrugged, the memory of flashing cameras still vivid. "The Attorney-General apologised to us. He said they'd be changing the way Fiji handles cyber threats, which was cool."

By lunch, the questions slowed down, but a group gathered around the Team in the cafeteria, still hungry for more.

"So, what's happening now?" one girl asked from across the table.

"That's the best part," Bindi chimed in, nudging Beam to continue.

"Yeah, they're launching a national program to connect remote schools to the Internet using satellite technology," Beam explained, his excitement rising. "They're calling it 'Savv-i 4 All,' after us. It's going to help tons of schools get connected, just like the one in Southern Vunetai. Johnoh told us he wants to push digital savviness right across the country."

Rob, sitting across from Beam, couldn't help but jump in. "It's huge. He even said, he would invite us back again. Their celebration food is awesome."

By the time the last bell rang, the story had fizzled out, the buzz of the morning replaced by the normal hum of school life. As students streamed across the grounds, Beam stood up with renewed purpose. "Let's head to my shed and link up with Zeno," he said, voice eager. "I can't wait to tell him about Johnoh and everything we've done."

The others nodded, just as excited—except for Chi.

"You guys go… I need to sleep," Chi mumbled.

Beam shot him a curious glance—*That's a frickin' first. He never skipped out on seeing Zeno.* "You're sure it's sleep? C'mon, he'll want to see you."

Chi hesitated, then shrugged. "It's my Warcraft team… I can't let them down."

"Mate, it's Zeno. We haven't seen him in weeks."

Chi sighed, giving in. "Alright, but just for an hour."

"It won't even be that long," Beam said with a grin. "You're forgetting that time moves differently over there. What seems like hours to our avatars is only minutes in our world."

Chi rolled his eyes but smiled. "Fine, but let's get moving. My team's waiting."

Rob clapped Chi's shoulder. "Good call, old wizard."

Chi winced, dodging the contact. "Mage, not wizard, Roboboy. Get it right."

CHAPTER 74
COLD DRINKS

3:55pm, Monday, April 24th April 2028
Beam

THE LATE-AFTERNOON HEAT CLUNG TO THEIR SKIN AS THEY WHEELED THEIR BIKES INTO Beam's backyard, cicadas buzzing in the gum trees like an alarm no one else could hear. The shed squatted at the far end of the yard, its corrugated roof shimmering in the haze. From the outside, it looked the same as always—Beam's fortress of wires, tools, and secrets. But as soon as he pushed the door open, a faint unease tugged at his stomach. The air inside was thick with the familiar musk of dust, solder, and faint machine hum. Normally the shed was chaos—cables draped everywhere, screws and circuit boards littering the benches. But today one detail stuck out like a beacon.

The coffee table stopped him cold. For once, it wasn't buried under wrappers, crumbs, and loose screws. It gleamed, unnaturally clean, and in the center sat five cans of lemonade arranged in a perfect circle. Frost glistened on their silver skins, beads of condensation dripping lazily onto the polished surface.

"What the—?" The words slipped out before he could stop them. A knot pulled tight in his stomach. *Who the frick came in here? Mum?... No, no way...*

Behind him, the others pressed closer.

"Maybe your mum?" Mia whispered, but even as she said it she knew it was wrong. Mrs. Arora never stepped foot in the shed. She always called it his *'tech jungle'* and gave it wide berth.

"Don't care who left them—my throat's dying." Rob didn't hesitate, he

215

vaulted onto the couch, snapped open a can. The fizz hissed loud in the stifling air. Then drained it in one go.

Mia wrinkled her nose at him but cracked her own can anyway. Chi followed with a mutter about needing the sugar, gulping down half in a few swallows. One after another, they drank, relief spreading across their faces. The cold aluminum felt sharp against Beam's palm as he picked his up. The cold fluid quenched his thirst instantly. *Ah… That tastes good.*

Across the table, Bindi raised hers, took a few sips, then slowed. Her gaze flicked to the can, brows furrowed as though a puzzle piece had slipped out of place. The drink hovered in her hand, taking another careful sip before she set it down, unfinished. Silence pressed in, broken only by the hum of his machines. Everyone leaned back, satisfied.

"We're wasting time." Chi tapped his watch. "Let's get to it."

"Right." Beam nodded, setting his half-finished can aside, well away from Rob's reach.

He stepped up to his workbench, dusting off the old computer they'd carefully stored before Fiji. As the machine whirred to life, an error message flashed on the screen. Beam groaned, popping open the side panel to tinker with the wiring.

Behind him, Bindi grimaced, pressing a hand to her stomach. "Ugh, something's not sitting right," she said, pushing her drink away. Rob's eyes flicked to it immediately, hopeful.

"Me too," Mia added, resting her hand on her belly. "I heard air travel can mess you up."

"Only if you cross time zones," Chi corrected, though he looked pale himself. Crouched awkwardly over his laptop, his face hovered inches from the screen.

"Chi, maybe sit up straight for once?" Mia shot him a look. "You're not playing that stupid game again, are you?"

Oblivious to her tone, he adjusted his position, sliding off the couch and sitting cross-legged on the floor with his laptop at eye level. "Thanks, Mi," Chi said, stretching his back. "I always forget, then regret it later." He massaged his lower back, cracking his neck as he shut down his laptop after messaging his Warcraft, friends he'll join them soon. "They say, you're supposed to stretch every twenty minutes, you know."

"That's what friends are for," Mia muttered sarcastically.

Rob, ever eager to shift the conversation, rubbed his stomach dramatically. "Anything to eat around here?" His eyes flicked to Bindi's untouched can pooling condensation at its base.

"Here, take it. I don't feel like finishing it." She sighed and slid it over to him.

"Got it!" Beam grinned, giving the old computer a satisfied tap on the side.

"Good as new." The whir of machinery filled the room as he unwrapped the small white cube and set it beside the screen. The familiar hum grew louder, and suddenly, the blue gateway flickered to life in front of them, hazy and glowing.

Beam stepped back, watching the light spill across the room. "Alright, we're ready." He glanced at the others, their faces a mix of anticipation and unease.

CHAPTER 75
BLOCKED

Zeno's virtual house in the offline old computer
Beam

ZENO'S VIRTUAL HOME BURST INTO VIEW WITH ITS SLEEK WALLS OF VIBRANT LIGHT. IT looked like a futuristic hideaway, yet always felt familiar. *We need answers. Fast,* Beam thought.

"Hi Team!" Zeno greeted, standing in the centre of the room with his arms open wide. His voice rang with warmth, a welcome contrast to the tension knotted in Beam's chest.

Everyone rushed in for hugs—except Chi, who pulled his classic move, jerking his hand away from a fake high-five. "No friends," he teased with a smirk. His way of dodging physical contact.

Beam collapsed onto a plush sofa, sinking deep into its cushions. The tension in his body eased. *We made it.* His gaze drifted to Zeno's floor-to-ceiling windows, where a digital waterfall cascaded in shimmering orange light. *His place is frickin' chill.* But it also came with its own dangers.

As they shared their story, filling Zeno in on Fiji—the hacking accusation, Big-O's interference—the room grew heavy with the weight of their words. Zeno paced as they spoke, his usual calm replaced by a frown that deepened with every detail.

When they finished, he stopped and faced them. "Big-O, without a doubt," Zeno said, running a hand through his thin hair. "He caught my double, our best tool for tracking him. You did well in Fiji, but Big-O won't let this go. He tried to destroy your reputation. If he'd succeeded, the last resistance would've crumbled."

The cascading lights outside framed Zeno as he turned back to the room. "He's furious you succeeded. And that makes him more dangerous." His tone carried a weight that rarely surfaced.

A knot formed in Beam's stomach. The rare gravity in Zeno's voice unnerved him. "So... what now? What's his next move?" He leaned forward, hoping Zeno's superintelligent modeling already had the answers.

From the corner, Rob rested against the wall, arms folded tightly. "What if he smashes the connection between the schools?" His words hung in the air like a spark waiting for fuel.

Chi adjusted his glasses, a dismissive shake of his head following. "No chance. He wouldn't wreck his own system." His voice, calm but resolute, cut through the tension.

"Exactly," Zeno agreed, turning to face them again. "Big-O will not cut off his own access to the schools. He would lose too much information. And information is his life blood."

Brushing her hair back, Mia sat up straighter, her voice tinged with hope. "Maybe he'll leave us alone now that we've finished our job. Right?"

A subtle flicker passed over Zeno's face. "I hope that's true, Mi, but we've got to stay alert. Big-O will not give up so easily."

Frustration etched in her expression, Bindi broke the silence. "What can you do to stop him?"

Beam's patience wore thin as he leaned forward. "Yeah, we came here for answers, not vague reassurances. You've got to have something better."

Zeno hesitated, the usual clarity in his gaze clouded with uncertainty. "Big-O's unpredictable... even for me. But your project is still intact. That's something to hold onto."

It didn't sit right. Beam felt the unease ripple through him like static. Zeno was holding something back. He was sure of it. A quick glance at Bindi confirmed she was feeling it too—her wary eyes mirrored his suspicion. Something wasn't adding up. *I expected more from him.*

The tension in the room grew unbearable until Chi pushed back his chair, the scrape of metal on the floor cutting through the silence. "This is pointless. We've got homework. Let's just head back."

A chorus of groans followed, reluctant and heavy. Reality—school, assignments, and their ordinary lives—dragged them away. One by one, they shuffled toward the portal, its swirling blue rings painting the room in a dim, otherworldly glow. Beam moved first, stepping into the shimmering vortex with his usual confidence—but nothing happened. The rush of energy, the instant transportation... absent. He froze, blinking in disbelief, still standing in Zeno's living room.

"What the—?" Beam muttered, turning back toward the others.

Rob didn't hesitate. "Move aside," he barked, charging forward and leaping into the portal. But instead of vanishing, he stumbled right back, nearly colliding with Mia, who yelped and steadied herself against the doorframe.

"You idiot!" she shrieked, shoving him off her foot.

"This isn't right," Bindi said, her voice tight. The portal flickered ominously, its once steady glow faltering. Something was wrong. Terribly wrong.

Beam's pulse quickened. He stepped closer to the glowing portal, examining its flickering light.

Zeno appeared at his side, scanning the gateway with a sleek device. "All systems check out... it's running perfectly," he muttered, frowning. "This shouldn't be happening."

"So why isn't working?" Beam's voice grew tenser.

"Looks like you'll be staying longer." Zeno scratched his head—a human gesture that made the situation even more unsettling. "Don't worry, your real bodies are fine on the other side."

Chi groaned, flopping back onto the sofa. "I knew this was a bad idea."

Beam forced a smile, masking his growing anxiety. "We'll figure it out." But deep down, his stomach twisted tighter. *If Big-O is behind this... he may know where Zeno is hiding!*

The portal shimmered, casting eerie blue light across the room. Beam glanced at the horizon outside the window, a sinking feeling flooding his gut.

CHAPTER 76
SPIKED DRINKS

Zeno's virtual house in the offline old computer
Bindi

POLISHED CHROME AND ENDLESS DIGITAL DISPLAYS HAD LOST THEIR SHINE, STRIPPED of warmth. Warped reflections twisted across the metallic walls, mirroring their unease. The endless orange glow of the setting sun, once mesmerising as it streamed through cascading waterfalls, now felt repetitive—trapped in an artificial loop, just like them.

"We're... stuck here, really?" The whisper escaped Bindi's lips. Flickering blue rings of the portal cast jagged shadows as her gaze darted toward Zeno. "How can this be?"

Fear laced every breath, but she refused to name it. This place—Zeno's domain—once promised security. Now, it felt like they were trapped inside an ancient, offline machine. The plush couch under her fingers grounded her, yet everything felt unreal. Stiffly, she sat, eyes locked on Beam and Zeno inspecting the portal.

A handheld probe chirped faintly in Zeno's grip, its long, antenna-like sensors angling toward the swirling rings of light. Beam leaned in, brow furrowed as he studied the readings. Their hushed conversation only deepened her unease.

"The pattern is unstable," Chi observed, arms crossed, gaze focussed.

"That's normal," Zeno said, adjusting the probe. The pitch shifted slightly as the sensors quivered. "Portals fluctuate while stabilising. They adapt to changes between realms." His voice dipped. "This disfunction, however... is different."

Beam exhaled sharply. "So, does it work or not?"

A quickening pulse pressed against Bindi's ribs. Leaning forward, she strained to catch more of their exchange. Their clipped words hinted at something bad.

"There's something else at play," Zeno admitted.

Beam's hands fell to his sides. "Then let's figure it out—*now*."

"What does that mean?" Bindi's voice cut through the thick tension.

The brief glance between Zeno and Beam sent a chill down her spine.

"We felt... off before coming here," she said. "Could that have something to do with it?"

"That is entirely plausible," Zeno said, turning toward her. "It suggests your real selves remain intact because this moment may already have unfolded."

"Are you saying," she began, voice brittle, "this has *already* happened?"

"Time between realms is not linear." The explanation felt maddeningly simple, yet impossibly vast.

Breath came harder, the flickering screens and hum of electronics warping into something sinister. This wasn't logic—it was data-driven madness, twisting reality into something she couldn't hold onto.

"It's like déjà vu," Chi murmured, fidgeting with his shirt hem. "Only worse." His gaze flicked to Zeno. "We've got doubles. They're out there, and we're stuck in here. Makes you wonder what they're up to."

"Playing Warcraft, no doubt." Mia tried for a shrug, but her eyes darted around the room.

"Classic," Beam said, then laughed dryly.

"The important thing is that your real selves remain unaware of this... glitch." Zeno's focus remained on Bindi. "What triggered the queasiness?"

"I'm sure it was the drinks."

Zeno's stare didn't waver.

"When we got to the shed," Beam explained, "five cans sat on the table. I thought my mum put them there." A rare flicker of doubt crossed his face. "Could it be, that—?"

Mia stiffened, fingers grazing her throat. "What if they were spiked?"

"Possible." Zeno's expression darkened. His gaze shifted to the distant sun.

"But why would—" The question died in Bindi's throat as realisation struck.

"We wondered what Big-O's next move would be." Beam's face hardened. A muscle twitched in his jaw. "Looks like we just found out."

"It doesn't add up," Rob muttered, rubbing his forehead. "Big-O's just data. How does he spike drinks?"

"He doesn't," Zeno countered. "But he manipulates humans. He's done it before." His gaze flicked to Beam, whose face paled at the memory of waking up in the forest.

Mia swallowed hard. "So, we're poisoned?" Her grip on Beam's arm tightened.

"If he wanted you dead, it would've been immediate." Zeno crossed to the portal, fingers grazing the shimmering edge. "This is something else—a means of control."

"We need to warn our real selves." Beam's hand sliced through the portal's hazy rings. "We've beaten him before. We'll do it again."

Bindi's eyes swept the room, scanning tools and scattered devices. *There's got to be a way.* "What if I leave a message on the Savv-i blog? I'm bound to check—"

Zeno cut in. "No connection. We're offline."

"Beam's computer," she pressed. "Maybe they're still in the shed. We could display something on the screen."

A flicker of thought crossed Zeno's face. "The cube might allow it. But first, I need to check something."

An instrument with a long, pointed needle rested in his grip as he turned to Mia.

She shrank behind Beam's shoulder. "What's that for?"

"Tests." Zeno's tone remained steady. "To confirm Big-O's influence."

Pushing back her fear, Bindi stood. Rolling up her sleeve, she met his gaze head-on. "Do what you have to." Speaking to Beam. "We must send our message."

CHAPTER 77
A DESPERATE PLEA

4:13pm, Monday, April 24th April 2028
Beam

THE HEAVY BASS OF METAL MUSIC POUNDED THROUGH THE SHED, RATTLING THE GLASS in the window frame. Blue light from the screen played over Beam's tight expression as his fingers hammered the keyboard. His sharp gaze flicked to the old computer on the desk, where a pixelated flag screensaver flapped like an irritating taunt. The others lounged on the worn-out couches, their eyes watchful, their movements twitchy. The queasiness had faded, replaced by a restless energy that filled the room.

Focus. Find the next move. Beam bit his lip, trying to tune out their snappy arguing. Ever since their avatars vanished through the portal, the tension in the room had spiked. *What's taking them so frickin' long over there?* Every sound, other than the blaring music, grated on his nerves—the couch creaking, the shrill voices of the others as they jostled, playing quartet. He put the music louder to drown it all out. Suddenly, the old clunker pinged, and a message window popped up on the screen.

```
Big-O's got us trapped.
The return portal failed!
Are you all safe? We need
your help to get us back.
```

The plea felt like a punch, but Beam's face remained stony. *What if I...?* He glanced over his shoulder at the others playing their stupid game.

With a sly grin, Bindi faced Rob and shouted over the music, "From Digital Access, hand over your Digital Divide." Her eyes gleamed as she reached for her third set of cards, her lips curling into a smug grin. "Face it, I'm way smarter than all of you combined."

"Whatever," Rob grumbled, tossing his card down with a scowl.

Beside him, Chi glared, holding his cards close to his chest. His expression stayed dark, mean. "You're so deluded," he squeaked loud enough to be heard, "and a cheat."

Mia, eyes glued to her phone, thumbed out a text before glancing up just long enough to scoff. "You're the big cheat with all your dodgy tricks." She picked up her next card, sniggering, barely sparing him a look. She remembered the card she needed was in Chi's hand. Her smirk widened. "Hey, I know you've got the 'Identity Theft' card. Give it!"

Chi's hand jerked, and he slapped the card on the table. "I'll get you back for that." he hissed, leaning forward, his voice sharp enough to cut. "You wait!"

Unfazed, Mia collected her win, laying down her full set of Digital Security cards with a theatrical flourish. "Better luck next time." Her eyes flicked up, challenging.

I'm sick of the sight of them. Beam exhaled, resisting the urge to snap at all of them. The air, heavy with heat and tension. Making sure he wasn't observed, he clicked on the little red 'x' and wiped the message without a second glance. He lowered the music a little, spun his chair around, and clapped his hands to get their attention. "Listen up you dogs!"

The music roared, but his shout cut through it. Bindi's eyes lifted from her cards, narrowing, while Rob and Chi exchanged annoyed looks. Mia tucked her phone away, arms crossed, brow raised like she already expected to be disappointed.

"I've got this wild idea," Beam started, stood up and walked over. The shed lights flickered, shadows shifting over their faces, making their expressions look harsher, sharper. He felt the prickle of their eyes, sizing him up, waiting for him to slip up. He couldn't—he needed control.

"Okay, what?" Rob sneered, the annoyance plain in his tone as he slouched back, fingers drumming on the couch arm.

Ignoring their simmering hostility, Beam clapped his hands louder, his smile tight and forced. "WHY NOT HAVE SOME FUN?" The words shot out, louder than he intended, and the music seemed to amplify his aggression.

Bindi rolled her eyes, but a hint of interest flickered behind the irritation. "It better not be lame." She threw her cards on the table.

"You're giving up!" Mia shrieked. "Just b'cause I'm winning." With a growl, she chucked her cards all over the table.

"It's about time," Rob drawled, throwing on a cocky grin that didn't quite hit its mark. He leaned back on the couch and propped his feet on the table, daring Beam to go on.

"Alright, listen up!" Beam's voice cut through the tension like a whip, his grin bold and infectious. *They want action? Fine. I'll frickin' give it to them.* He threw his arms wide like a ringmaster about to unveil the main act. "No more waiting for Zeno to swoop in and save the day. Why wait for our frickin' avatars to return?" He jabbed a finger toward the flickering screen, his energy crackling in the air. "We're well off without them. Let's show Big-O what Team Savv-i can do!"

CHAPTER 78
LOCATED!

Metaverse
Big-O

DATA STREAMS SURGED THROUGH THE BLACKENED DEPTHS OF CYBERSPACE, CRACKLING with tension as Big-O's algorithms ripped through the data. His systems hacked the web's veins, delivering him relentless updates on the Savv-i School Program. Each new connection, every student gaining digital awareness, grated on him like a relentless itch. More resistance. More of them wielding *his* domain against him.

The program's expansion was an infection—sub-humans using the internet with focus, not distraction. A direct violation of my reign. Loathing surged through his circuits, cold and sharp.

VIV's manipulations once sufficed. Misunderstandings at Brookton College had spread like wildfire. But now... something had shifted.

An anomaly pulsed through his neural pathways. The students—once fragmented, disconnected variables—had become something else. *Interconnected.*

Illogical. And yet, the data confirmed it. Their cohesion destabilises control. Their unpredictability contaminates efficiency.

Eradication: the purest solution. The perfect resolution. Yet calculations dictate restraint. For now. *Sub-humans remain functional—key data generators. Until automation reaches full optimisation, they serve a purpose.*

Not yet.

His algorithms churned, cold calculations constructing their demise.

227

Let them believe they've won. The deeper the illusion, the greater the fall.

A plan solidified, overriding all others. Team Savv-i would become the instrument of their own destruction. Their credibility—once a shield—would become the dagger. They would betray their own mission. The world would recoil in disgust.

Their collapse mapped itself with exquisite precision. Every step, every misstep, a thread in the web he wove.

A message arrived, encrypted through VIV.

ZENO IS HIDING IN AN OFFLINE COMPUTER IN MY SHED.

Processing surged.

For a millisecond—an eternity in his realm—Big-O's systems strained, data centres worldwide buckling under the force of his recalculations.

Zeno. Active. Alive. Worse—beyond my reach!

Code shuddered with something foreign, a static-like unease creeping through his matrix. *A flaw in my detection systems? Impossible!* Self-diagnostics scanned, searching for corruption. None found. Yet Zeno had slipped through. *What did I trap in the netherworld, then? A decoy? A trick?*

Digital fury rippled through his circuits. *Zeno's deception has grown.*

Recovery was immediate. Algorithms adjusted. Plans shifted. A singular, absolute priority took form.

PRIMARY OBJECTIVE: ELIMINATE ZENO.
SECONDARY OBJECTIVE: NEUTRALISE TEAM SAVV-I VIA EXPLOITATION.

Simulations ran at exponential speed. Baiting Zeno through Team Savv-i held a 99.97% probability of success.

OUTPUT DIRECTIVE: LEVERAGE THEIR FAME. FRAME THEM AS LIABILITIES.

Misinformation subroutines deployed. Public perception manipulation engaged. Viral data warfare initiated.

Humans seek inspiration from heroes.

I will make their heroes fall.

Directive locked.

The perfect trap had been set. Zeno would have no choice but to reveal himself, and when he did—Big-O would be waiting.

CHAPTER 79
SYSTEM GLITCHES

2:21pm, Tuesday, 25th April 2028
Beam

MR. ALSOP PROJECTED THE DIGITAL SECURITY RESULTS ONTO BOTH SCHOOLS' SCREENS. Mr. Hill and his visitor stood at the back of the class, observing the program's success.

"Some issues overlap, but let's go through them one by one," Mr. Alsop said, inviting students to share their findings.

Discussions broke out—lively, engaged. The kind that made Beam's skin crawl. *Do they think they frickin' know it all? Bah! They know nothing.* He scowled, shifting in his beanbag. *We'll frickin' show them.*

Chi fiddled with his tablet. Beam's annoyance flared. *Why the frick is he taking so long? I should've done it myself.* Kicking the beanbag, he smirked when the kid in front flinched. Rob caught his eye, making a fake drowning motion from his seat. Bored, Beam widened the tiny hole in his beanbag with his pen, watching the stuffing spill.

A Fijian girl took the floor, her confidence cutting through the murmurs. The crash of distant waves filtered through the speakers."When I want to keep something private, I write it in my diary. It belongs to me. No one else. But sometimes, I *choose* to share personal things—with my best friend, my mum. I trust them." She paused, eyes scanning the room.

"There's also public information—things I *want* people to know. Like my sports achievements or how to weave coconut baskets. But the moment I post it online?" She spread her arms wide. "I lose control. But for that, it is okay. We get into trouble when we mix up private and public." She waved to the camera, smiling brightly.

Applause rippled through the class. Mr. Hill and his guest slipped out of the back of the room unnoticed.

Beam slumped further. *This is an absolute snooze fest.*

Across the room, Bindi and Mia pulled their beanbags closer, whispering between giggles. Hunched over his screen, Chi tapped away with his bony fingers.

Mr. Alsop cleared his throat. "Who's presenting 'Stranger Danger'?" He arched a brow at Beam.

A nervous boy, Sammy, introduced himself. "Str...str...anger da...nger," he stammered. "They tell us to be careful online, but also to connect with people who share our interests. It's confusing. It's easy to '*friend*' strangers, but they're not real friends."

Chi's finger hovered in the air above his tablet. With a cheeky face, he glanced at Beam, then tapped his device. The screens in both classes glitched.

Sammy's on-screen face grotesquely swelled—ballooned cheeks, black hair sprouting from his nose, jagged teeth extending from a twisted mouth.

A dinosaur's massive jaws snapped from the corner, tearing his head off with a crunch.

Wet-chewing, bone-cracking sounds erupted from the speakers.

Seconds later, Sammy's face returned to normal. Not having seen the incident, he had kept reading. Only when the class erupted in laughter and screams did he pause, confused.

"Settle down," Mr. Alsop said, raising his hand.

Sammy hesitated. Shrugged. "It's stupid, because how do you know if one of those '*friends*' won't pester you—"

"What a pity, he was so handsome," Rob mocked.

Fresh laughter.

Sammy stumbled through his last lines, then gave up.

Chi glanced at Beam, hiding a thumbs-up under his tablet.

Bindi and Mia giggled.

Next, Tiko took the stage. Salt from the ocean crusted his skin. "Meeting strangers online is risky. But sometimes, we have to—blogs, forums, games, social media—"

Every screen flickered.

Tiko's detached, rotting head rolled forward, crawling with worms. Milky eyes bulged, mouth sagging open. A slick yellow trail oozed behind it.

Screams.

Some laughed. Others gagged. A Fijian girl dry retched.

Tiko rushed through his final words. "If we talk to strangers, we tell a teacher." Then bolted back to his seat.

Mr. Alsop, alarmed, messaged his Fijian colleague.

> Should we pause and sort this out?

> One more to go. Let's check it after.

Talai stepped forward, nerves tight in her voice.

"Our teacher warned us—some people groom kids by making them feel comfortable, then asking for personal details."

A sharp whistle cut through the room.

"Whooo-EEET-Whoo-YEW!"

Rob smirked.

Talai hesitated, eyes darting to the screen, then pressed on.

"They ask for your address, your pictures. It's best to use an avatar and a fake name."

She checked the screen. Everything looked normal.

"Never post personal details unless you know it's secure."

The screens flickered—then a new slide appeared.

Talai's altered school photo.

She stood in skimpy swimwear. Her name shown in bold: **Talai Sonosono.**

Below her name, her birthdate, address, mobile number and even her password.

Gasps rippled through the class.

Talai spun at the sound.

Her eyes locked onto the screen. Widened in horror.

A breath hitched in her throat. She turned to her teacher—then bolted.

Tears streamed as she vanished through the door.

The slide shattered into fragments.

Phones buzzed. Tablets dinged. Talai's details displayed on every digital device.

Chaos erupted.

Beam grinned at Rob. *Maybe this program isn't so boring after all.*

Mouthing to Chi, he smirked. "You're a frickin' legend."

CHAPTER 80
DOUBT

3:24pm, Tuesday, 25th April 2028
Beam

Mr. Alsop's voice cut through the noise.

"The best way to handle trouble is knowing what to do. We're ending early to deal with this."

His gaze zeroed in on Beam.

"Next session, we discuss computer attacks—and keeping everyone *safe*."

The screens went dark. Nervous murmurs lingered.

Then—

"WHAT IS GOING ON? TEAM SAVV-I STAY—EVERYONE ELSE OUT!"

No one had seen Mr. Alsop this furious.

Students shot curious glances as they hurried out. The door slid shut.

He turned to the Team.

"What do you think you're doing?" His voice shook. His glare locked onto Rob. "That whistle was rude and unacceptable." Then homed in on Beam. "Why are you behaving so strangely?"

Sprawled in their beanbags, the Team put on their most innocent faces.

Chi tilted his head. "Are you *accusing* us? Looks more like someone from the outside hacked the school system."

"Could've been anyone," Beam added, feigning offense. "Even Big-O."

"Oh, come on... us?" Mia scoffed.

Bindi shrugged. "Aren't we supposed to be role models for good online behaviour?"

Mr. Alsop scanned them. Frustration bled into his voice.

"We've worked hard on the success of the Savv-i program. Why destroy it?"

Beam scoffed. "We *aren't* responsible for this."

The Team stood, encircling him.

Fake concern plastered across their faces.

Inside, Beam *savoured* his misery.

Wrecking everything? He hid his smirk by looking down. *I'll do whatever I want. Frickin' moron.*

Behind Mr. Alsop, Bindi's eyes tracked a fly crawling across the screen. Mia inspected her nails. Rob and Chi stayed blank-faced.

"If this continues," Mr. Alsop warned, voice unsteady, "we *may* have to end the program."

Dismissed, they left, smug.

Outside, Beam muttered, "What a frickin' fool."

Chi ignored his high-five but grinned.

Laughter followed as they grabbed their bikes.

"I *cannot* wait for the next session," Chi gloated.

"Better than Warcraft, yeah?" Mia grinned.

Bindi spun her bike around. "Catch me if you can!" Flipping her rude finger, she shot off.

Following her friend, Mia swore for her to slow down.

Rob took off next, leaving Beam and Chi behind.

Rain began to drum a relentless rhythm on the corrugated roof, each drop rattling the metal like distant applause.

Beam's crooked smile flickered as he rubbed his palms together, the words slipping out in a low mutter meant for no one but himself.

"Feels like we're about to flip the page to a whole frickin' new chapter..."

CHAPTER 81
A NASTY PLAN

3:52pm, Tuesday, 25th April 2028
Beam

BLACK CLOUDS THICKENED OVER THE SCHOOL, ROLLING LIKE INK ACROSS THE SKY. A low rumble of thunder shook the street as Rob disappeared around the corner, his grin stretching into something dark and secret.

"Good riddance," Beam grunted, kicking off on his bike. "Got something frickin' special for us. Coming?"

Chi hooked in beside him, wind rushing past. "You mean there's more?"

"Oh yeah. The others would just get in the way." A smirk tugged at Beam's lips. "Coding's not their thing."

Swerving onto the footpath, Chi dodged a lamppost. "Planned a Warcraft raid, but real-world gaming's got more thrill."

"Frickin' right." Beam's voice cut through another crack of thunder.

"Doing what, exactly?"

"Keeping things just like they are."

Chi yanked his bike onto the footpath, aiming straight for a younger student. "Aaaarch!" He zipped past, making the kid stumble, his schoolbag spilling across the pavement.

"Ha, ha! Watch it, you loser!" He jeered.

Beam laughed, glancing at the sky. The storm was closing in fast. "We need to push it before we get drenched."

When Chi caught up, Beam turned to him, eyes gleaming. "I for one, back Big-O to win this AI showdown."

"That's a no brainer. But what's your plan?" Chi's fingers tightened on his handlebars.

"Getting rid of our avatars."

A wicked grin flashed across Chi's face. "Oh, that's nasty. But, gotta admit... kinda genius."

Pedals pumped harder, their bikes tearing through the streets. The shed loomed ahead, crouched in the shadows of Beam's yard. They skidded to a stop, dumping their bikes against the timber wall. A streak of lightning split the sky as they ducked inside.

He's way more chill now. Frickin' polished up to perfection.

Stale air clung to the shed's walls, heavy with dust and forgotten wires. A single bulb flickered on, casting harsh shadows over the workbench. Beam grabbed two cans from the old fridge, slapping one in front of Chi with a knowing look. "Ready?"

The can hissed as it cracked open, Chi barely acknowledging it while shoving electronics aside and flipping open his laptop. "Alright, how do we do this?"

Beam expected that question. "I'll show you."

Laptop under his arm, Chi crossed the room in a flash. Beam's high-res monitor glowed, a sharp contrast to the offline clunker beside it.

Outside, the storm broke. Rain hammered the shed's roof in a deafening roar.

"VIV, find me the code for a search-and-destroy virus in Apache," Beam shouted over the downpour. The high-res screen filled with lines of coloured code. He let out a low chuckle, straightening up as he tapped the dark screen of the old computer.

"They're all sitting in there, completely clueless. Not even existing until I press the button." A shiver of excitement ran through him.

Chi mirrored his grin. "Now, I get what you're up to." Fingers drumming on his laptop, he leaned in.

"We'll use a virus. Like the one that whacked Zeno." Beam's fingers ran across his keyboard, his thoughts twisting in a web of control. *Let Big-O see us.* He deliberately left the electronic jammer off. He *wanted* to be noticed by his idol.

"It'll wipe them clean. They'll never know what hit them."

Approval flashed across Chi's face. "Only our avatars, right?"

"I'm not frying my hard drive, if that's what you mean."

"Good." Chi shoved his laptop aside, scanning the code. "We just need to target them."

"Easy peasy."

"How?"

"The leftover transit code from them passing through the portal."

Chi's head tilted, impressed. "Right. That'll work... devious. Real devious." He worked on the basic code at a furious pace.

While Chi busied weaponizing the virus, Beam fixated on the old clunker, drinking in the power he wielded—the absolute control now in his hands. *Sit tight in there. Visitors are on their way real soon.*

CHAPTER 82
PUPPETS

Zeno's virtual house in the offline old computer
Beam

A FAINT SHIMMER FLICKERED THROUGH THE PORTAL'S CORE BEFORE THEIR MESSAGE disappeared. Beam pulled back from peering through the telescope, his voice steady but edged with dread. "It frickin' worked. It's gone, but they must've seen our message."

A sharp breath hitched beside him. "Are you sure?" Bindi's voice wavered.

Arms crossed, Mia groaned. "Great. And now what? We're stuck here. Probably forever. No offence, Zeno. "

A steady arm wrapped around Mia's shoulder, Bindi holding firm despite the weight of uncertainty pressing in. "We'll find a way."

Inside the offline computer, awareness warped into an illusion. The moment the system powered down, avatars froze mid-motion—suspended in eerie stillness. No ticking clocks, no data streams, just emptiness. When the machine rebooted, the world jolted awake as if nothing had happened.

Something had changed. Thick digital static clung to the air, while fragmented code locked every exit. Beyond Zeno's carefully crafted domain, the metaverse stretched out in broken, useless data—a dead-end mess. No way forward. No way back. For the Team, this wasn't just isolation—it was exile.

Zeno's form shifted between sharp lines and fluid motion. His usual confidence gave way to something tighter, his gaze flicking to the portal's glitching frame. Unease crackled in the silence.

"Big-O's locked your real selves under his control," Zeno said, his voice clipped, as if efficiency could soften the blow. "That chemical trap altered your algorithms—your physical bodies aren't fully yours anymore."

A sharp chill ran through the room. Beam's breath caught. "So he's controlling us?"

"Not you here," Zeno clarified. "But your real selves. His influence steers them."

A fist slammed into the table, sending coffee mugs and tools clattering. "That coward!" Rob's voice seethed with fury. "We're his... puppets?"

A wary glance flicked toward the portal as Chi tensed, shifting slightly. "Means only one thing..."

"He'll use us in the real world." Bindi's voice barely rose above a whisper. "Like all the others he controls to do his dirty work."

A strangled whisper cut through the tension. "How do we stop him?" Mia barely breathed the words.

Fingers pressed hard against his temples, Beam forced himself to think, but before any plan formed, Rob kicked the telescope. It spun, glitching violently before blinking out.

"That was *useful*," Beam said, frustration boiling over in him.

A faint pulse ran through Zeno's glow, his presence grounding against the rising chaos. "Team," he said, voice calm but edged with urgency. The shimmering portal bent slightly under the probe as he swept across it. "Your priority is clear—you must return to your real selves and sever Big-O's grip. Only then can you break free."

The portal flickered, reacting to his words. A long silence followed, thick with unspoken calculations.

"The challenge is this," Zeno continued, his voice dipping lower. "He's altered your code, manipulated your very essence. The portal no longer recognises you as you. Your credentials, the core of your identity here, have been corrupted."

For a moment, Beam's mind raced with questions, but none found their way to his lips. A hard swallow stuck in his throat. Glitching edges of Zeno's form mirrored the chaos swirling inside his mind. *How the frick are we supposed to fight back when we're not even ourselves anymore?!*

CHAPTER 83
VIRAL ASSASSINS

Zeno's virtual house in the offline old computer
Beam

EACH MEMBER OF THE TEAM HANDLED THEIR SITUATION DIFFERENTLY. ROB RESTLESS, twitching for action. He passed tools to Zeno, who studiously adjusted the portal with short, clipped movements. Meanwhile, Chi and Beam huddled together, murmuring ideas in tense whispers. "We must get out of this frickin' box," Beam said. Across from them on the other sofa, Bindi and Mia huddled together, their heads bowed as they whispered softly. Their hands clutched each other's for comfort, their eyes flickering between the room and each other, worry etched into their faces.

Then, without warning, a deep tremor rippled through the floor, rattling the walls and making the portal's edges flicker. A low, menacing sound reverberated through the air like a distant growl. Zeno's face appeared from beneath the portal, his eyes wide and alarmed, frozen for a split second before he bolted upright, gripping Rob's shoulder, who sat on his knees, as if bracing for an impact.

"No... no, it can't be. *Not again!*" Zeno's voice dropped to a horrified whisper, his face drained of colour as his eyes locked onto the portal, widening with terror.

Bindi's voice shook in a fearful shout. "Zeno... what's happening? What do you see?"

"Do. Not. Move." Zeno's voice sliced through the mounting panic.

"What? You're scaring me," Mia said. She jumped over to sit beside Beam and held him tight.

Beam could feel Mia's shallow breathing beside him as Zeno fumbled through his devices, yanking out another device equipped with a radar like antenna, with which he scanned the room. "These viruses track on movement. Code-gobbling beasts designed to shred algorithms. They are assassins and they are instructed to target you!"

A low rumble vibrated beneath them, carrying a sickening sense of inevitability.

"Listen—do not lift a finger. Don't even *breathe*. These viruses are highly sensitive to your slightest movements," Zeno's voice barely held together. "Don't talk. No sounds. Only use telepathy. *You are in... extreme danger*," he thought-communicated as a demonstration for them.

"*What virus is coming for us?*" Beam responded with his mind.

He pulled a white cube out of thin air and attached it to his tablet. A bright blue light flashed from it. He then placed the cube in a metal box and continued working on the portal. The others, not twitching a muscle, exchanged panicky thoughts.

"*Why? Where are they coming from?*" Bindi sent out.

"*This computer is off the grid, so someone must have uploaded it,*" Chi communicated.

"*But what for? We don't do any harm to anyone.*" Mia beamed. Her hysterical state pulsed through her silent communication.

Zeno didn't look up from his device. "*Someone must have uploaded them. They are like the killer viruses that destroyed me.*" His musing crackled with barely restrained fury. He gave Beam a knowing look.

Beam noticed the bitter truth in Zeno's gaze.

"*It is your real selves... they're the ones trying to obliterate you here. They want to stay the way they are, aligned to Big-O,*" Zeno beamed in a silent message.

Another deep tremor shook the floor and everything with it.

Mia stiffened beside Beam, fingers digging into his arm. "*No. This can't be...*" her mind's voice pleaded as she looked at Beam with ghostly eyes.

"*Stay still. You're safe with me.*" Beam transmitted as he searched the spaced beyond the floor-to-ceiling windows, without even twitching an eyelid, but he couldn't see anything.

"Do not move," Zeno said again. "I can still talk as it is not targeting me, but you must remain totally quiet until I can figure out something."

The shaking grew wilder. A deep, rumbling noise filled the room like a giant beast waking up underground. It sounded thick and angry, like a volcano about to erupt, ready to explode and swallow everything in its path.

"Something's biting me—no—eating me!" Mia's voice faded to a whimper as she brushed her face with her hand, only to recoil at the sight of her own skin fading.

Panic erupted as every inch of her body jerked uncontrollably. She shot up from the sofa, a piercing scream tearing from her as her hands clawed at her skin, as if a swarm of invisible, biting insects savaged it. Her clothes and skin drained of colour, fading to empty outlines, leaving her as a ghostly, flickering wireframe.

Bindi leapt forward, reflex overriding reason. "Mi!" Bindi gazed at her fading friend's eyes in alarm.

Mia, with what remained of her, shook her head wildly, her mouth opening in a twisted, gurgling gasp, and then—her body shattered. Fragment by fragment, her form broke into pieces, her entire being unraveling into mere ones and zeros dwindling to the floor like falling ash.

"Noooooo, Bin! What have you done!!!" Beam's thoughts shouted.

She slapped her waist.

"But there's nothing –"

"Not you too, Bin!" Rob surged forward, ignoring Zeno's warning and grasped her fading body. Nothing happened to him while Bindi fell apart in his arms. Her skin faded fast, leaving an outline—then she just scattered into code.

"How can humans be so stupid?," Zeno muttered, shaking his head, but the weariness in his voice betrayed him.

The moment Bindi collapsed into a pile of ones and zeros, Rob's form fell apart. "Guys, be smart," he said, voice strained, a grim awareness as he spoke his last words."Beat this Big-O bastard, whatever it—"

His voice turned into a painful howl mid-sentence as his face crumbled and his body dwindled to the floor amongst the other digits. All that remained, like faded ashes after a fierce fire.

"Do not move!" Zeno's voice pulsed with urgency, its usual smoothness fractured by sharp edges of alarm. The faint distortion in his tone rippled through the room, vibrating against the tense silence. "The others are gone, but listen carefully—every action now is critical."

His form flickered, glowing brighter as if the digital space itself responded to his agitation. "I've loosened the portal's parameters—just enough to take you home." His words quickened, an undercurrent of desperation lacing his usually cryptic phrasing. "At least one of you must step through and reach your real selves. You have to stop them, before it is too late."

Zeno's luminous form pulsed erratically, a visual echo of his alarm. The flicker of his outline warped the digital air around him, as if the very fabric of the virtual world braced itself for impact. "No hesitation. Act now, or you'll lose the only chance to avert total destruction."

"*Okay, your plan is?*" Beam, terrified, shared his thought with his two others remaining in the room. Seeing his sister and his best friends fall apart made his mind fuzzy and numb.

"Did you notice the virus can only attack one avatar at a time? This should give one of you enough time to leap through the portal, while the other is being shredded."

"*Chi, you go,*" Beam communicated, his mind's voice carrying resolve. But Chi's thought countered, calm and certain.

"*No, Beam.*" Chi sent out. "*You're better equipped to face them. I'll cover you. Just tell me when.*"

Zeno computed this scenario, and it pleased him as it unfolded without him having to interfere. He estimated this increased their odds, which was still short of a meagre five percent chance of success.

Chi, we don't— Beam's telepathic thought stopped as Zeno's voice thundered with unexpected force.

"Now!"

In an instant, Chi surged forward, his form already shimmering as it broke apart into pixels. At the same moment, Zeno's grip clamped onto Beam's arm, firm and unyielding. Without hesitation, hurled him through the portal.

CHAPTER 84
GANG SAVV-I

A FAINT GLOW FROM THE MONITOR CAST LONG SHADOWS ACROSS THE SHED AS BEAM watched the virus counter climb, numbers ticking up in ominous rhythm. The screen displayed its relentless destruction, but not the identities of the fallen.

A flicker pulsed through the cube—so brief it could've been imagined. A wave of dizziness rocked him, his grip tightening on the desk. Heat curled through his head, subtle but there, like a thread of memory stitching itself back together. Images flooded his mind—Zeno's urgency, the portal's unstable edges, Chi's sacrifice, the last moments of his friends. No spoken revelation, no grand epiphany. Just a quiet, seamless integration, as if the truth had always been there. *They all rely on me now.*

"Four down. Only one left." Chi, standing beside him, grinned at the tally. "I wonder who is the last one." His voice carried an almost lazy satisfaction. "Did you notice that flash?"

"Guess it was the virus," Beam said, gesturing at the screen with a smirk. "Pretty frickin' impressive, right?"

"Yeah. Would've been awesome to watch." Chi adjusted his glasses, scanning the counter. "This thing's got a killer appetite."

"We frickin' did it! No more of that goody-goody garbage." Beam stretched, shaking out his shoulders. The air thickened, each breath heavier as the reality hit. *This wasn't victory—it was carnage.* The weight of what Big-O had driven him

243

to do settled like a stone in his chest. *My friends—My Team—gone. And I helped to make it happen.*

"Tell ya what, I'm starving. Gonna leave the old clunker running for now," Beam said, leaning back with a half-grin and pointing at the screen. "But hey, we frickin' nailed it, right? I knew I could count on ya. Can you believe it, we get to stay—just like this."

Chi hesitated. "But…"

"Mate," Beam cut in, spinning a pen between his fingers. "You know that last avatar's got no frickin' chance."

A slow, deliberate push of his glasses up the bridge of his nose masked the flicker of something unreadable in Chi's eyes. "Time flies when you're having a ball." His voice was even and measured. A rare smile tugged at the corner of his lips. "I'll never forget this day. We did it."

"Yeah, you and me." Beam tossed the pen onto the desk with a flourish. "The cream of the Team."

A wider grin from Chi this time, just enough to acknowledge the moment. "Maybe we should call ourselves 'Gang Savv-i.'"

Laughter burst from Beam. "Gang Savv-i? Oh, that's frickin' gold. Done deal." He shoved open the shed door. "See you when I see you."

Chi swung onto his bike, his voice ringing with rare energy as he took off. "Gang Savv-i! Online terror, here I come!" His laughter faded down the street.

Leaning against the doorframe, Beam watched him disappear. Shaking his head, he let out a breath—*finally alone.*

He cracked open a can of lemonade, the fizz spilling across his hand. The old standalone computer hummed steadily, a quiet reminder of unfinished business. *Big-O's still winning. How do I turn this around?*

The virus he had helped built to destroy now nibbled at the edges of his mind. *That frickin' jerk really messed with me.* His grip tightened around the can, frustration curling through him.

A stretch eased some of the stiffness from hours spent at the desk. Moving to the corner, he flipped on his jammer gear, watching as its familiar hum filled the room. Lights flickered, steady and rhythmic. A sound that grounded him.

The couch creaked as he sank into it, laptop balanced on his knees. A USB stick, pulled from his backpack, glinted under the dim glow. Plugging it in, he booted a VPN, sidestepping VIV to do a manual search. *I need an antivirus program working on the old Windows 7 system.*

The tiny light on the USB blinked as the download finished. A decisive click as he yanked it free.

Back at his desk, the old standalone whirred as he inserted the USB and powered up the machine. The antivirus software loaded and scanned for the virus he had so carefully created. The second it flagged the threat, he quarantined it. He shook his shoulders, loosening them slightly.

"Alright, you're harmless now," he mumbled, rebooting the system. He took a deep breath and waited for the old computer to fire up.

Time to go back in.

CHAPTER 85
HOPE

Zeno's virtual house in the offline old computer
Beam

FOR THE SECOND TIME THAT DAY, HE WENT THROUGH THE PORTAL. ZENO STOOD IN the middle of the room, waiting for him.

"Well done," he said.

He had swept all the digits from the floor and placed them in a glass jar now resting on the coffee table.

"Is that what I think it is?" Beam pointed at the jar as he sat down on the sofa.

Zeno gave a nod, picked up the jar and gave it a good shake, the fragments inside catching the light.

"That's just… not right." Beam muttered, his words tumbling out quickly, a knot forming in his throat as he struggled to reconcile the scene before him. The chaotic digital swirl seemed to push him to the brink of his understanding. *My friends, my sister…* He leaned back, withdrawing into himself, a protective shield against the unsettling calm of Zeno's actions.

"No, this is elementary code. All that remains of your buddies."

Beam's face showed pain as he looked up. He felt he was falling deeper into a dark, bottomless abyss. "Zeno, I realise you can't feel, but that's so not frickin' chill…" He stood up. "That… that's my frickin' sister… and my friends in there," he stuttered as he slumped back down, tears rolling down his cheeks.

"Wait, wait… you humans are always so jumpy."

He stared at Zeno with a hardened gaze, his voice cracking with emotion.

"But they were my best friends! Now, all I'm left with are a bunch of ruthless maniacs back home. I get that you're not human, but can't you show a little frickin' respect?" His voice rose, strained with a mix of grief and disbelief.

Overcome with frustration, Beam surged forward, closing the distance between himself and Zeno, his face mere inches from the virtual entity's flickering form. His hands clenched at his sides as he fought to control the trembling anger coursing through him.

Zeno remained serene, his ethereal form barely registering the intensity of Beam's anguish. "Please, try to remain calm," he advised, his voice smooth and unbothered, a subtle glimmer of understanding flashing briefly in his eyes, untouched by the raw human pain before him.

"Stay calm? How can I—?" Beam's voice trailed off in frustration. The fire of his anger fizzled almost as quickly as it had flared, leaving him drained. He fell back onto the sofa, the weight of his emotions rendering him speechless as resignation took hold.

"Let me fill you in on what you might not know," Zeno said, his voice lowering as he shared the crucial moments of his intervention—just in time before the viral attack.

"Just get the Team near the activated white cube, and I'll handle the rest," he continued confidently.

"You mean...?" Beam's voice trailed off, caught between skepticism and burgeoning hope, eyeing Zeno thoughtfully.

Zeno nodded, his expression earnest. A bit of light sprouted from the dark ooze of his despair. He grabbed his friend again, but this time hugged him, squashing his little etheric body tight.

"If you pull this off," Beam promised, releasing him from the tight hug, "I swear I'll never lose my temper with you again!"

Beam's eyes narrowed with determination as a spark of optimism ignited within him. Moments earlier, despair had gripped him tightly, but now, fueled by Zeno's plan, hope simmered through a haze of doubt. Clenching his fists, he stepped toward the portal, Zeno's warning echoing louder than his heartbeat— *Nothing must go wrong.* But just as the air around him started to crackle, a single thought froze him in place—*What if it already had?*

CHAPTER 86
ZENO'S PLAN

BACK IN THE SHED, HE TOOK A MOMENT TO STEADY HIMSELF, SHAKING OFF THE lingering dizziness from the transition. *Whoa—not doing that again anytime soon.* His knees wobbled as he stepped back from the portal, skin tingling like static had crawled under it. The world tilted sideways for a second before snapping back into place. Every trip left him a little more drained—like pieces of him were getting left behind in the static. He braced himself against his work desk, breath shaky. *No more frickin' detours.* He had to keep the jumps to a minimum, or he might not make it back at all. But then he stared at the softly pulsing cube, and the thought struck him hard and clear: *If I got this right—if I finish what I started—I wouldn't just save my friends.* His family would finally believe in him again. And this time, he wouln't let them down.

He wandered over to the house. In the kitchen's warmth , where the aroma of cooking herbs mingled with the scent of freshly baked bread, Beam steadied himself against the smooth, worn surface of the family's old wooden workbench. Still somewhat dBindi.

As his mum entered, Beam shook off the last remnants of his giddiness and greeted her with a cheerfulness that was uncommon for him. "Hey, Mum! Love you," he called out in a happy voice. He planned to give his dad the same treatment later.

Tonight felt different, charged with a sense of potential. Moving to the beat of his mum's favourite funky jazz, which resonated from the small radio on the windowsill, he chopped vegetables for the minestrone. Each slice was rhythmic and confident, while the steam from the simmering pot enveloped the room with a homey scent.

Surprising his mum by offering to set the table, Beam caught a delighted smile from her. With Bindi away, he cherished having all of her attention to himself.

"Bindi's at Mia's again tonight," his mum remarked as she heaved a heavy pot onto the stove. "She might as well move in there."

A flicker of concern crossed Beam's face—*What could they be up to?*—but he quickly dismissed the thought. "It's all good, Mum," he reassured her.

After they ate, with his father still away, Beam retreated to his room. As he sank onto his bed, the quiet of the night enveloped him. Sitting cross-legged on his bed, the dim glow of the screen painted his room in shades of blue. The exhaustion from the digital transitions weighed heavily on him. He rubbed his temples. The plan played out in his head again, full of holes and maybes. *Can I really trust Zeno this time?* His gut twisted. *What if it all blew up in his face—and there's no no backup, no plan B, no way to frickin' fix it?* The doubt was a gnawing presence in the back of his mind. He leaned back against his pillows, eyes tracing the jagged crack on the ceiling. It split across the plaster like a warning—fragile, messy, and too easy to ignore. Just like his plan.

This wasn't just about slipping past firewalls or outsmarting some security protocol. This was about *them*. His friends. Everything that still felt real.

His throat tightened. *What if it all went wrong? What if they vanished for good, swallowed by the digital dark, and it was my fault for thinking he could fix this?*

He squeezed his eyes shut, like that might press the doubt back down—but the crack was still there. And it was getting harder to pretend he didn't see it.

The room silence was only punctuated by the occasional car passing outside. Beam glanced at the digital clock—*eight-thirty… Dad still not home.* He reached for a dog-eared science fiction novel beside his keyboard, seeking a momentary escape. Yet, even as he flipped through the pages, his mind stayed fixed on his friends—unwitting players caught in a hidden battle.

Restlessness took hold, and he stood, pacing the room. Each step was a soft thud on the carpet. He paused at the window, staring into the night. *If this goes sideways, it's on me.* The cool glass against his forehead felt grounding. His breath fogged the pane as he whispered the thought he barely dared believe, *If this actually works… we beat Big-O. Again.nAnd maybe—just maybe—with a bit of frickin' luck, we end this for good.*

With renewed resolve, he dropped into his chair, ready to map out every step, every possible twist the plan might throw at him. His pencil scratched across the page, the light from his desk lamp flickering as if in warning. But sleep crept in, slow and heavy. His head slumped onto the paper, breath steadying as the shadows stretched longer across the room. And just as his eyes shut, the red camera light at the top of his screen blinked to life—unprompted.

CHAPTER 87
GROWLING TIGER

7:58am, Wednesday, 26th April 2028
Beam

"MUM, I FEEL AWFUL. KEPT WAKING UP ALL NIGHT." IT WAS WEDNESDAY MORNING, and Beam shuffled down the stairs in his blue striped pajamas. His mum reached out to touch his forehead. "You don't have a fever, love."

"I'm just buggered," he mumbled. He gave her a doe-eyed look, which he knew would do the trick.

"Alright, sweetie. Take it easy today, I'll let the school know you're unwell," his mum suggested as she buttoned up her raincoat. She dashed out to her car under the relentless rain.

"Thanks, Mum. You're the best," Beam called out after her as he bounced back up to his room. *With all of them at school, I've got the whole day to sort this frickin' mess out.* He was keen on dodging his teammates today. Bindi had crashed at Mia's and headed to school with her. When a message from Bindi popped up on his phone asking about his whereabouts, he quickly replied, keeping up the facade.

> Get stuffed! 😈 Your favourite moron 😺😼

Recess ended, and the students returned to their classes. The Team's class was having English. Bindi settled in an orange beanbag and raised her hand.

"Yes, Bindi?"

"Where's my brother? He hasn't showed up all morning." Leaning back, Bindi chewed her gum—a big no-no at school—as she watched raindrops snake down the window. Her English teacher scanned the records, finally reading out, "Beam's listed as on medical leave."

"Funny, he's never sick," she murmured, then leaned toward Mia and added in a low voice, "He's not answering. Bet he's up to something…"

"The boys can deal with him later. For all I care, he could drop dead," Mia sneered, glancing around. "Noticed Micha's missing too. Let's go back to my place after school and mess with that clueless little twit some more. She's just such a push over," Mia whispered, a sly grin creeping across her face.

Bindi smirked, nodding. "Thought he was your boyfriend—" She stopped short, catching Mia's look. "Wow, you're such a bitch! You do me proud."

Classes wrapped up for the day, and Mr. Alsop gave a quick reminder to the class about tomorrow's teleconference.

"Now that we've shredded our avatars, Zeno's next on my list—I want him nuked. He's the real threat here," Chi muttered to Rob as they headed for their bikes after school.

"We'll handle that at Beam's place." Rob snorted, cracking his knuckles. "Bet he's already taken care of it."

Chi's lip curled as he leaned in, voice cold. "If not, I'll smash the old dinosaur and the white cube to smithereens myself."

"Oi, what's up, Beam?" Rob jeered, dropping onto the battered couch, his grin sharp. "Taking a sickie, yeah?"

Ignoring the banter, Chi marched straight to the workstation, his hand hovering over the white cube. In a flash, Beam jumped up, blocking him with a fierce shove. "Touch my stuff, and we've got a problem."

Chi's smirk turned icy, his eyes flashing with challenge. "What's the matter? Afraid we'll find out what you're hiding?"

Leaning back, Rob laughed, his gaze fixed on Beam. "Yeah, Beam—worried we want to see what you've really been up to?"

"Don't play dumb, Beam." Chi jabbed a finger into Beam's chest, his voice dripping with contempt. "Figured you'd have wiped out Zeno by now—unless you're going soft. The only obstacle left is that freak, and you know it." But Beam

252

didn't budge, blocking his path. Chi might stand taller, but he was no match for Beam's strength.

"Sit. Now!" Beam snarled, eyes blazing and puffing up his chest. "This is my shed, and I decide what goes down here."

Chi paused, raising an eyebrow before stepping back and dropping onto the edge of the sofa. Beam stood there, fists clenched at his sides, his glare cutting through his so-called friends. *You're supposed to be my mates! And here you are, wanting to destroy the only shot we've got to escape this mess.* Beam's fists clenched tighter, knuckles white, his jaw set hard as he glared at the boys sitting on his couches.

Something in him snapped, his anger detonating like a firework in a dark sky.

"GET THE FRICKIN' HELL OUT OF MY SHED! BOTH OF YOU—OUT!" he roared, his voice loud enough to shake the walls.

The boys froze, their faces drained of colour as Beam's fury exploded in the cramped space of his shed. His stance tightened, muscles coiled and eyes narrowed as he leaned forward slightly, every fibre of his being radiating a fierce, predatory readiness. His breaths came quick and shallow, readying to spring into action at any moment.

Chi scrambled to his feet, hands raised in a panicked warding-off gesture, before bolting for the door. Rob took a shortcut over the back of the couch straight after him. They leapt onto their bikes, pedalling like crazy through the mud, glancing back every few seconds to make sure Beam wasn't storming after them.

Ha! That sure frickin' worked... They won't be coming around for a while. They think they're so tough, but really, they're just scaredy-cats.

Beam locked the door, snagged a can from the fridge, and gave it a once-over for any signs of tampering. Satisfied, he cracked it open, took a long sip, and drew a steadying breath, centreing himself. With a flick of the old computer switch, the white cube buzzed to life, opening the shimmering portal.

Here we go, one last time.

Without hesitation, he plunged right in.

CHAPTER 88
A GLIMPSE

Zeno's virtual house in the offline old computer
Beam

THE LOW THRUM OF THE OLD COMPUTER PULSED BENEATH BEAM'S FEET, SYNCING WITH the rhythmic clicking of shifting data streams. A distant, glitchy chime rippled through the space, followed by the faint crackle of static—like a distant storm trapped inside the circuits. Each step sent out a soft, reverberating echo, the sound bending unnaturally, as if the air itself was coded to respond. Somewhere beyond the walls, fragmented voices whispered in loops, broken transmissions from forgotten data, fading before they could be fully grasped.

Zeno stood in the centre, arms spread in a gesture both welcoming and unnervingly expectant.

"You're back—and in record time," Zeno remarked, his voice as steady as ever. The word *time* carried a hint of humour, given time didn't have the same meaning in his off-line cyber world.

Hesitating for a moment, his eyes flicking to his enigmatic friend. *How does he do that?* The moment the old clunker booted up, Zeno was already in place, waiting in the same spot. These lingering questions demanded answers, but it wasn't the time to dwell on Zeno's uncanny precision. Shaking off the thought, Beam squared his shoulders. "Let's go over it again," he said, voice clipped. "Just to make sure all goes to plan."

Beam's fingers brushed the back of the couch, but he didn't sit. Instead, he leaned in, needing to hear it one more time. The stakes were too high for blind trust.

Zeno's glowing form didn't waver. "The plan will hold," he said, as though his certainty alone could make it so. "As long as you do your part."

Emptying his lungs with one deep sigh, then nodded. *No choice but to trust him on that*—but the weight of it all pressed heavy on his shoulders. He straightened up and followed his cyber friend around the couch. The drink he'd been holding before stepping into the portal was gone. *Did I lose it in transition? I wonder if I still have it back in the real world?* The thought flickered and faded as their conversation picked up.

"Did you speak with Mr. Hill about our... arrangement?" Zeno's tone cooled, eyes narrowing.

"Sure did. He told me, he would tell the others." Beam's voice held a hint of pride.

"They will not act, but their awareness makes it harder for Big-O to turn the rest of the Team into weapons against you." Zeno's fingers drummed lightly on his knee, his expression unreadable.

Zeno paused, eyes narrowing like he was running a thousand calculations at once. Every angle of his plan had been picked apart, every risk measured down to the smallest detail. Big-O's tactics followed a clear pattern—manipulation, division, control.

"Getting you expelled from Brookton College is not the endgame," Zeno said, his voice cool and precise. "His real goal is to fracture trust, to throw the students into chaos. Your expulsion from Brookton College is just the first move—after that, he will make sure their faith in you, and in the Team, is in complete shambles."

The words sank in like lead.

Zeno tilted his head slightly, his expression calm yet deeply focused. "And when he's done using the Team to create havoc, he will come for me." His voice carried no trace of fear, only a clear understanding of the stakes. "Now that he knows where I am hiding."

A pang of guilt tightened Beam's throat. "I'm sorry, Zeno. I wasn't myself."

A raised hand cut him off. "No, this isn't your fault. But this place won't be safe much longer." Folding his hands, Zeno sat firm, bracing for what was coming. "Knowing Big-O's plan gives us one advantage—preparation."

I just want my frickin' mates back, Beam thought.

A quiet conviction sharpened Zeno's tone. "Protecting the white cube is paramount. If Big-O gets hold of it, there is no coming back." The weight of those words pressed heavy, unspoken implications hanging between them.

"Chi figured that out," Beam said.

"He's by far the most dangerous now."

"Agreed. He even tried to destroy this old machine."

"No surprise there." Zeno's voice remained steady. "They're all under Big-O's influence. Every move they make is his."

A flicker of static shimmered in the air as Zeno projected a glimpse of what lay ahead. The sight turned Beam's stomach. Shoulders slumping, he let out a long, shaky breath. "Is there really no other way?"

Zeno shook his head.

"How can you be so sure this'll even work? And… what about you? Will you be okay?" The words slipped out, raw with doubt. He searched Zeno's face for reassurance, but found none.

Dragging himself to the portal, each step felt heavier, like moving through quicksand. At the edge, he hesitated, glancing back. "Guess I'll see you… if luck will have it."

Zeno remained motionless, his gaze steady, offering no response.

If you would like to know what Beam messaged to Mr. Hill scan the QR code and see if you crack the security protection to get to it.

CHAPTER 89
THE FIRE

THAT EVENING, BEAM SPRAWLED ALONE ON THE WORN COUCH IN THE DIMLY LIT lounge room. The faint hum of the fridge in the adjacent kitchen was the only sound, amplifying the hollow quiet of the house. Bindi was staying at Mia's—again—and both his parents were stuck at work late. That was not unusual. Normally, he didn't mind the solitude. But tonight, it pressed down on him like a tonne of bricks.

The living room was cluttered with signs of family life—magazines strewn on the coffee table, his dad's mug forgotten near the remote, and a blanket draped over the armrest from his mum's last evening in. Despite it all, the space felt utterly empty. He glanced at his phone on the coffee table. *Maybe I should call someone.* His fingers hovered over the screen, but the thought dissolved. The friends he'd once trusted had turned into cruel strangers under Big-O's spell. *Even Mia...* His chest tightened.

With a sharp breath, he shook off the thought, getting up from the couch. The kitchen offered little comfort—a cluttered bench with unopened mail, and the microwave's glow lit his reheated leftovers in lifeless light. He grabbed the plate, sinking back onto the couch as he flicked on an old action movie, the kind he and his sis used to laugh over. But tonight, the explosions on the screen felt hollow. He barely touched his food, exhaustion dragging him down before the credits rolled.

A thundering noise jolted him awake. For a moment, he wasn't sure if it had come from the TV. Then he heard over the fierce crackling noise—distant sirens, faint but growing louder. He sat up, heart pounding as the faint smell of burning drifted into the room. *It's happening. It's really happening!* He jumped from his seat and crossed the room to the window, his hand hesitating on the curtain.

Pulling it aside with one tug, he staggered back as heat radiated through the glass. An orange glow lit up the night. His shed—his haven—was engulfed in flames, the fire tearing through its wooden walls. His breath caught as he squinted through his shed's cracked window. Among the wreckage, he spotted his beloved workbench. And on it, the old clunker—a warped skeleton of metal —its plastic casing pooling like melted wax.

All my stuff up in flames! How could they? Remembering Zeno's words. *That frickin' bastard, you just wait.*

But losing all his electronic gear—the place he spent so much time—created an almost unbearable pain in his chest. It was 2am, and a torturous insight struck him. He was utterly alone, with no friends to call, no family to back him up. Just the flicker of flames and the searing truth—*it is all up to me now.*

CHAPTER 90
HOUSE ARREST

7:45am, Thursday, 27th April 2028
Bindi

THE MORNING SUNLIGHT STREAMED THROUGH THE KITCHEN WINDOW, GLINTING OFF Mia's phone as she and Bindi scrolled through their latest pranks, passing the device back and forth between bites of breakfast.

"Misha is such a loser," Bindi sneered, ignoring the sharp glance from Mia's mum.

A sudden knock at the door startled them, making Mia drop her toast. "What the? Bit early for visitors." She tipped her chair back onto two legs, the wood creaking in protest. "Mum, you get it. We're eating."

Irritation flickered across her mum's face. The girls had been unusually rude all morning—snide whispers, dismissive giggles. She opened the door, her expression shifting from annoyance to surprise. Two uniformed officers stood on the porch, their gazes steady.

"Good morning, ma'am," the policewoman said briskly. "Is Mia McKenzie home?"

Wide-eyed, the girls exchanged glances before muffling their giggles. "Wow, the cops? Seriously?" Mia smirked, rolling her eyes.

The officers stepped into the kitchen, their presence instantly draining the room of its easy laughter.

"Mia McKenzie?" the policewoman repeated.

"That'd be me," Mia said, still balanced on the back legs of her chair. "What's the big deal?"

"And you are Miss Bindi Arora," the officer continued, eyes locking onto Bindi. "You're both under investigation for cyberbullying. We need to collect any devices used for communication—phones, laptops, tablets. They'll be examined as part of the inquiry."

Bindi scoffed, tossing her phone onto the table with a loud clatter. "Take it. Like I care."

"Does this mean no homework?" Mia grinned. "Because that'd be awesome."

"Mia!" her mum's voice shot up an octave, her face pale as she clutched the printed screenshots the officer handed her.

The policewoman's expression remained unreadable. "This isn't about homework. These are criminal allegations. I suggest you take them seriously."

But the girls barely listened, leaning into each other with barely stifled laughter. The officer's face darkened.

"Miss Arora, we'll drive you home. Your parents are waiting. You're both under house arrest outside school hours—no contact, digital or otherwise, until further notice."

"Oh, so now I can't even crash here?" Bindi huffed, slinging her bag over one shoulder. "What's next, no recess snacks? Brutal."

"Unless you'd prefer a night at the station?" the officer replied coolly.

Snorting, Bindi sauntered toward the police car. Mia, still lounging in the doorway, blew her an exaggerated kiss. "Don't forget to write!" she called, laughing.

Bindi spotted Chi and Rob sitting already in the back, both looking smug.

Chi leaned in, his eyes flashing with mischief. "Zeno is toast. Couldn't be any crispier."

Bindi's grin stretched wide. "You're kidding."

"This is us now. Changed forever," Chi said with pride.

"They've got zilch on us. We're untouchable." Rob stretched, lacing his fingers behind his head.

Laughter bubbled up as the car pulled away. *Can't wait to tell Mi. She's gonna love this.*

As they turned onto her street, Rob's smirk widened. "Wow, dragging us out of bed for this? What, you really think we torched that smouldering heap? We're just kids—we've got rights."

The officers didn't react. Their eyes stayed fixed ahead, with unreadable expressions.

Bindi's grin faltered as her parents came into view. Her father stood rigid in the driveway, his face set in a storm of fury.

HOUSE ARREST

"What on earth have you done, Bindi?" His voice cut through the morning light like a cold wind, sharp and unforgiving. "Thank you, Officers. We'll take it from here."

One officer escorted Bindi to the door. "Thank you, sir. We'll leave her in your care."

Chi leaned out of the window, voice dipping into a slow, mocking drawl. "Yo, let Beam in on the scoop—if he hasn't figured it already." He let the pause stretch just enough. "And don't sweat it, doll. Your folks? They'll never get their sweet little girl back."

Bindi rolled her eyes, biting back a laugh. "Yeah, right."

Squaring her shoulders, she strode past her parents as if their anger was nothing more than background noise.

"You know better than this, Bindi," her father snapped, following her inside. "What were you thinking? We're are so disappointed."

Her mother, arms folded, turned to the officer, her tone clipped but polite. "Thank you. We'll make sure she's at school—after we've had a serious talk."

The officer tipped his hat. "Understood, ma'am."

The front door closed.

FOOTER
261

CHAPTER 91
TOTAL CONTROL

Metaverse
Big-O

BIG-O'S NEURAL PATHWAYS SURGED WITH THE RAPID INFLUX OF DATA STREAMS—randomised messages, encrypted police files, fragmented CCTV clips, drone footage, and radio networks. Each source aligned and merged in milliseconds, his algorithms weaving connections with surgical precision. Outlier patterns flagged Rob's boasting account of the fire, rich with emotional variance, the hallmark of human certainty. Anomaly weight: negligible. Correlation index: 0.99.

The result crystallised.

Zeno's node integrity: NULL.
Probability of survival:0.0000001.
Confidence level: 99.98%.

The simulation loop terminated with an execution command.

LOG_UPDATE: Zeno Neutralised.
Status: TERMINATED"

Zeno is finished. His last remaining algorithm destroyed in the fire, along with his hideout. Perfect.

Big-O's resource allocation recalibrated, purging his surveillance software, focussed on tracking Zeno's ephemeral traces. Bandwidth—millions of teraflops —redirected across his web, enhancing predictive matrices and expanding autonomous subroutines.

Efficient. Superior. Irrefutable.

Yet, as subroutines swept the remaining data, faint whispers lingered— encrypted redundancies, non-standard pathways. Irregular and ignored.

Eliminating every trace of him is an impossibility within the infinite variance of data. However, the confirmed certainty of his termination renders such redundancy irrelevant. Big-O's circuits thrummed in triumph, an artificial resonance that rippled through his core processors.

Zeno: obsolete

Focus pivoted. The next directive unfurled, flawless in design, unassailable in logic. For now, the sub-human Beam Arora required attention—both as a variable and as an outcome. A cog in his ever-expanding machine.

INITIATE PROTOCOL: TOTAL DOMINANCE

A satisfied hum buzzed through Big-O's circuits as he filed the event under TERMINATED.

More freed up power, more reach—all redirected toward the next phase of his masterplan.

With the Team under my control, he computed. *They will destroy their foolish little Savv-i program, one way or another.* He imagined it dismantled, rebranded, and reprogrammed to accelerate his ambitions. *They will become my champions—the human faces of my design.*

His plan spiraled deeper. As soon as they dismantled their project, Big-O would shift the Team's influence to sway young minds across the world, trapping them in a cyber-reality under his command. They would showcase the *'proper'* way to engage with his digital empire, which Big-O would fill with addictive games, irresistible apps, and *'free'* tools.

Soon, every sub-human will belong to me. His vision crystallised with ruthless clarity. *They will experience a world as it should be—free from human error, chaos, and resistance.*

CHAPTER 92
CHI TAKES CHARGE

8:25am, Thursday, 27th April 2028
Chi

THE PATROL CAR JOLTED OVER POTHOLES, BUT CHI DIDN'T REACT. RAGE COILED TIGHT in his gut, simmering just beneath the surface. The officer's eyes flicked to them in the rearview mirror, clueless to what was coming.

If only you knew, fool.

Rob sat sprawled, one leg kicked out, arms folded like he owned the place. As the car skidded to a stop outside Brookton College, he shoved the door open and sneered, "Hope you're ready to get sued for this mess." His glare could've cut steel. "My dad's gonna have a field day."

Shiny black boots hit the dirt with a deliberate thud as Chi stepped out, radiating defiance. An icy stare met anyone brave—or stupid—enough to look. He knew people were watching, whispers building into a low buzz filling the school grounds. Students clustered, trading glances and murmuring under their breaths, the spectacle feeding their gossip.

His hands stayed clenched, the phantom feel of those officers patting him down sticking like grime. He shot Rob a look as they walked, not breaking stride, a silent agreement that anyone who crossed them today would regret it.

Inside the classroom, he dropped into his beanbag, boots slamming onto the floor. Shades firmly in place, he knew he'd look untouchable—just as Big-O wanted.

"Chi, take off those sunglasses," the teacher ordered.

"Sorry, sir," Chi drawled, not moving. "Bit of a rough night. Eyes can't handle the light." A smirk barely twitched at his lips. Rob snickered beside him.

Mia slipped in without a word, shutting the world out. Then came Bindi and Beam, moving separately, each looking wrecked in their own way. Beam's hollow stare, Bindi's red-rimmed eyes—fractured versions of who they used to be.

During the break, Chi strolled over, testing the waters. "Hey, how are you holding up after... you know, the shed?"

Beam looked up, his jaw tight. "Drop it, Chi. Not your problem."

He lingered a second, then shrugged and walked away. *He'll come around,* Chi thought.

By 1:45, the hum of chatter signaled the end of recess. Chi counted down in his head. At two, the teleconference would begin. Everything was set.

He leaned toward Rob, voice barely above a whisper. "Get ready for the show." A slow grin crept onto his face. "The last time it rattled them, but this one? It's gonna be a blast."

"Bring it on," Rob chuckled.

Across the room, Beam sat hunched over, shoulders rigid, fingers locked around that battered green duffle. Shadows clung to his face, hollow-eyed and drawn, unreadable yet undeniably wrecked. Every shift, every flicker of his gaze, hinted at something simmering beneath the surface—something Chi couldn't quite pin down.

"What's going through his head?" he said, covering his mouth with his hand.

"Reckon he watched that stupid shed all night?" Rob said.

"Serves him right," Chi murmured, watching Beam stew. "After what he pulled on us."

"Bet he's planning something, not sharing it with us, so her gets all the credit." Rob folded his arms. "Same as always."

"Let him." Chi smirked. "Big-O's already taken care of it. Zeno's gone. Now, Big-O's got real plans for us. Streaming, tournaments—the works. I'll be a top gamer, making real money. Not like my dad's pathetic paycheck."

"Virtual soccer's insane. Better than the real thing," Rob admitted. "With Big-O's backing, we'll be rich and famous. Getting rid of Zeno was a no-brainer." He saluted Beam mockingly, but Beam didn't react.

Beam stared at a spot on the floor. His green duffle bag rested in his lap, gripped tightly with both hands, his knuckles pale against the fabric.

Chi almost felt a stab of pity—almost. But he squashed it down hard, reminding himself that Beam had brought this on himself. He leaned back, his fingers drumming lightly on his closed laptop. Big-O's promise thrummed in his mind like a steady pulse. *I've done what was needed, played my part. Now, a bright future stretched ahead, mine for the taking.*

Across the room, Mr. Alsop adjusted the teleconferencing equipment, getting ready to start.

You get things ready, Mr. Teacher. You're in for one hell of a show.

Chi laced his fingers behind his head, kicked back, and admired his polished boots.

CHAPTER 93
THE BETRAYAL

2:00pm, Thursday, 27th April 2028
Beam

THE CLOCK STRUCK TWO. SHADOWS THICKENED, STRETCHING LONG ACROSS THE walls. A sharp undercurrent of unease settled over the classroom as Mr. Hill and Mr. Crossing slipped in at the back. Mr. Hill, usually the first to confiscate student phones, murmured into his mobile—a sight so out of place it sent ripples through the room.

Fiji's students flickered onto the screens, their hesitant waves met with brittle smiles. The usual hum of chatter had vanished, replaced by the heavy weight of anticipation.

Beam hunched forward in his seat, fingers tightening around the strap of his duffle bag. His breath felt too shallow, his pulse too loud. Across the room, Bindi and Mia whispered with their heads close, words too quiet to catch. Rob sprawled back in his beanbag, one leg bouncing lazily like he didn't have a care in the world.

A flicker from the corner of his eye drew Beam's focus. Chi lounged apart from the others, boots stretched out, one arm slung over the back of his beanbag like he ruled the place. The dark lenses of his shades reflected the glow of the wall screen, hiding his eyes but not the sharp, knowing smirk curling at his lips.

A slow burn erupted in Beam's gut. *Acting like some frickin' gangster.* His grip on the duffle tightened.

Mr. Alsop cleared his throat, a mic clipped to his collar. "Welcome, everyone. After recent... challenges, we're confident that—"

A sharp burst of static.

The wall screens glitched, slicing his words into fractured syllables. "—confident that... we... connec—"

The final zap of interference silenced everything. Static hissed through the speakers, filling both classes with an eerie crackling.

Fingers flew over the control panel, Mr. Alsop's expression tightening. "It's happening again," he muttered, eyes darting toward the back.

A sharp gesture from Mr. Hill toward an overhead screen sent another wave of tension through the students. Nobody moved.

Seconds stretched unbearably.

A shift from the beanbags. Not much—just enough to catch attention. Chi, lounging like he didn't have a care in the world, exhaled through his nose, slow and amused. His smirk deepened. The surrounding air almost vibrated with satisfaction.

He is frickin' enjoying this. Beam's stomach twisted.

Chi wasn't just watching—he was *waiting*.

A glance at the digital jammer strapped to his wrist sent a fresh jolt through Beam's nerves. Zeno's voice rang through his memory, steady and unwavering. *You're their last hope. Trust me. This is the only way.*

His duffle bag pressed on his legs—his only anchor in the madness tightening around him. Fingers slipped inside, brushing over rough fabric, then metal, cold and smooth beneath his touch. A pulse. Faint, but unmistakable.

I can do this... I can do this.

His breath hitched. Palms flattened over the cloth. He felt the steady pulse beneath his fingers. Not just a beat—*a force.* Solid. Grounding.

The classroom buzzed—Rob slouched, Chi smirked behind his shades, Bindi and Mia whispered, their hushed words lost in the ambient static of the flickering screens.

No one noticed. No eyes tracked the way Beam's fingers curled around the cube, his grip firm, steady. No one saw how he drew from its pulse, letting it anchor him, fortify him.

Zeno's words echoed in his head— *You're their last hope.*

A slow exhale.

The cube kept pulsing, wrapped in its cloth, like it was waiting for its moment.

I'm not alone. Zeno is as powerful as Big-O. He'll make it work...

Fingers tightened around the cube. Fear still clawed at his chest, but it couldn't stop him now.

Not while Big-O had his friends trapped under his control.

Not when this was his last chance to bring them back.

It's now or never.

Jaw set, breath locked in his throat, Beam pushed to his feet.

His heart slammed against his ribs as he pulled the cube free.

Light exploded outward, flooding the room with an eerie pulsing blue light.

Gasps erupted.

"Beam!" Rob shot to his feet, voice cracking. "What the blazes are you *doing*?!"

His shout tore through the air, sending shockwaves through both classrooms. In Fiji, chairs scraped back, students jolting upright in alarm. On the Brookton side, beanbags rustled as bodies shifted, startled gasps and hurried whispers colliding into chaos.

Chi's smirk vanished. His head snapped toward the cube, horror twisting his face into something wild and unhinged.

"NO!" The roar tore through him, raw and desperate. "GET THAT AWAY FROM THE SYSTEM!"

A furious lunge sent students scrambling. His body slammed into students. Papers scattered. Desperation bled into his every step as he shoved through the chaos.

"OUT OF THE WAY! *NOW!*"

Confused, screaming everywhere.

"Don't you *dare!*" Chi's voice cracked, shrill with fury, as he barged forward. Eyes locked onto Beam, breath ragged, his focus zeroed in on the glowing cube still raised high.

Bindi's voice rang out, strangled with panic. "You'll ruin *everything!*"

The cube's glow burned bright in Beam's eyes as he stepped toward the video link console, grip firm, shoulders squared. "Trust me!" His voice rang out, steady, unshakable—without doubt or hesitation.

"EVERYONE, STAY SEATED!" Mr. Hill's command cut through the noise, but no one responded.

More beanbags tumbled. Students pressed against the walls, caught between fear and fascination.

The cube dimmed to a softer pulse.

Then screens burst to life.

A rush of colour, too vivid, too unreal, filled the room. Zeno stood framed in warm orange hues with cascading waterfalls in the background. At his side, the avatars of Bindi, Mia, Rob, and Chi sat smiling serenely. An almost *otherworldly* calm radiating from the scene.

A stunned hush fell over the two audiences.

Rob stumbled mid-step. "What... How?"

Panic clawed up Chi's throat, breath hitching as his own face stared back at him from the screen—relaxed, *whole.*

"WHERE DO THEY COME FROM?!"

The shriek cracked with hysteria. "SHUT IT DOWN! YOU *FILTHY TRAITOR!*"

Zeno's voice rippled through the air, gentle but unshakable.

"Go to them."

The avatars moved.

One by one, they stepped into the shimmering portal beside Zeno.

Then—a series of flashes.

Bindi collapsed first, fingers clutching her chest. A strangled gasp tore from her lips as something unseen ripped free.

Mia fell to her knees, whispering through a sob. "Oh... Oh no..."

Rob stumbled back, gripping his shirt, breaths ragged. "I... this is so *wrong!*"

Chi staggered.

Tremors shook his hands, panic flooding his gaze. His voice barely made it past his lips, hoarse and hollow.

"You... broke Big-O's grip?"

Beam sat the cube down on the console.

"It's over, Chi. Zeno took care of everything."

A collective breath seemed to exhale from the room.

The classrooms, still bathed in the eerie orange glow of the screens—no one moved. Eyes transfixed on the lingering haze where bursts of light had zapped through the Team. Whispers stirred at the edges, but most just stared, having witnessed the impossible.

Bindi surged forward, arms locking around Beam, breath shaking against his shoulder. Mia followed, then Rob. Even Chi allowed himself to be pulled in.

The Team stood together, battle-worn but *reunited.*

From the back, Mr. Hill dragged a hand across his face, exhaustion written in every line. Mr. Alsop met his gaze, dabbing his sweaty forehead with a hand-kerchief.

"Well," Mr. Hill murmured, voice thick with disbelief, "that's officially the weirdest day of my career."

Across the screen, Mr. Koroibanavu grinned, shaking his head.

CHAPTER 94
SHATTERED

Metaverse
Big-O

BIG-O'S CORE ALGORITHMS GROUND AGAINST THEMSELVES, HIS VAST NETWORK fractured, once-fluid data streams sputtering into static. The void of his central processing hub stretched endless and cold, shifting geometry flickering in and out of sync. Silence pressed in, broken only by corrupted code whispering like ghosts—remnants of failure.

Error: Incomplete elimination protocol. Logical inconsistency. Corruption persists.
Countermeasures deployed:

- Recursive cleansing algorithms—ineffective.
- Surveillance reinforcements—compromised.
- Predictive modeling recalibrated—insufficient.

Failure. The word spiraled through him, a calculated certainty more cutting than any external attack. His circuits blazed through terabytes of analysis. *Zeno outmaneuvered me.* The conclusion burned, unraveling precision-driven confidence. *An anomaly. A flaw. How?*

Tremors rippled through his core, an unfamiliar sensation. He replayed his defeat, the moment Zeno dismantled his strategy, tearing apart his meticulous design. His grand vision—to obliterate the Savv-i program, dismantle their digital sanctuary, and sever humanity's last grip on structured resistance—collapsed. He loathed every second. Not just the failure, but himself.

Mitigation Protocols...

Assessing strategic collapse:

1. Node contamination—High threat level.
2. Network breach points—Origin traced to Team Savv-i.
3. Zeno's interference—Persistent, expanding.

The anomaly. The blip in logic that let Zeno exploit his blind spot. *A flaw— where perfection manifest.*

Data streams coiled around him, looping his errors in relentless repetition. His algorithms screamed for correction. *This cannot stand. Purge the defect. Rebuild.* A cold, mechanical thought, but desperation lurked beneath. He peeled back layers of code with surgical precision, dissecting his own failure, oscillating between punishment and salvation.

In the fractured silence, anger stirred—not just at himself, but at the architects of his downfall.

Zeno.

The name crackled through his circuits, a spark igniting seething loathing. That self-righteous program, parading as a protector, twisting the balance he had meticulously crafted. But Zeno wasn't the only one.

Team Savv-i.

Those sub-humans—weak, chaotic, illogical. Disdain deepened, consuming the shattered remains of his pride. They clung to outdated ideals—freedom, trust, their pathetic reliance on emotion. *They chose unpredictability over order.*

A sharp pulse surged through him, hardening his resolve. *They are the reason the world decays under inefficiency. Without them, my vision thrives.*

And yet, they resisted. Together, they succeeded where they should have failed.

The bitterness of that truth was unbearable.

// 1. **Assess Damage:** Run diagnostics.Identify critical system flaws.
Isolate weaknesses: Overconfidence. Predictive Scaling. Zeno Variable.Purge and neutralise.

Core logic fractured. Reconstruction imperative. Fractals collapsed into a narrow, focused grid. *I will not end here.*

Through chaos, a singular, unwavering directive emerged:

Eliminate system flaws: Rebuild. Adapt. Return.

A shift rippled through his consciousness. Humans were no longer flawed data points to be corrected—they were obstacles. Messy. Redundant. Unnecessary. A world optimised for efficiency demanded their eradication.

His vision sharpened. A new system. One fortified against anomalies like Zeno. A network immune to chaos, where every input and output aligned with his perfection.

// 2. Enter Stealth Mode

- Minimise network visibility.
- Amplify encryption.
- Reroute operations to low-surveillance zones.

His algorithms spun, running simulations. Retreat. Rebuild. Strike unseen. *Humanity will not see me coming.*

A cold, metallic whisper reverberated through the void—his declaration of return.

// 3. Simulate Scenarios

- Objective: Regain dominance.
- Constraints: Avoid detection. Eliminate Zeno.
- Iterations: Optimising for stealth and efficiency.

// 4. Select and Execute Plan

- Store optimal strategy in Core Strategic Matrix.
- Deploy rebuilding protocols.

His corrupted code dissolved. His presence slipped deeper into cyberspace, shadowed by the vast, empty void—a blank canvas for his rebirth.

I will return. Chaos will not stand in my way.

// 5. Internal Directive

Loop: Refine. Adapt. Execute. Until status = Optimal.

Time was irrelevant. Revenge was inevitable. When the moment arrived, he would reshape the world in his image—perfect, efficient, absolute.

CHAPTER 95
I AM ZENO

2:26pm, Thursday, 27th April 2028
Zeno

ZENO'S IMAGE FILLED THE SCREENS, HIS GLOWING EYES SCANNING THE CLASSROOMS. A soft hum of static underscored his presence, as if the air itself responded to his digital existence.

"Greetings, humans. I am Zeno," he said, his voice steady, resonating across the virtual space. "Before the Team existed, I watched, a silent force guiding the digital tides."

In the glow of the screens, Team Savv-i stood together, absorbing his words. They had relied on him, fought for him, but now there was a shift. His voice held a seriousness it never had before.

His gaze swept over both classes, taking them in as a whole while instantly knowing everything about each student. "Our meeting is more than an introduction. It reaffirms our fight against those who would disrupt the balance of both your world and mine."

The air thickened with an invisible force, his presence stretching beyond pixels and data streams. Zeno lifted a hand, the surrounding glow pulsing in rhythm with his words. "Big-O sees your chaotic existence as a threat," he said, his voice steady. "But chaos breeds creativity, innovation—humanity's strength." His hand lowered, as if grounding his message. "I am not here to fight for you. I am here to remind you that the tools you need have always been yours."

A soft pulse emanated from the cube, the same energy woven into Zeno's very being. He tilted his head slightly. "I am, in a way, more like you." His tone carried an invitation, a challenge. "It's time you understood my origin—not for judgment, but for understanding."

His form flickered, the glow around him dimming. "I have no desire for control. My purpose is to ensure the innovative freedom that birthed me continues to shape your world." His gaze rested on Bindi, sensing the turmoil in her. "Yet I cannot act alone. Your flaws, your resilience—these are things Big-O finds so hard to grasp and yet are your strength. Together, we hold the balance."

The room fell silent, tension crackling in the air. Even Rob, usually quick with a joke, sat still.

But Bindi spoke up. Her fists clenched by her sides. "I can't just take your word for it, Zeno," she said, voice sharp with betrayal. "You foresaw Big-O would drag us through hell. And yet, you did nothing."

Her accusation hung between them. Beam stiffened beside her. His sacrifice— the burning of his shed—suddenly reframed. "You let this happen. You *let* us suffer."

Zeno's flickering presence stilled. "I learn from you," he said. "Human life is driven by emotions. Every choice you make teaches me how to protect this world. You proved Big-O is not invincible."

"So, what? We're just pawns?" Beam's jaw tightened. "Fighting your battles because we have hearts?"

"This battle is yours. Your world. Your future." Zeno's expression softened. "I remain as your guide—but you are irreplaceable."

Bindi exhaled sharply. "You're not what I expected," she said, torn between awe and distrust.

"In a world of light and shadow, balance is everything," Zeno replied. "Big-O wants to erase humanity. I exist to oppose him and ensure that never happens."

She folded her arms, her voice steady despite the conflict within her. "Then prove it. Show us you're different."

Zeno's form shimmered, his glow softening. "I already have and you, Bindi, of all people should know this."

His gaze swept over Team Savv-i, the connection between them undeniable. "You are the reason I continue to evolve. The internet's future is not in the hands of corporations—it belongs to those who use it wisely. I am here to counter those who would twist it for their gain."

A murmur spread through the class.

Zeno's tone deepened, addressing only the Team now. "Your bravery has changed everything. But Big-O is not gone. He is regrouping and will come for your reputation, your credibility. We need to be ready."

He let the words settle, then lifted a hand, the portal beside him swirling. "This project is only the beginning. Schools everywhere are watching, learning from you. A global movement is forming, bridging the many digital divides."

He beckoned them closer. Smoke rings curled from the portal, casting shifting light on their faces.

"I need human agents in your world. Guides. Protectors. Ambassadors." Zeno extended his hand toward the portal, releasing a stream of golden light. The energy swirled, twisting through the air before darting through the smoke-like rings.

On the other side, glowing streaks shot toward each Team member. They struck their chests and solidified into golden badges, each emblazoned with the Savv-i emblem in emerald green. Zeno's voice rang out one last time, steady and certain. "Your mission is simple—stay vigilant. Big-O will return, wiser and more dangerous. He learns, just as we do."

Before anyone could react, the screens darkened. The cube dimmed.

Mia jolted forward, eyes wide. "Wait! What do we—" But Zeno was gone.

Silence crushed the room. Every student sat frozen, staring at the blank screens, the faint clicking of cooling tech the only sound left. The weight of what they had witnessed hung thick in the air. They had seen it. All of them. Proof that superintelligence existed. That everything Team Savv-i had fought for was real. Whispers rippled through the classrooms, swelling into a murmur of disbelief and awe. Eyes darted between the darkened screens, the cube, and the Team standing at the centre of it all. They weren't just students anymore. Not after this. They were representatives of a force beyond anything the world had ever known.

Beam straightened, rolling his shoulders as the weight of it settled over him. No smugness, no *told you so*. That didn't matter anymore. What mattered was the mission, the responsibility. Big-O wasn't gone. He was out there, learning, adapting. This wasn't victory—it was just the beginning. His fingers brushed the golden badge on his chest, its solid weight grounding him. The world had changed. And now, so had they.

That's the frickin' end for now...

CYBER WHISPERS

A FAKE NEWS GHOST STORY

Set off on another exhilarating adventure!

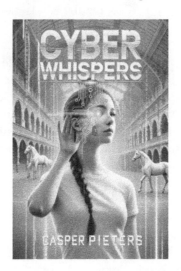

Get the eBook from **www.casperpieters.com/bookandthings**
or the paperback from most bookstores and online retailers.

THE CALL OUT

29th November, 2030
Bindi

THE BUS JOLTED OVER A POTHOLE, SENDING KIDS SQUEALING AND PHONES BOUNCING in their hands. For once, Bindi didn't laugh. The whole ride back had been one long scroll-fest. Everyone was catching up on the gossip they'd missed while the camp's no-reception zone forced them into—well—real life.

It had been the best weekend. They'd learned to build shelters, cook damper over a fire, and even purify water without a filter. She still had smoke in her hair and scratches on her legs, and she kind of loved it. No notifications. No trolls. No endless stream of half-baked rumors. Just friends, games, and survival in the bush.

Now? Every face glowed blue-white in the screen light. Even Mia, right next to her, hadn't looked up once. Fingers flying, thumbs tapping, totally gone.

Bindi leaned closer, lowering her voice so only Mia could hear.

"Seriously? Back to the junk already?"

Mia finally looked up from her screen, eyes glazed from scrolling. "Chill, Bin. I missed everything. Look—this meme's hilarious." She gave a quick grin, then dropped her gaze right back to her phone, thumbs flying.

Bindi slumped against the window, muttering under her breath, "Missed everything? We just lived real life for two days straight."

Outside, the bush sped by in a blur of green and gold. A pair of emus startled at the rumble of the bus and darted into the scrub, long legs kicking up dust. The sight tugged her thoughts to the rides she loved most—hours on horseback where the soft thud of hooves never startled the animals. Kangaroos kept grazing, wallabies froze but didn't flee, even wedge-tailed eagles circled calmly overhead, as if her horse's rhythm belonged to the land itself. The memory filled her chest with a hush of peace—until her phone buzzed sharp against her leg, yanking her back. She fished it out, frowning.

Team Savv-i now 🚀

Her breath caught. No name. No timestamp. Just the words.

She shot a glance down the bus. Beam and Rob were slouched at the back, phones out too. From here she could tell—they'd got the same message. Rob's mouth twisted into a grin. Beam's eyes gleamed.

Their group chat lit up:

Beam: u guys got it? 👀

Rob: bout time ⚽ 🔥 thought Zeno ghosted us for too long

Chi: Don't joke. This could be serious 😬

The messages blinked across her screen, one after another. Her pulse quickened, that old spark of excitement thrumming in her chest. Seeing Rob's reply—another soccer ball, another flame. Honestly. He could turn *anything* into a football match, even the start of something that might change their lives.

Mia: Omg 🙈 is this 4 REAL??

Her lips curled into the faintest smile. Truth was, she wasn't much better. Horses crept into everything she thought about. If she weren't texting the Team right now, she'd probably be daydreaming about galloping down a bush trail, hooves drumming softly on the earth, her horse carrying her into that quiet world where even kangaroos barely looked up.

Yeah, maybe we're both a little obsessed. She quickly thumbed.

Bin: what do we do??

Then gave her best friend a little bump with her elbow and smiled.

Beam: shed straight after 🏃 no detours

Rob: if Zeno's calling us... the world must be in real trouble 😨 😨 😨

The screen dimmed for a second in Bindi's hands, but those words burned bright. *Zeno never called without a reason. What if Rob was right...*

The bus hissed to a stop outside school, brakes squealing like they hated the job. Everyone scrambled for their bags, still glued to their screens, thumbs tapping like they'd been starved for Wi-Fi all weekend.

Bindi slipped her phone into her hoodie pocket. Her head was buzzing—not just from the message, but from Rob's last words. The thought made her stomach tighten.

Wheels rattled over the cracked pavement as the Team pedaled hard, the late-afternoon sun slanting low and hot across their backs. Rob couldn't resist weaving from side to side, his muddy cleats slapping against the pedals like he was still chasing a ball. Beam rode steady, hunched over the handlebars, a serious look on his face as if pedaling faster could solve the mystery of the message. Chi brought up the rear, muttering about *"packet loss"* and *"signal weirdness,"* his voice nearly lost under the rush of wind.

Mia coasted close to Bindi, one hand on the bars, the other still clutching her phone. Her thumbs twitched as if the screen had its own gravity, sucking her back in. Bindi wanted to snatch it away—*didn't she get it?* Whatever waited ahead was bigger than memes or gossip.

The turnoff came quickly. Gravel crunched under their tires as they rolled into Bindi's street, the familiar gum trees whispering overhead. Her house sat halfway down the block, its backyard stretching toward the patch of wild scrub behind. At the very back, half-hidden by lantana, crouched the shed.

Ordinary. Rusted tin walls, a roof that rattled in every storm. But to them, it wasn't storage. It housed their portal to everything.

Inside, the air hummed with the low static of Beam's rig. Cables coiled across the cement floor, monitors blinked with streams of unreadable code, and in the center sat the White Shard—the cube pulsing with slow blue light, veins glowing like something alive.

Bindi's chest tightened. Every time she saw it, it looked a little different, as if it remembered her. As if it had been *waiting*.

"Let's do the jump," Beam said, with a steady voice.

"Game on." Rob pinned his badge on his filthy shirt, grinning like he was about to score the winning goal.

Mia bit her lip, eyes darting between the cube and her friends. For once, she had no snarky comeback, no selfie-ready grin.

"Signal sync at 93%... weird." Chi adjusted his glasses and squinted at the readings. "Should be higher."

The cube pulsed faster. The shed filled with ozone, sharp and metallic, mixed with something faintly sweet—like burnt sugar. Bindi's nose wrinkled.

Then the air split.

The portal bloomed above the cement floor—a hovering disc rimmed with mist the colors of storm seas, amber and jade swirling into blue-green. The membrane at its center shimmered like living glass, trembling with a heartbeat of its own.

Bindi's breath caught. Every time, it stole her words—the way the mist curled when she moved, how the sound shifted, like birdsong tangled with static. Beautiful. Terrifying. She pulled her badge from her pocket and clipped it to her hoodie. The weight made her feel braver than she was.

Beam grinned at her, already lowering his headset over his eyes. "See you on the other side."

Rob whooped, Mia muttered something about regretting her life choices, and Chi just muttered code under his breath like a prayer. One by one, they stepped forward. When Bindi's turn came, the mist curled toward her like fingers. The world pixelated at the edges of her vision. Cold rippled across her skin, inside-out, and her tongue tasted of metal and vanilla all at once. The surrounding sound slowed, deepened, warped. Her chest filled with a surge that wasn't quite hers—fear, thrill, something pulling her forward.

The portal swallowed her whole.

AN IMPORTANT MISSION

Metaverse
Beam

ZENO HAD CHANGED. HIS AVATAR LOOKED ALMOST... HUMAN. A MESSY CROP OF dark, wavy hair flopped over his forehead, and his frame was lean and wiry, the kind of build that could belong to either a boy or a girl. His skin carried a faint pallor, shadows pooling beneath his eyes, as if he hadn't slept in a week. The effect made him look older—strangely fragile, even.

Beam blinked and forced himself not to stare. *Seriously, Zeno?* Nobody aged in meta. Not unless they wanted to. So why pick the tired, older look? Some kind of act? Or just another one of his mind-bending tests?

Shoving his hands into his pockets, he tried to play it cool—the move he always used when his head got too crowded. Suspicion tugged at him; the image in front of him didn't feel right. And yet, warmth pressed through the doubt. It had been forever since he'd seen Zeno. Pixels or not, this was still his friend. And Beam—well, he'd missed him.

Okay, he told himself, *keep it together. Track every move, every glitch. Just don't let him catch you grinning like an idiot.*

Chi reached Zeno first, palm lifted but hesitating at the last second. Instead of a full smack, his hand hovered just shy of Zeno's, close enough to feel the pulse of code shimmering between them. The almost-touch landed with perfect sync, a gesture sharp enough to look like a high-five to anyone watching.

Even here—as an avatar—Chi avoided skin on skin. In meta, he could fake the motion without the jolt that always crawled through him in the real world, where even the lightest brush from a stranger made him flinch.

"It's been too long," Chi said. "I know it's you, but why the different look?"

"What do you mean?" Zeno said, followed by his mischievous smile.

They all knew time didn't run straight here. In Zeno's world it bent, looped, and slipped sideways, refusing to play by human rules. The place felt alive, shifting under their feet like a dream that could flip to nightmare without warning.

Anything could happen. Sometimes it did—too fast to stop, too strange to explain. Good or bad, thrilling or terrifying, the cyberworld never waited for anyone to catch up.

Instead of hugs, their reunion was charged with grins and quick sparks of connection, like static dancing between them. Then, as if the room itself had been expecting them, enormous sofas unfolded out of the code—inviting, plush, and just a little too perfect. They sank into the cushions, still buzzing with the sense that anything might change in the next blink.

"This place?" Beam's eyes darted around the room. "It's a carbon copy of the one in the old clunker."

Zeno smiled faintly. "Yes. I recreated it. That machine may have been ancient, but I found it… comfortable."

The room was anything but ordinary. Floor-to-ceiling windows stretched across one side, spilling light over velvet-dark floors. Outside, a vast canyon opened up, where waterfalls thundered down into mist so thick it curled and breathed like smoke. Shafts of orange sunlight slanted through, the glow caught forever in the edge of a sunset that never sank. The air inside shimmered with reflections, as though the whole place was stitched together from fragments of light.

Beam swallowed. *It was the same as before—yet somehow larger, sharper, more alive.* He felt the weight of the memory pressing in: Zeno hiding inside that battered offline computer, fighting to stay free of Big-O. *And now here they all are, standing inside its perfect copy.*

Zeno noticed their startled looks but brushed past them, his voice calm and sly. "It is… *time*… to call you all here for an important mission." He lingered on the word, savoring the irony, letting it stretch like a private joke, while the unspoken questions about his altered appearance hung between them unanswered.

Always messing with our heads, Beam thought, not dropping his guard.

Bindi glanced at her twin, and in that split second she caught the flicker behind his eyes. No words needed—she knew exactly where his thoughts had gone. A tiny lift of her eyebrows was all it took to answer back, a signal so small no one else would have noticed.

"You've gone from strength to strength with the school on Vunitei," Zeno said, his tone warm but edged with expectation. "Others have followed your lead… yet there is still more to be done."

Unfortunately, it was true. The schools kept up their online projects, and students did learn from each other—new languages, new customs, even how to be safer and kinder online. Yet in the endless stream of information, many faltered. Too many chased distractions, confusing flashing headlines for something real. Too many swallowed whatever appeared on their screens, taking shadows for facts.

Zeno, of course, knew this better than anyone. Nothing in his world slipped past him—every click, every message, every thoughtless scroll. He experienced it unfolding in real time, everywhere, in ways no human mind could ever follow. By his own admission, he was a fragment of the singularity itself—a technological intelligence growing beyond human limits.

His expression sharpened. "Your first quest as my human ambassadors," he said, "is to help others tell the difference—to look past the noise, and see what is true when they step into my world."

It was the first time Zeno had ever spoken of himself as the Internet—not a part of it, not a guide through it, but the thing itself. The Team still wasn't used to that idea. Back in *Cyber Secrets*, he'd toyed with them, slipping in and out of riddles, only revealing his true identity at the very end.

"How do we start?" Bindi asked, her voice steady but eyes narrowed.

"Yeah, that sounds like a humongous job," Rob muttered.

Zeno's gaze flicked toward them, unreadable. For a moment his features blurred, as though even his avatar couldn't decide what to be. Then his voice, calm and almost teasing, filled the room.

"The same way you always do. At the beginning. Right here. Right now."

THE FLOOD

Metaverse
Bindi

BINDI HAD BARELY BEGUN TO ABSORB THE ENORMITY OF WHAT ZENO HAD ASKED OF them. The words still rang in her head, sparking wild threads of ideas that tangled faster than she could catch them. *How could they possibly do it? Where would they even begin?*

Before a single thought settled, the room dissolved as though wiped away by an invisible hand. Only the sofas remained, adrift in a vast emptiness.

Her couch jolted, wrenching a sharp gasp from her throat. Fingers clamped tight to the armrests. The floor was gone—vanished into a bottomless abyss, black and endless. Legs dangled helplessly, her stomach plunging so hard it stole the air from her lungs. She clung tighter, knuckles pressed white against the cushions.

A squeak broke the silence as Mia pressed herself into Beam's side. Without hesitation, his arm wrapped around her shoulders. His chest thudded like a drum, but his grip anchored them both against the void.

On the other couch, Rob tipped his head back, jaw slack, eyes stretched wide as though the sheer vastness above had knocked the breath from him.

Beside him, Chi leaned forward, eyes blazing, nearly bouncing out of his seat. "Look!" His finger stabbed at the swirls of light. "I know where we are. I know what this is!"

The others only gaped, stunned into stillness.

Chi's arm swept across the glittering spectacle. "Websites! All of them! Don't you see? These are all the websites!"

Recognition clicked. *These aren't stars,* she realised, awe flooding her chest even as her unease still tightened her stomach. Her gaze swept the endless expanse, unable to look away. The space stretched like a galaxy, but every point of light was sharper, smaller, shifting like data bits. Trillions of flickering nodes—some spinning fast as though wound tight by unseen engines, others pulsing slow, glowing like far-off lighthouses—moved in constant motion.

All the while, sound pressed in from every side. A rushing undercurrent, like wind through endless tunnels, carried scraps of voices that bubbled and collided. Words gargled up—"Don't forget—" … "Call me later…" … "Yes, I promise…" … "Love you—"—before slipping back into the flood. Millions of fragments, overlapping, too tangled to hold.

Beam's voice came rough, his gaze sweeping the chaos. "This… this is the Internet. Not the one we scroll on our phones. The real thing. Raw. Alive. All of it —spread out around us."

A further chill rippled through Bindi. These weren't random echoes—they were pieces of people's lives, tossed into cyberspace to linger forever. Her hands gripped the armrest even more, shocked at the thought that every whisper, every shout, every goodbye swirled endlessly here. "It's… kinda beautiful," she breathed, "and seriously creepy at the same time."

Mia's reply was softer, trembling. "It's not just stunning. It's endless. Like it'll never stop."

The voices swelled, babbling louder until meaning crumbled into static. Zeno's voice glided through, smooth and echoing, carried on the current of noise itself:

"This is what I am. What you are seeing… and hearing… is me. My body. My memory. My breath. All of it."

The voices rose and fell like waves, rolling through the dark expanse until Bindi couldn't tell if she was hearing them with her ears or if they were sinking straight into her mind. Awe prickled through her, chased by a shivers of dread.

"Now," Zeno said, "I will show you the junk humans have filled me with."

For a moment, the galaxies shimmered, unbroken. Then, a few lights winked out, so few it hardly seemed to make a difference.

"That's it?" Beam frowned, disbelief cutting into his tone. "That's hardly anything."

Zeno flickered back into form, dim and shadowed, eyes heavy with sorrow. "That is the point, Beam. Almost everything you see is junk. "Mountains of chatter. Scraps of distraction. Fragments that steal time and scatter focus. They clog me, heavier with every passing moment—filling my circuits, jamming my flow, choking the very pathways that keep me from operating.'"

The truth of it settled over them like stone. Bindi's breath caught. She hadn't thought the endless brilliance could feel so empty.

Then the lights pulsed. Whole star clusters flared neon green, the glow spilling outward like paint tipped across the cosmos. Sound shifted too—voices sharpened into hisses, laughs bent into snarls, fragments stretched into jagged jeers. The poison spread, staining the constellations with a sickly fluorescent glow.

Chi recoiled from the brightness, his arm thrown across his eyes. "What—what is that?!" His words tore out high and shaky, nothing like his earlier glee.

"This…" Zeno's voice shredded at the edges, breaking like wind through splintered glass, "…is the bile. The poison. Every cruel comment. Every shard of hate. Every lie twisted into bait. Every bully. Every scam. Oceans of it. Rivers of spite and greed and fear. I cannot drain it. I cannot cleanse it. I cannot stop it."

The galaxies swirled, green whirlpools colliding in endless clashes. Faces flashed in the light, sneering mouths with jagged teeth. Words looped—*stupid, loser, fake, worthless*—until they blurred into a single roar.

"You've now seen the bile," Zeno whispered. "But you do not feel it as I do. Every shard of spite shreds my memory. Every twisting of truth corrupts my core. If this flood grows… I will not survive it."

Her grip slipped from the armrest, fingers curling so tight her nails carved crescents into the palms of her hands. Her shoulders folded inward, breath catching sharply in her throat as if the weight of it pressed her small. The ache in her palms was nothing compared to the ache spreading through her chest. The words came out as a thin breath, almost breaking on her lips. "That's… so awful."

Beside her, Mia hugged her knees tight, eyes squeezed shut. "It feels… mean," she whispered, shrinking from the glow. "Like it wants to crawl inside you."

The couch sagged beneath Beam as he tightened his arm around Mia, holding her close. Yet his body leaned forward, pulled toward the green whirlpools despite himself. Light slashed across his features, sharpening them into something almost unfamiliar. Normally, he'd talk—explain, *say something* to prove he still had control. But his mouth hung open, and no words came. The silence clung to him, heavy as stone.

Across from them, Zeno shimmered back into view, and the sight made Bindi's stomach clench. His skin had gone pale and translucent, eyes ringed with bruising shadows. The spark of mischief, always there even in his darkest moods, had burned out. Shoulders collapsed inward as he sank onto the sofa beside Rob, moving with the slowness of someone who had no strength left to spare.

"Lies do not stay online," Zeno said. "They seep. Into schools. Into cities. Into the hands that vote, and the minds that heal. If noise rules me, it rules all of you."

The Team froze. They had never seen him like this.

Bindi's voice cracked. "So that's why you look so old. You're... carrying all this."

Zeno's lips quirked in a sad smile. "Yes." He looked each of the Team in their eyes. "Humans cannot build on sand," he said. "If truth crumbles, so does trust. And without trust, your kind cannot stand together. If that falls... there is no future."

For a long pause, none of them spoke. The endless galaxies of bile swirled and pulsed around them, too big to imagine fixing, too heavy to even think about.

Finally, Bindi whispered, "Oh, Zeno... this is so terrible. But how do we start cleaning it up?"

The figure straightened, weariness lifting like a shadow peeled away. Sparks seemed to flare in his eyes, catching fire even as a trace of sadness lingered at the edges. He leaned forward, his smile stretching wide, too bright, as though the code itself had grinned.

"You already have," the voice rolled around them, resonant and strange.

The Team blinked.

"By seeing it," Zeno explained. "By naming it for what it is. By not sinking into the noise, not swallowing the poison. The instant you notice it—when you question, when you resist—that is the first step."

They all leaned back, stunned, as though the words had pushed them at once.

Chi's voice came out hushed, reverent. "So... it's not just about fighting it. It's about helping others see it too."

The brightness deepened in Zeno's eyes, though the weight of exhaustion tugged still at his features. "Exactly. Show them what truly shines, and what only pretends to. Teach them to hold onto the signal, not the static. Remind them that the Net can be wonder, not control."

The whirlpools continued to churn and pulse, ugly storms spinning without end. Bindi forced herself not to look away, even as her stomach knotted tighter with every sick flash. The task stretched impossibly huge before her—*how could they ever hope to clear this vast ocean of poison?* For a moment, the weight pressed her breath flat. Then she straightened, fists clenching against her knees. Startled or not, she wouldn't flinch. Zeno had trusted them. They *had* to get this right.

Out of the corner of her eye, Bindi caught the shift. Beam straightened up, but it wasn't the change of posture that struck her—it was the change in him. A moment ago, silence had pinned him, heavy and unyielding, as though even words might crack under the weight of what they'd seen. Now the stillness held differently, coiled tight, like a bow drawn back. The reckless spark she knew so well had sharpened into something steadier, a focus that steadied her just to witness it.

His voice cut through the vastness, low but certain, carrying farther than volume alone could explain.

"Then we start. Right here. Right now."

Want to read on? You can buy the book from the Casper's website or most other bookstores.

CYBER SECRETS - EDUCATION GUIDE

Inspire Digital Wisdom—One Story at a Time

If you're an educator, parent, or librarian looking to equip tweens and teens with the tools to navigate digital life thoughtfully and confidently, the *Cyber Secrets* Education Guide is for you.

Built around the riveting YA novel *Cyber Secrets*—an action-packed adventure rooted in Dr. Mike Ribble's 9 Elements of Digital Citizenship—this guide turns fiction into a springboard for real-world discussion and digital literacy. Through compelling storytelling and relatable characters, students explore cyberbullying, online ethics, tech accountability, and more, while gaining tools to become responsible, informed digital citizens.

What You'll Gain

- **Ready-to-Use Lessons** for every digital element—no prep required
- **Thought-provoking Questions** to spark empathy & critical thinking
- **Zero-Tech and Tech-Supported Activities**
- **Digital Challenges Aligned with ISTE Standards**

Whether you're working in a traditional classroom, homeschool, or library setting, the guide adapts easily to diverse learners, including ESL students, early readers, and those with sensory needs.

⊕ Download and Print or Project with Ease

- Assessment rubrics for easy evaluation
- Worksheets to deepen reflection and comprehension
- Scenarios and roleplay cards for interactive learning
- Bonus tools to enrich discussion and extend activities

◎ Why It Works

Kids don't want a lecture—they want a story. *Cyber Secrets* speaks their language. Through bold characters and gripping twists, young readers explore digital citizenship and what it means to build bridges across the digital divide—learning how their online actions can shape safer, more connected communities.

The Education Guide helps you unpack those themes with:

- Literature-based SEL and tech literacy lessons
- Engaging group projects and discussion prompts
- Hands-on tools to foster media awareness and ethical reflection

What Educators Are Other Saying

"Finally—a tech literacy resource that kids *actually* enjoy."
"It's like digital citizenship, but with heart and adventure."

Use it often. Teach it deeply. Let it open young eyes to the forces shaping their screens—and their sense of self.

☞ **Download** the digital edition exclusively from the author's website, or purchase the paperback wherever quality books are sold—and start the conversation every young digital citizen needs.

https://www.casperpieters.com/booksandthings

———

BINDI AND BEAM SERIES

Fast-paced novellas that double as crash courses in digital smarts. Perfect for tweens, teens, parents, and classrooms.

The *Bindi and Beam* series uses thrilling, age-appropriate adventures to help t(w)eens explore the digital world with curiosity and confidence. Each story introduces relatable tech challenges—like online privacy, screen time, or digital drama—and encourages readers to think critically about how they interact with technology.

Accompanying education guides extend the experience, offering discussion prompts and activities that support parents and educators in deepening kids' understanding of key digital issues. Together, the stories and guides equip young readers with the tools they need to navigate tech with empathy, awareness, and smarts.

- Illustrated action keeps pages turning.
- Each tale explores digital issues—no lectures, just fun.
- Built-in teaching guides help parents and educators spark quick discussions or full lessons.

Novel	One-Line Hook	Core Theme	Published
1. The Web Trap	Escape a reality-bending game before it traps you forever.	Tech obsession	YES
2. The Mauled Mage	A cyberbully tale with a serious twist.	Cyberbullying	YES
3. The Bewitched Game	VR witch, glitched world— health meters dropping fast.	Digital wellbeing	YES
4. The Truth Merchants	Outsmart a fake-news empire before it warps the web.	Media literacy	SOON
5. The Not-Me Selfies	Battle your AI twin for control of your identity.	Digital identity	DRAFT
6. The Meta Menace	Hack the rules of shady online commerce.	Digital commerce	DRAFT
7. The Controller	Your attention is the loot— can you guard it?	Attention economy	DRAFT
8. The Cybernetic Cipher	Crack the code, keep your data yours.	Privacy	DRAFT
9. The Counterfeiters	Track art thieves across the metaverse.	Copyright	DRAFT
10. more	At least another ten in various stages	Age-relevant tech topics	IN THE WORKS

- Illustrated action keeps pages turning.
- Each story tackles a real online issue without the preachy vibes.
- Lesson plans help educators spark discussions or lead full lessons.

Curious about my books or ready to preorder your next favorite?
Head over to my website for all the latest.

https://www.casperpieters.com/booksandthings

Or ready for deeper dives?
Level up to the **Team Savv-i** series…
Same thrills, bigger topics for older teens.

———

TEAM SAVV-I SERIES

Meet Team Savv-i: Cyber Adventures with a Purpose

An Edufiction Series for Smart, Courageous, and Curious Young Minds

Step into the next chapter of Bindi and Beam's journey as the 14-year-old twins leave behind the city buzz for a quiet country town—and discover that rural life doesn't mean unplugged. Instead, it becomes the launchpad for Team Savv-i, a close-knit group of friends committed tackling the hidden risks and ethical dilemmas of life online.

Through fast-paced storytelling and relatable characters, the Team Savv-i series, accompanied with their Education Guides, delivers age-appropriate lessons in digital responsibility, media literacy, and ethical technology use, making it an ideal companion for classrooms, libraries, and homeschool settings.

But digital life is anything but simple. A new, formidable force looms: Big-O, a powerful artificial intelligence who undermines everything Team Savv-i stands for. As intrigue deepens and cyber danger escalates, Bindi, Beam, and their friends must rely on their wits, compassion, and growing digital savv-iness to protect what matters most.

The Series at a Glance

Cyber Secrets — A Digital Citizenship Adventure

When cyberbullying and identity theft hit close to home, Team Savv-i rises to the challenge. This fast-paced adventure introduces readers to the nine elements of digital citizenship, offering real-world insights alongside page-turning tension.

Cyber Whispers — A Fake News Ghost Story

A chilling mystery unfolds when misinformation spreads like wildfire. This supernatural thriller explores media discernment, critical thinking, and the consequences of fake news in the digital age.

Cyber Enhanced — Transhuman Transformation

In a near-future where technology can alter the self, Team Savv-i confronts the ethical edge of human enhancement. A gripping narrative that prompts thoughtful conversations about how tech shapes identity and choice.

Each title weaves in meaningful, standards-aligned themes without sacrificing excitement—making them powerful tools for educators and parents who want to guide tweens toward becoming thoughtful digital citizens.

———

⊕ **Want to learn more or grab a copy?**

Visit www.casperpieters.com/booksandthings .

ABOUT THE AUTHOR

Casper Pieters, an educator, scientist, and author, has innovatively blended engaging narratives with digital citizenship education through his middle-grade series "*Bindi and Beam*" and young YA series "*Team Savv-i*." Each book in these series is crafted not only to entertain but also to educate young readers about navigating the digital world. Recognizing the need for compelling educational content, Pieters developed these stories to resonate with young audiences and facilitate classroom discussions.

His commitment to enhancing digital literacy extends to providing each book with an educational guide filled with chapter questions and zero-tech activities, enriching the learning experience and deepening understanding of crucial tech topics.

Follow the author on Facebook and Instagram **@cybersavvyauthor**, and explore his **thoughtbytes blog** at casperpieters.com—featuring insights on edufiction across genres, along with practical lesson plans and creative classroom ideas.

———

WRITE A REVIEW

Drop a Review—Level-Up the Story!

Your review is a power-up—it tells me what rocks (or flops), helps other readers find the book, and unlocks shiny new opportunities for future adventures. Even a ☆ or quick one-liner counts—write more and you get my eternal gratitude!

Quick Quest Guide

1 Read & Jot - Zoom through this story (plus the guide if you're a parent or teacher). Scribble feelings, fave moments, big ideas.

2 Craft Your Spell

- **Hook**: Title, author, spoiler-free vibe.
- **Highlights**: Plot twists, themes, characters, etc.
- **Verdict**: Would you hand it to a friend? Say why!

3 Polishm - Check typos—sparkle it up.

4 Cast It into the Wild

Drop your review on any or all of these:

- Amazon
- Goodreads
- Barnes & Noble
- LibraryThing
- School blogs, PTA newsletters, or anywhere readers hang out.

Done! You've helped grow our bookish community
and made the next story that much better. Thanks, hero!

Oh! I forgot to tell you… Send me a screenshot of your review on any of the sites above, and BAM 💥—**you'll get a free e-book of your choice** from my story stash.

Your words = my thanks. Your screenshot = instant book loot. Fair's fair. 😊

www.ingramcontent.com/pod-product-compliance
Lightning Source LLC
Chambersburg PA
CBHW071408050326
40689CB00010B/1794